S0-AKA-723

Literature 4
Student Guide

3rd Edition

k¹²

About K12 Inc.

K12 Inc., a technology-based education company, is the nation's leading provider of proprietary curriculum and online education programs to students in grades K–12. K¹² provides its curriculum and academic services to online schools, traditional classrooms, blended school programs, and directly to families. K12 Inc. also operates the K¹² International Academy, an accredited, diploma-granting online private school serving students worldwide. K¹²'s mission is to provide any child the curriculum and tools to maximize success in life, regardless of geographic, financial, or demographic circumstances. K12 Inc. is accredited by CITA. More information can be found at www.K12.com.

Copyright © 2015 K12 Inc. All rights reserved. K¹², the K¹² logo, and Unleash the xPotential are trademarks or registered trademarks of K12 Inc. or its affiliates in the U.S. and other countries. Other names may be trademarks of third parties.

No part of this document may be reproduced or used in any form or by any means, graphic, electronic, or mechanical, including photocopying, recording, taping, and information retrieval systems, without the prior written permission of K12 Inc.

978-1-60153-465-1

Printed by LSC Communications, Kendallville, IN, USA, April 2017

Table of Contents

Unit 1

Foundational Skills 1
"Child's Play" 2
How Do You See It? 4
Guidelines for Peer Discussion 5
"Chanticleer and the Fox": Session 1 6
"Chanticleer and the Fox": Session 2 9
The Barnyard Evening News 11
"It Could Always Be Worse" 15
"The Bear Boy" 18
A Change for the Better 20
"The King and His Hawk": Session 1 21
"The King and His Hawk": Session 2 23
"The Green Glass Ball": Session 1 25
"The Green Glass Ball": Session 2 29
"The Green Glass Ball": Session 3 31
Looking Back 32
Lessons Learned Story Review 35

Unit 2

"How Bear Lost His Tail" 37
Guidelines for Peer Discussion 40
"From Tiger to Anansi" 41
"Brer Rabbit Gets Brer Fox's Dinner" 44
"Brer Rabbit Goes Back to Mr. Man's Garden" 47
Compare and Contrast Tricksters, Session 1 50
More Fun with Tricksters 53

Unit 3

All Kinds of People 55
Guidelines for Peer Discussion 58
Your Thoughts 59
Such Strange People! 61
Humorous Characters 64
Picturing the Pirate 67
Speaking for Themselves 69
Speaking for Yourself 72
Dramatic Reading 74
Peer Review 77

Unit 5

"Noah and the Ark" 79
Noah: Choices and Consequences 81
Bible Character Chart 83
Guidelines for Peer Discussion 84
"Joseph and His Brothers": Session 1 85
Story Timeline 87
"Joseph and His Brothers" Session 2 90
"The Story of Moses" 92
Moses: Choices and Consequences 94
Choices that Matter 97
Bible Character Chart 99

Unit 7

Robinson Crusoe: Chapters 1–6 101
Guidelines for Peer Discussion 105
Robinson Crusoe: Chapters 7–11 106
Robinson Crusoe: Chapters 12–18 109
Robinson Crusoe: Chapters 19–24 112
Important Decisions 115
Robinson Crusoe: Chapters 25–29 116
Look Before You Leap 118
Happy As a King 120
Message in a Bottle 122
Robinson Crusoe: Chapters 30–33 123
Footprint in the Sand 125
Robinson Crusoe: Chapters 34–35 126
The Story Behind the Story 128
Robinson Crusoe: Chapters 36–37 129
Robinson Crusoe: Chapters 38–40 132

Unit 8

"Keepers of the Prairie": Session 1 135
Guidelines for Peer Discussion 140
Parts of a Magazine 141
Prairie Dog Town 143
Chain of Events 144
Guidelines for Peer Discussion 145
"Keepers of the Prairie": Session 2 146
The Prairie Dog Post 148
"The Wolf in the Dog": Session 1 151
Wolf in the Dog 154
Organization Station 155
What I Know, What I Wonder: Session 1 156
Burning Questions: Session 1 158
"Feathers" 159
Classify and Categorize 162
"Amazing Sea Lions" 163
Compare and Contrast 166

What I Know, What I Wonder: Session 2 167

Burning Questions: Session 2 168

Finding the Answers 169

"Incredible Giraffes" 170

Unit 9

Surprises 173

Inventions of Imagery 177

The Little Hero of Holland 179

Troublesome Doctors and Terrible Cooks 183

Rhyme Schemes 187

Through the Eyes of a Child 189

Reading with Rhythm 193

Unit 10

"Louis Pasteur: Battle with Death": Session 1 195

The Fact Detective 198

Guidelines for Peer Discussion 199

"Louis Pasteur: Battle with Death": Session 2 200

An Interview with Dr. Pasteur 201

"Elizabeth Blackwell: A Pioneering Physician": Session 1 204

"Elizabeth Blackwell: A Pioneering Physician": Session 2 207

Dear Dr. Blackwell 208

"Sir Alexander Fleming: The Accident That Changed the World": Session 1 210

Who? What? Where? When? Why? How? 214

"Sir Alexander Fleming: The Accident That Changed the World": Session 2 215

Looking Back 217

Semester Review 219

Fast Facts 223

Mix and Match 227

Unit 14

"The Hodja Speaks" 229

Guidelines for Peer Discussion 234

Wisdom from Around the World 235

"Younde Goes to Town" 236

Wisdom from Around the World 240

"The Little Smoke Thief" 241

Wisdom from Around the World 245

"The Gold Coin" 246

Juan's Journey 250

Wisdom from Around the World 252

"The Grateful Stork" 253

Wisdom from Around the World 257

Review and Reflect 258

"Rikki-Tikki-Tavi": Session 1 260

Making Inferences and Drawing Conclusions 263

"Rikki-Tikki-Tavi": Session 2 264

Wisdom from Around the World 268

Unit 15

"What Good Is a Forest Fire?" 269

Adaptation Cube 273

Adaptation Cube 275

Main Idea and Details 277

Guidelines for Peer Discussion 278

"Frogs on Ice" 279

Take Note! 282

"Desert Home" 283

Surprises, Surprises 286

"Seed Travel" 288

Amazing Adaptations 291

Unit 16

Analyze a Presentation and Choose Your Topic 293

Research a Topic and Organize a Presentation 295

Create a Presentation 300

Practice a Presentation 303

Peer Feedback: Tell Me About My Presentation 305

Deliver Your Presentation 308

Unit 17

Your Not-So-Silent World 309

Onomatopoeia Chart 313

Guidelines for Peer Discussion 315

Moon and Stars 316

Hoofs, Howls, and Feathers 320

Wonderful Words 325

Unit 19

Welcome to the Middle Ages 331

Peter the Page's Journal 335

Guidelines for Peer Discussion 336

Knights and Castles 337

Your Coat of Arms 340

Peter the Page's Journal 341

Work and Play in Medieval Times 342

Peter the Page's Journal 345

Travel, Medicine, and Celebrations 346

Peter the Page's Journal 350

Burning Questions 351

The Middle Ages Today 352

Squire's Certificate 355

Peter the Page's Journal 357

An Illuminated Manuscript 358

Unit 20

"The Rightful King of the Britons" 359

My Code of Chivalry 364

Guidelines for Peer Discussion..365

"The City of Dreams and the Sword of Legend" 366

"Guinevere and the Gift of the Round Table" 370

"Pretty-Hands" 374

The Round Table..377

"The Hideous Lady" and "Epilogue: The Fate of Camelot" 379

The Fate of Camelot 383

Adventures in Camelot 385

Unit 22

Gulliver's Travels—"A Voyage to Lilliput": Session 1 389

Inventory 393

Guidelines for Peer Discussion..395

Gulliver's Travels—"A Voyage to Lilliput": Session 2 396

Choices and Consequences..399

Gulliver's Travels—"A Voyage to Brobdingnag": Session 1 400

Gulliver's Travels—"A Voyage to Brobdingnag": Session 2 403

Gulliver's Travels: Review 406

Chart the Choices 408

Unit 23

Metaphors in Nature 409

Guidelines for Peer Discussion..413

Metaphors in the Manmade World..414

A Metaphor Riddle 418

Seeing Metaphors...420

Metaphors to Think About 423

When Dreams Grow 427

Unit 24

"Wilbur and Orville Wright: Men with Wings" 429

World Map..433

World Map..435

World Map..437

World Map..439

"The Challenge: Bessie Coleman's Story"...441

"Dangerous Adventure! Lindbergh's Famous Flight" 443

Similarities 446

"Go, John Glenn!" 447

Hero's Welcome..450

Firsthand Accounts 451

Two Pieces on the Wright Brothers..453

Read and Research: Session 1 454

An Interview with Bessie Coleman 456

Charles Lindbergh Speaks 459
John Glenn's Transcript 461
Similarities and Differences 464
Read and Research: Session 2 465
Polish Your Draft 467
Revising and Proofreading Checklist 469

Unit 26

Semester Review..471
Mix and Match 473
Name That Character! 474
Take Note! 478

Name _____ Date _____

Foundational Skills

Learn about what to expect in this course and review some strategies for understanding what you read. Then answer questions about reading strategies.

In This Course

Complete this online activity to learn about the course that you are about to begin. You will learn about resources in the course and review reading strategies for being a better, more effective reader.

Check Your Listening

Complete this online activity to answer questions about your understanding of reading strategies.

© 2015 K12 Inc. All rights reserved.
Copying or distributing without K12's written consent is prohibited.

Name _____   Date _____

"Child's Play"

Have you ever thought about sailing across an ocean? Do you think you could do it on a log? Meet two children who see an adventure differently.

Vocabulary
You will find these words in today's reading.

cargo: (n.) a load of goods carried by a ship, airplane, truck, or other vehicle
The truck delivered its *cargo* of fruits and vegetables to the store.

parrot-fish: (n.) a fish that has tusk-like teeth that look like a beak
I read about the unusual teeth of the *parrot-fish* in an encyclopedia.

peevishly: (adv.) in a cross or annoyed manner
My friend spoke to me *peevishly* when she did not agree with what I said.

Think Ahead
1. Look through the pages of *Classics for Young Readers*. Use the table of contents to locate the story "Child's Play" and open to the first page.
2. Preview the story by scanning its paragraphs and looking at the picture. What do you notice about the structure of the story? How is the structure of the story different from the structure of poems and/or plays that you have read?
3. What does it mean to *pretend*?

Read
"Child's Play" in *Classics for Young Readers,* Vol. 4A, pages 6–7.

© 2015 K12 Inc. All rights reserved.
Copying or distributing without K12's written consent is prohibited.

Questions

Answer the following questions in complete sentences in your Reading Notebook.

1. What does the second child see the first child doing by the roadside?
2. When the first child sees the water, what does the second child see?
3. Describe the island scene the first child spots from the boat.
4. Why does the second child stop playing with the first child?
5. How does the first child react when the second child walks away?

Discuss

1. Why do you think the second child doesn't like the game the first child is playing?
2. What does it mean when the first child says, "It's all the same"?

How Do You See It?

When you read a story, there are many ways to learn about its characters. The story may have details about the characters or only give clues about them. In this story we are not given physical descriptions of the boys, but we do learn about them from their words and actions.

Think about how the first child and the second child are different. What does each boy think of the other? Answer the questions on the page called How Do You See It?

© 2015 K12 Inc. All rights reserved.
Copying or distributing without K12's written consent is prohibited.

Name _____   Date _____

How Do You See It?

Read each quotation from the first and second child in "Child's Play." Identify who made each statement.

"I think you are pretty dull to play things that aren't really there." Who said this?

_____

"I think you are pretty dull to see nothing but what is under your nose." Who said this?

_____

Write one or more paragraphs explaining which child's statement you agree with and why.

_____

_____

_____

_____

_____

_____

© 2015 K12 Inc. All rights reserved.
Copying or distributing without K12's written consent is prohibited.

Guidelines for Peer Discussion

Share your thoughts, ideas, questions, and feelings about a text with a peer or others. Listen carefully to what everyone has to say about the text. During your discussion, follow these guidelines.

1. Be prepared to discuss what you think about the text. You should have already read the assignment. Come prepared to discuss your ideas, and use examples from the text to support your thoughts and answers.

2. You will be asked questions about the text. Be ready to answer them, and bring some questions of your own to ask others, such as:

   "Who was your favorite character? Why?"

   "What was your favorite part of the text? Why?"

   "What fact did you enjoy learning? Why do you find this fact interesting?"

   "What question would you ask if you had the chance to meet the author?"

3. Listen if it's not your turn to speak. Pay attention to what others say so that you can add your ideas. Speak clearly and in complete sentences.

4. If you don't understand what someone says, ask a question, such as:

   "What do you mean when you say . . . ?"

   "Can you give an example of . . . ?"

5. If you don't agree with what someone says, explain why.

   "I don't agree with that because . . . "

6. Keep discussions positive! You can disagree, but don't argue. Be respectful.

© 2015 K12 Inc. All rights reserved.
Copying or distributing without K12's written consent is prohibited.

Name _____ Date _____

"Chanticleer and the Fox": Session 1

Chanticleer the rooster and Reynard the fox both learn an important lesson about trust.

Vocabulary

You will find these words in today's reading.

burnished: (adj.) polished
The autumn leaves were the color of *burnished* gold.

flattery: (n.) excessive praise spoken by someone who doesn't really mean it
The fox tried *flattery* to get the crow to sing, so that when she opened her mouth, she would drop the grapes she was holding.

sprightly: (adj.) spirited, lively
The *sprightly* puppy wiggled about as I tried to pet him.

Think Ahead

1. Think about the last time someone complimented you. How did it make you feel?
2. How did you know that the person really meant the nice things he or she said about you? Why might someone pay a compliment he or she really doesn't mean?

Read

"Chanticleer and the Fox" in *Classics for Young Readers,* Vol. 4A, pages 8-11.

© 2015 K12 Inc. All rights reserved.
Copying or distributing without K12's written consent is prohibited.

Questions

Answer the following questions in complete sentences in your Reading Notebook.

1. What is Chanticleer's voice compared to?
2. Describe Chanticleer's bad dream.
3. What does Chanticleer say his dream might be warning him about?
4. What trick does Reynard use to capture Chanticleer?
5. What trick does Chanticleer use to escape from Reynard?
6. After Chanticleer escapes, what does Reynard say to him?

Discuss

1. Why do you think each character is so easily fooled by the other?
2. Do you think that Reynard might try to trick Chanticleer on some other day? What makes you think so?
3. How is the lesson Reynard learned different from the lesson Chanticleer learned?
4. There is an old saying, "Fool me once, shame on you; fool me twice, shame on me." What do you think this means? How does the saying fit this story?

Lessons Learned

The story of "Chanticleer and the Fox" was first told over 700 years ago. Why do you think people still like to read and tell this tale? Are the lessons in the story ones we should remember today? Why?

A Book of Wisdom

People long ago wrote down important sayings and quotations in a "Commonplace Book." They would read the sayings and think about how the lessons related to their lives.

© 2015 K12 Inc. All rights reserved.
Copying or distributing without K12's written consent is prohibited.

Make the first page in your own "Commonplace Book." Tell the lessons Chanticleer and Reynard learned. Write the lessons neatly on a page. If you wish, add an illustration or some design. Save the page because you will add more pages to it later.

© 2015 K12 Inc. All rights reserved.
Copying or distributing without K12's written consent is prohibited.

Name _____ Date _____

"Chanticleer and the Fox": Session 2

What would Chanticleer want to tell about Reynard's attack? Would Reynard say that it never happened? Pretend to be each character and tell **your** version of the story. But first, learn some important tips for having a productive and enjoyable discussion of a story.

Speaking and Listening

Complete the online activity to learn how to participate in a discussion of something you've read.

Think Ahead

1. Have you heard the old saying, "There are two sides to every story"? What does the saying mean?

2. Imagine that Chanticleer and Reynard are both looking back at the events that just happened between them. What might Chanticleer say if he were telling his version of what happened?

3. What would Reynard say? How would his perspective be different from Chanticleer's? For example, do you think that Reynard might insist that he really did just want to hear Chanticleer sing?

The Barnyard Evening News

Complete *The Barnyard Evening News* page. Helena Hen from *The Barnyard Evening News* has come to interview Chanticleer and Reynard. Take turns pretending that you are first Chanticleer and then Reynard. Answer Helena's questions as you think they might.

The first response has been completed for each.

© 2015 K12 Inc. All rights reserved.
Copying or distributing without K12's written consent is prohibited.

Discussion: *The Barnyard Evening News*

After completing *The Barnyard Evening News* page, share your answers about how each character would respond to Helena Hen's questions with others. Listen as others share their answers with you.

Then talk about why you imagined the characters responding as you thought they would. Discuss the reasons for your answers, describing how each character feels and thinks, and listen as others talk about the reasons for their answers.

Remember to be polite, express yourself clearly, and try to build on the points made by others. If needed, summarize or restate ideas to make sure that everyone understands them.

As always, use appropriate language.

© 2015 K12 Inc. All rights reserved.
Copying or distributing without K12's written consent is prohibited.

Name _____   Date _____

The Barnyard Evening News

Helena Hen: Good evening! This is Helena Hen with *The Barnyard Evening News*. I am reporting to you live from the barnyard where a frightful confrontation occurred today between Chanticleer the rooster and Reynard the fox. Chanticleer and Reynard have joined me so I can ask them a few questions about the day.

Chanticleer, I hear today's events all started with a dream you had. Tell me about it.

Chanticleer: Yes, Helena. I was sleeping in the barnyard and was startled by a terrible dream. In the dream, a fierce beast jumped out of the woods and captured me. It was horrible!

Helena Hen: Did you find out who the beast in your dream was?

Chanticleer: _A Fox_____

_____

_____

Helena Hen: You seem like a smart rooster. How did Reynard trick you?

Chanticleer: _I wanted to impress him._

_____

_____

© 2015 K12 Inc. All rights reserved.
Copying or distributing without K12's written consent is prohibited.

The Barnyard Evening News

Helena Hen: What did you do once he captured you?

Chanticleer: Trick him into letting me go.

Helena Hen: How did you manage to escape?

Chanticleer: By tricking him

Helena Hen: Now let's hear from Reynard the fox. Tell us, sir, is Chanticleer telling the truth? Were you the beast he dreamed about? Did you plan to harm him?

Reynard: I don't know what Chanticleer is talking about! I don't know about any dream. Chanticleer has a wonderful voice and I just wanted to invite him to my home so I could hear him sing.

Helena Hen: What did you tell Chanticleer to get him to think about coming to your house?

Reynard: I said I wanted to see if he was better than his father

© 2015 K12 Inc. All rights reserved.
Copying or distributing without K12's written consent is prohibited.

The Barnyard Evening News

Helena Hen: Why did you grab Chanticleer around the throat and run off?

Reynard: _So I could eat him_

Helena Hen: Why did you let Chanticleer go?

Reynard: _He tricked me_

Helena Hen: Why do you think Chanticleer would not come to your home?

Reynard: _because he knew I would eat him_

Helena Hen: What were you saying as you ran away from the scene?

Reynard: _He who talks should be silent_

© 2015 K12 Inc. All rights reserved.
Copying or distributing without K12's written consent is prohibited.

The Barnyard Evening News

Helena: Thank you, Chanticleer and Reynard. Ladies and gentlemen, it's plain to see that there are indeed two sides to every story! That's all the time we have. This is Helena Hen with *The Barnyard Evening News* saying good night and be safe.

© 2015 K12 Inc. All rights reserved.
Copying or distributing without K12's written consent is prohibited.

Name _____   Date _____

"It Could Always Be Worse"

Sometimes you need to look at a situation from a new perspective. Read how one man's life changes after he takes the advice of a wise rabbi.

Vocabulary

You will find these words in today's reading.

fray: (v.) to become worn down, such as along the edge of cloth when threads start to come loose
Danny wore his favorite jeans so often that the fabric began to *fray*.

misfortune: (n.) bad luck; trouble
The little girl had the *misfortune* of accidentally letting go of her balloon.

Think Ahead

1. Like "Chanticleer and the Fox," the story you will read today has been told many times over the years. Can you recall some of the reasons people like to retell certain stories?

2. In "Chanticleer and the Fox," the two main characters had different perspectives about the events. In this story the main character's perspective changes.

Read

"It Could Always Be Worse" in *Classics for Young Readers,* Vol. 4A, pages 20-21.

© 2015 K12 Inc. All rights reserved.
Copying or distributing without K12's written consent is prohibited.

Questions

Answer the following questions in complete sentences in your Reading Notebook.

1. Why is the man so unhappy?
2. What does the rabbi tell the man to do with his cow, goat, and chickens?
3. How does the man's life change after the cow, goat, and chickens are in his house?
4. How does the man describe his life at the end of the story?

Discuss

1. What lesson does the man learn?
2. Does the man's situation improve as the rabbi promises?
3. Do you think the man realizes that his life at the end of the story is the same as it was at the beginning?
4. Why do you think people enjoy retelling this story?

Perspective

There is more than one way to look at a situation. For instance, if you have a glass of water filled to the halfway point, is the glass half full or half empty? Is either view incorrect? No, they are just different *perspectives*.

- What is the man's perspective at the beginning of the story?
- Does it change at the end of the story, or does he still see things in the same way?
- What makes the man change his perspective?

Dear Diary

Pretend you are the man in the story. Write a diary entry that tells what happened to you. Remember to put the events in the correct order. Write the entry in your Reading Notebook.

© 2015 K12 Inc. All rights reserved.
Copying or distributing without K12's written consent is prohibited.

For example, Chanticleer's diary might have this entry:

Dear Diary,

    I awoke this morning from a terrible dream. In the dream, a beast grabbed me. I knew that it was a sign of terrible things to come. Later, that sly fox Reynard came by and tried to convince me to come to his house to sing. He told me that he liked my father's singing and had heard that mine was even better. Just as I began to crow, he grabbed me by the throat and started to run. Suddenly I knew that Reynard was the beast in my dream. But Reynard didn't get the best of me. I tricked him into teasing the animals that were chasing us. When he opened his mouth, I flew right out and perched up in a tree.

A Book of Wisdom

Think about the lesson in this story. What did the man learn? What do you think the story tells us about being happy with what we have?

Write the lesson learned in this story on a page to add to your "Commonplace Book." Illustrate the page if you like. Save this page.

© 2015 K12 Inc. All rights reserved.
Copying or distributing without K12's written consent is prohibited.

Name _____   Date _____

"The Bear Boy"

Read about a lesson that a story character learns from someone very unexpected.

Pronunciation
Pueblo (PWEB-lo)

Vocabulary
You will find these words in today's reading.

initiation: (n.) the trials or tests that a person, often a young person, has to go through to become part of a group
The young Pueblo boy had to run a course, shoot a bow, and throw a spear as part of his *initiation* into manhood.

mesa: (n.) a large, high rock with steep sides and a flat top
From the *mesa,* we could look down on the rocky cliffs and deep canyons below.

Think Ahead
1. "The Bear Boy" is a story from the Native American people known as the Pueblo. Most Pueblo people live in the southwestern part of the United States. Find Arizona, New Mexico, Utah, Nevada, and Colorado on a map of the United States.

2. If a story is about a father and a son, which character do you think is the most likely one to learn a lesson? See if that turns out to be true in this story.

Read
"The Bear Boy" in *Classics for Young Readers,* Vol. 4A, pages 12-16.

© 2015 K12 Inc. All rights reserved.
Copying or distributing without K12's written consent is prohibited.

Questions

Answer the following questions in complete sentences in your Reading Notebook.

1. What is Kuo-Haya's father like at the beginning of the story?
2. What is Kuo-Haya like at the beginning of the story?
3. Compare how the mother bear treats Kuo-Haya to the way his father treats him.
4. How does the medicine man help Kuo-Haya's father?
5. What does the father do to get his son to come back home?

Discuss

1. Describe Kuo-Haya at the end of the story. How has he changed from the beginning of the story?
2. What lesson does Kuo-Haya's father learn from the mother bear?
3. What lesson does Kuo-Haya learn from the bears?

A Change for the Better

Both Kuo-Haya and his father change in the story. To see how each character changes, complete a chart comparing what the character is like at the beginning of the story to what he is like at the end.

Use the page called A Change for the Better. In the first column describe the character at the beginning of the story. Then think about how the characters change and list those changes in the second column.

A Book of Wisdom

Add another page to your "Commonplace Book." Think about the lessons in this story. What did Kuo-Haya's father learn? What did Kuo-Haya learn?

Write the lessons learned in this story on a page to add to your book. Illustrate the page if you like. Save this page.

© 2015 K12 Inc. All rights reserved.
Copying or distributing without K12's written consent is prohibited.

Name _____ Date _____

A Change for the Better

In the first column, describe the character at the beginning of the story. In the second column, tell how the character is at the end of the story.

Kuo-Haya

Beginning of Story	End of Story
timid	
doesn't know how to wrestle	

Kuo-Haya's father

Beginning of Story	End of Story
does not treat his son well	
is not helping his son prepare for his initiation into manhood	

© 2015 K12 Inc. All rights reserved.
Copying or distributing without K12's written consent is prohibited.

Name _____   Date _____

"The King and His Hawk": Session 1

Read what happens when Genghis Khan, a great king and warrior, makes a judgment without knowing the facts.

Vocabulary

You will find this word in today's reading.

> **clamber:** (v.) to climb with effort, usually by using both hands and feet
> The boy *clambered* up the rocks to reach the top of the mesa.

Think Ahead

Have you ever heard the saying "Think before you act"? What does it mean? Can you describe a situation in which it's important to think before you act?

Read

"The King and His Hawk" in *Classics for Young Readers,* Vol. 4A, pages 17-19.

Questions

Answer the following questions in complete sentences in your Reading Notebook.

1. Describe Genghis Khan.
2. How do hawks help their masters hunt?
3. Why did the king grow angry at his pet hawk?
4. What did the king discover at the end of the story?

© 2015 K12 Inc. All rights reserved.
Copying or distributing without K12's written consent is prohibited.

Discuss

1. Why didn't the king try to figure out why the hawk was diving at him?
2. What lesson did the king learn?
3. What could the king have done instead of acting in anger?

Righting a Wrong

Genghis Khan acted rashly when he struck at his hawk, and he learned a very hard lesson. He didn't know all the facts, yet he acted anyway.

Pretend that you are Genghis Khan. Now that you know what the hawk was trying to do, you regret your actions and you want to keep other people from making the same mistake. You decide to write a letter to your subjects and soldiers to tell them about your actions and the lesson you learned.

In your letter tell:
- What happened
- What you learned from what happened
- What you want others to do to avoid making the same mistake
- How you will honor the memory of your friend, the hawk (for example, with a statue or monument)
- How this event will affect your future actions

You need to know the story well in order to be able to write this letter, so begin by *rereading the story*.

Begin to write the draft of your letter today. You will finish it in the next lesson.

If you want to, you can use the following sentence to begin your letter:

> My people, I, your king, have acted unwisely. I wish to tell you what happened so that you may benefit from the hard lesson I have learned.

© 2015 K12 Inc. All rights reserved.
Copying or distributing without K12's written consent is prohibited.

Name _____   Date _____

"The King and His Hawk": Session 2

Revise, proofread, and publish your letter.

Think Ahead

Read aloud your draft. What do you like best about it? What would you like to change to make the writing clearer or more interesting for your reader?

Revise Your Draft

When an author *revises* a draft, he goes back and makes changes to improve what he has written. Reread your draft, and think about the following questions:

- Does your letter sound like it was written by the king? Do you use "I," "me," and "my"?
- Do you tell what happened?
- Do you tell what you learned from the event?
- Do you tell what you want others to do to avoid making the same mistake?
- Do you tell how you will honor the memory of your friend, the hawk?
- Do you tell how this event will affect your future actions?
- Are your paragraphs and sentences in the right order? Do they make sense?
- Are there words or sentences you should add?

Proofread and Publish Your Draft

Take out your magnifying glass! You're going to *proofread* your draft. Look for and correct all the spelling, punctuation, and grammar errors you can find.

When you finish, write a final copy of your draft. You may draw a picture of the monument to your hawk if you wish. You may wish to

© 2015 K12 Inc. All rights reserved.
Copying or distributing without K12's written consent is prohibited.

add an inscription, for example, "He was such a true friend that he gave his life to save mine."

Now share your letter with family or friends. Think about how Genghis Khan would have sounded when he spoke to his people. Stand straight and tall and speak clearly in a loud voice. Speak with expression. You may wish to practice before a mirror and add gestures to emphasize the points you feel are important.

A Book of Wisdom
Think about the lesson in this story. What did the king learn?

Write the lesson the king learned on a page to add to your "Commonplace Book." Illustrate the page if you like. Save this page.

© 2015 K12 Inc. All rights reserved.
Copying or distributing without K12's written consent is prohibited.

Name _____   Date _____

"The Green Glass Ball": Session 2

The old woman warned the Tinker to be careful using the green glass ball. What do you think his wish will be?

Vocabulary

You will find this word in today's reading.

bog: (n.) an area of soft, wet ground found next to a body of water. When the man drove too close to the pond, the wheels of his car sank into the *bog*.

Think Ahead

You looked for clues in Scene 1 that foreshadow what will happen in the rest of the play. What prediction did you make about what will happen? What do you think the Tinker will wish for?

Read

"The Green Glass Ball": Scene 2 in *Classics for Young Readers,* Vol. 4A, pages 29-35.

Questions

Answer the following questions in complete sentences in your Reading Notebook.

1. Why is it a good day for the Tinker?
2. At the beginning of Scene 2, how does the donkey feel about the green glass ball?
3. What does the donkey want the Tinker to wish for?
4. What does the Tinker wish for?
5. What lesson does the old woman say they have learned from the green glass ball?

© 2015 K12 Inc. All rights reserved.
Copying or distributing without K12's written consent is prohibited.

Discuss
1. Why does the tinker wait for Tim to help him make his wish?
2. Why doesn't the ball seem beautiful to the Tinker after he makes his wish?
3. Was anyone besides the donkey affected by the Tinker's foolish wish?

Creating a Character
Prepare to play a part in "The Green Glass Ball." First choose the character that you would like to play, then choose the scene. Use information from the play to answer the following questions in your Reading Notebook:

1. What costume will you need?
2. What do you think this character's voice sounds like?
3. How does this character move? What actions will you do?
4. What props will you need?

A Book of Wisdom
Think about the lessons in this story. What did the Tinker learn? Write the lesson learned by the Tinker on a page to add to your "Commonplace Book." Illustrate the page if you like. Save this page.

© 2015 K12 Inc. All rights reserved.
Copying or distributing without K12's written consent is prohibited.

Name _____ Date _____

"The Green Glass Ball": Session 3

Ready! Set! Perform a scene from "The Green Glass Ball"!

Think Ahead

1. Review the notes you took about your character. Think about how your character feels during this part of the play. How can you say your lines to show what the character is feeling? Gather any props you will need and prepare your costume.

2. Rehearse your lines. Practice reading with expression. You don't have to memorize your lines, but you should be able to read them smoothly in a loud, clear voice. Practice some of the gestures you will use. Rehearse in front of a mirror and pretend you are speaking to the audience. Think about where you will stand on the stage as you deliver your lines.

3. Be prepared to give your audience a summary of what happens in the parts of the play that you do not perform. Be sure to include the important characters and events.

The Curtain Rises

Welcome your audience and give a brief summary of what has happened in the play up to the scene you are performing. Then act out the lines of the character you are playing. Use gestures and look up from your lines from time to time. Speak clearly, in a voice that everyone can hear.

© 2015 K12 Inc. All rights reserved.
Copying or distributing without K12's written consent is prohibited.

Name _____ Date _____

Looking Back

Revisit the stories and use the story details to complete one of the activities.

Think Ahead

Complete the Lessons Learned Story Review page by writing the names of the main characters under each story title. Then use the pages you created for your Book of Wisdom to help you identify the lesson learned in each story.

Save the review page to use in the next session.

A Book of Wisdom

Assemble your book.

- Put the lesson pages in the same order as the stories in your *Classics* book.
- Make a construction paper cover for your book. Write the title "Commonplace Book" in the center. Illustrate the border if you like.
- Share your book with a family member or friend.

Similarities and Differences

Review the Commonplace Book of Wisdom that you created. With fellow students or with your Learning Coach, discuss what happens to the characters in this unit. Talk about the mistakes the characters in this unit make and the the lessons that they learn from their experiences.

As you talk, think about and try to answer the following questions:

- How are the mistakes that characters make similar? How are they different?
- How are the lessons that the characters learn similar? How are they different?

© 2015 K12 Inc. All rights reserved.
Copying or distributing without K12's written consent is prohibited.

- Are you surprised that characters from such different cultures could learn similar lessons? Why or why not? What does that show?
- Which lessons from the stories in this unit could apply to your own life? How?

Whenever possible during the discussion, use specific examples from the stories in this unit.

Looking Back at Lessons Learned (Optional)
Choose one or more of the following activities to complete.

Interview with a Character
Use the interview from "Chanticleer and the Fox" as a model to create an interview with another character. In your interview, be sure to include questions and answers having to do with the lesson the character learns and how he learns it. Write your interview in your Reading Notebook.

For example:

> **Reporter:** This is Imagine Ation with the *Creativity Evening News*. I am here with our village tinker who tells me he was given a most amazing green ball. Tell me, sir, why were you given this ball?
>
> **Tinker:** I mended a kettle for Old Mother Blakewell. She didn't have any money to pay me, so she gave me a green glass ball. She said the ball was magic.

Dear Diary
Choose a character from the unit who learns an important lesson. Pretend you are that character. Write a diary entry explaining the lesson you learned and how you learned it. Be sure to include details and events from the story.

© 2015 K12 Inc. All rights reserved.
Copying or distributing without K12's written consent is prohibited.

For example, here's the beginning of an entry in the Tinker's diary:

> When I woke up today, I thought it was going to be a great day. My donkey didn't agree with me. He complained from the minute I saw him.

Lights! Camera! Action!

A skit is a short play that has one scene. Choose a part of a story to turn into a skit. Try to stick close to the words and actions in the story, but you may make small changes to improve your skit as long as you remain true to the story. For example, here are some lines you might write for a skit based on "Chanticleer and the Fox."

Reynard: (*speaking in soothing tones*) Your father once visited my house; I should so love to see you there, too. I wonder if you remember your father's singing? I never thought to hear so wonderful a voice again – until I heard you sing this morning.

Chanticleer: (*puffing out his chest feathers*) Oh? Why thank you, kind sir.

Use "The Green Glass Ball" to guide you in writing stage directions, dialogue, and other details. Write your skit in your Reading Notebook or on a separate sheet of paper.

© 2015 K12 Inc. All rights reserved.
Copying or distributing without K12's written consent is prohibited.

Name _____   Date _____

Lessons Learned Story Review

List the main characters under each story

title. "Chanticleer and the Fox"

_____

"It Could Always Be Worse"

_____

"The Bear Boy"

_____

_____

"The King and His Hawk"

_____

"The Green Glass Ball"

© 2015 K12 Inc. All rights reserved.
Copying or distributing without K12's written consent is prohibited.

Name _____ Date _____

"How Bear Lost His Tail"

In this Native American tale, Bear learns a lesson he will always remember thanks to a tricky fox.

Pronunciation
Iroquois (IR-uh-kwoy)

Vocabulary
You will find these words in today's reading.

possession: (n.) something a person owns
My silver locket is my most valuable *possession.*

glossy: (adj.) shiny
Before his bath, our dog's coat was dirty and dull, but after his bath, it was clean and *glossy.*

twitch: (v.) to move suddenly
The rabbit's whiskers *twitched* when it smelled the fox.

Think Ahead
1. Today you will meet a new kind of character, called a *trickster.* What kind of character do you think the trickster will be? Write down your prediction in your Reading Notebook.

2. "How Bear Lost His Tail" is a trickster story from the Native American people called the Iroquois (IR-uh-kwoy). Many Iroquois people live in what is now the state of New York. Find New York on a map of the United States.

Read
"How Bear Lost His Tail" in *Classics for Young Readers,* Vol. 4A, pages 36-39.

© 2015 K12 Inc. All rights reserved.
Copying or distributing without K12's written consent is prohibited.

Questions

Answer the following questions in complete sentences in your Reading Notebook.

1. What does Bear's tail look like at the beginning of the story?
2. Why does Bear want to stick his tail into the icy lake?
3. How long does Bear sit on the ice?
4. How does Bear lose his tail?

Discuss

1. Look back at the prediction you wrote about tricksters. Think about what you read in the story. Which parts of your prediction were correct? Which parts do you want to change?

2. Do you like Fox? Would you want him as a friend? Why or why not?

Summarize the Plot

The *plot* is what happens in a story. To *summarize* a plot means to tell in order the main events in a story. In a summary, you only need to tell the most important events.

For example:

In the story "It Could Always Be Worse," a poor man goes to a rabbi for help because his house seems crowded and noisy. First, the rabbi tells him to put all the farm animals in the house with them. Then, he tells the man to take the farm animals out one at a time. Finally, when the animals are all back outside, the man is happy because now the house seems quiet and peaceful.

Summarize "How Bear Lost His Tail" in your Reading Notebook. Use the words *first, next, then,* and *finally* to help you put the events in the correct order.

© 2015 K12 Inc. All rights reserved.
Copying or distributing without K12's written consent is prohibited.

Trickster Trading Cards

Fox is only the first of many tricksters you will meet in this unit. Make a Trickster Trading Card to remember him as you read about other famous tricksters.

On the blank side of your index card, draw a picture of Fox and write his name. On the lined side, answer these questions:

- Describe Fox's character. Is he funny? Is he mean? Is he clever?
- How does Fox trick Bear?

© 2015 K12 Inc. All rights reserved.
Copying or distributing without K12's written consent is prohibited.

Guidelines for Peer Discussion

Share your thoughts, ideas, questions, and feelings about a text with a peer or others. Listen carefully to what everyone has to say about the text. During your discussion, follow these guidelines.

1. Be prepared to discuss what you think about the text. You should have already read the assignment. Come prepared to discuss your ideas, and use examples from the text to support your thoughts and answers.

2. You will be asked questions about the text. Be ready to answer them, and bring some questions of your own to ask others, such as:

   "Who was your favorite character? Why?"

   "What was your favorite part of the text? Why?"

   "What fact did you enjoy learning? Why do you find this fact interesting?"

   "What question would you ask if you had the chance to meet the author?"

3. Listen if it's not your turn to speak. Pay attention to what others say so that you can add your ideas. Speak clearly and in complete sentences.

4. If you don't understand what someone says, ask a question, such as:

   "What do you mean when you say . . . ?"

   "Can you give an example of . . . ?"

5. If you don't agree with what someone says, explain why.

   "I don't agree with that because . . . "

6. Keep discussions positive! You can disagree, but don't argue. Be respectful.

© 2015 K12 Inc. All rights reserved.
Copying or distributing without K12's written consent is prohibited.

Name _____   Date _____

"From Tiger to Anansi"

Is stronger always better? Decide for yourself while reading this story about one of the smallest tricksters of them all.

Vocabulary
You will find these words in today's reading.

tremble: (v.) to shake with fear
I *trembled* as I watched the scary movie.

feeble: (adj.) weak
The newborn kitten was so *feeble,* it was not strong enough to stand up on its own.

noose: (n.) a loop of string with a knot in it that tightens as the string is pulled
I slipped a *noose* of string around the door handle, and pulled until it tightened.

Think Ahead
1. What kind of character is a *trickster?* What words describe a trickster? What kinds of things do you expect a trickster to do?
2. Today's trickster tale comes from an island called Jamaica, in the Caribbean Sea. Find Jamaica on a map or globe.

Read
"From Tiger to Anansi" in *Classics for Young Readers,* Vol. 4A, pages 40-45

© 2015 K12 Inc. All rights reserved.
Copying or distributing without K12's written consent is prohibited.

Questions

Answer the following questions in complete sentences in your Reading Notebook.

1. Who do the animals say is the strongest animal in the forest?
2. Who do they say is the weakest?
3. Why does Tiger ask Anansi to bring Snake to him?
4. Describe the three ways Anansi tries to catch Snake, and how Snake escapes.
5. How does Anansi trick Snake?

Discuss

1. Do you think Anansi is the weakest animal in the forest? Why or why not?
2. Why does Anansi play the trick on Snake? Why does Fox play the trick on Bear? How are Anansi and Fox the same, and how are they different?

Mr. Snake's Diary

Pretend you are Snake. Write a diary entry that tells what happened to you in the story. Remember to put the events in the correct order.

For example, if you were writing in Tiger's diary, you might say:

This morning I was sitting on my throne and all the animals were sitting around me. Anansi came into the clearing. He bowed so low that his forehead touched the ground. But I ignored him. He is such a weak little thing. Anansi asked me if I would let him name the Tiger Stories "Anansi Stories." Ha! No way. So I decided to play a trick on him. I told him he could have the stories if he could bring me Mr. Snake alive. He said he would, and everyone laughed. I think that is the last we will hear from Anansi!

© 2015 K12 Inc. All rights reserved.
Copying or distributing without K12's written consent is prohibited.

Trickster Trading Cards

Make a Trickster Trading Card for Anansi. On the blank side of an index card, draw Anansi and write his name. On the lined side, answer these questions:

- Describe Anansi's character. Is he brave or cowardly? Is he mean?
- How does Anansi trick Snake?

© 2015 K12 Inc. All rights reserved.
Copying or distributing without K12's written consent is prohibited.

Name _____   Date _____

"Brer Rabbit Gets Brer Fox's Dinner"

Meet Brer Rabbit, a trickster from the American South.

Vocabulary

You will find these words in today's reading.

shingle: (n.) a small, thin piece of material, usually wood or clay, used to cover a roof
The builder laid the *shingles* on the roof in neat, overlapping rows.

outskirts: (n.) a part far away from the center
You'll find offices, stores, and homes in the center of a town, and fields and forests on the *outskirts*.

resume: (v.) to start again
I stopped doing my math problems to help my baby sister tie her shoe, then I *resumed* my work.

Think Ahead

1. Describe the two tricksters you have met: Fox and Anansi. How are they alike? How are they different?

2. "How Bear Lost His Tail" is an Iroquois legend from the northeastern part of the United States. Today's story is from the southeastern part of the United States. Find Georgia on a United States map.

3. A little more than a hundred years ago, a man named Joel Chandler Harris started writing down tales that he remembered hearing slaves tell on a southern plantation. He wrote the stories as though they were being spoken by a kind old slave named Uncle Remus. The story you will read keeps some of this voice, so keep your ears open!

© 2015 K12 Inc. All rights reserved.
Copying or distributing without K12's written consent is prohibited.

Read
"Brer Rabbit Gets Brer Fox's Dinner" in *Classics for Young Readers,* Vol. 4A, pages 46-48

Questions
Answer the following questions in complete sentences in your Reading Notebook.

1. Why is Brer Fox hammering?
2. Does Brer Rabbit really want to help him?
3. Why doesn't Brer Fox stop Brer Rabbit from taking his dinner?

Discuss
1. Why do you think the author says Brer Rabbit and Brer Fox "weren't enemies and weren't friends"? What do you think that means?
2. How does Brer Rabbit trick Brer Fox?

Interview with the Characters
Pretend you are a reporter. Interview each character about what happened in the story.

For Example:
    Reporter: So, Anansi, tell me about how you caught Snake.
    Anansi: Well, it wasn't easy. I tried every trap I knew, but Snake just kept escaping. I decided to trick him. I told him I had to tie him to a bamboo pole to prove he was the longest animal in the world.

Use the questions below to help you get started, or make up questions of your own. Remember to write an interview with each character.

- Why were you hammering?
- How did you feel when Brer Rabbit took the dinner pail?
- Will you be friends or enemies from now on?

© 2015 K12 Inc. All rights reserved.
Copying or distributing without K12's written consent is prohibited.

Trickster Trading Cards

Make a Trickster Trading Card for Brer Rabbit. On the blank side of an index card, draw Brer Rabbit and write his name. On the lined side, answer these questions:

- Describe Brer Rabbit's character. Is he cruel or kind? Is he trustworthy?
- How does Brer Rabbit trick Brer Fox?

© 2015 K12 Inc. All rights reserved.
Copying or distributing without K12's written consent is prohibited.

Name _____   Date _____

"Brer Rabbit Goes Back to Mr. Man's Garden"

Brer Rabbit is up to his tricks again! But this time, will he get dinner or become dinner himself?

Vocabulary
You will find these words in today's reading.

holler: (v.) to yell or shout
At dinnertime, Sarah *hollered* for us so loud, we heard her halfway down the street.

stoop: (v.) to bend down
I *stooped* to lift the heavy box up off the ground.

quiver: (v.) to shake
I *quivered* with excitement as I waited for my turn to play in the piano recital.

Think Ahead
1. Describe Brer Rabbit's character.
2. What is this kind of story character called?
3. Do you think Brer Rabbit will get caught in this story? Why or why not? Write down your prediction.

Read
"Brer Rabbit Goes Back to Mr. Man's Garden" in *Classics for Young Readers,* Vol. 4A, pages 49-52

© 2015 K12 Inc. All rights reserved.
Copying or distributing without K12's written consent is prohibited.

Questions

Answer the following questions in complete sentences in your Reading Notebook.

1. How does Brer Rabbit trick Janey into letting him have some sparrow grass?
2. How does Brer Rabbit trick Janey into letting him have some peas?
3. How does Mr. Man trick Brer Rabbit in the peanut patch?
4. Why does Brer Fox get into the box?

Discuss

1. Look back at your prediction. Which parts were correct? Which parts do you want to change?
2. If you were Mr. Man, what would you have done with Brer Rabbit? Why?
3. What advice would you give Janey? What advice would you give Brer Fox?

Exploring Language

When Joel Chandler Harris wrote down these stories, he decided that he wanted to make them sound the way the slaves told them. How is the language in these stories different from the language you usually see in books and stories?

Write each phrase in your Reading Notebook. Then put the phrase into your own words.

1. "Ain't got time to be flapping gums with you."
2. "I ain't never nailed nobody's tail before."
3. "He said I couldn't have no sparrow grass today, but it would be all right if I helped myself to the English peas."
4. "Mr. Man, I know I done wrong. And if you let me go, I promise I'll stay away from your garden."

© 2015 K12 Inc. All rights reserved.
Copying or distributing without K12's written consent is prohibited.

Act It Out!

Choose your favorite scene from the story. Practice reading it aloud. Here are some questions to think about while you practice:

- How does each character sound?
- How is the character feeling when he or she speaks? Excited? Frightened? Angry?

When you're ready, act out the scene. You may wish to make props and costumes for your performance.

OR

A Letter to Mr. Man

What do you think should happen to Brer Rabbit if Mr. Man catches him again? Why? Write a letter to Mr. Man explaining your opinion.

© 2015 K12 Inc. All rights reserved.
Copying or distributing without K12's written consent is prohibited.

Name   Date

Compare and Contrast Tricksters, Session 1

Fox, Anansi, and Brer Rabbit have some traits in common. But they are also very different. How must a character behave to be called a trickster?

Think Ahead

Review your Trickster Trading Cards. Which character did you like best? Which did you like least? Why?

Compare and Contrast the Tricksters

- Compare the pairs of animals in the trickster tales. Which is usually the stronger animal, a fox or a bear? A tiger or a spider? A snake or a spider? A rabbit or a fox?

- Are the trickster animals strong? What words would you use to describe them?

- Would the stories make you laugh if the trickster were a strong animal tricking a weak one? Why or why not?

- Describe two or more ways the tricksters are alike.

- Describe two or more ways the tricksters are different from each other.

Write About Tricksters

Draft an essay about the two tricksters you think are the most interesting.

Prewriting

First, choose the two tricksters you think are the most interesting. Choose two you have strong feelings about. Which made you laugh the most? Which made you angry?

© 2015 K12 Inc. All rights reserved.
Copying or distributing without K12's written consent is prohibited.

Use this Venn diagram to think about how the two tricksters are alike and different. Label each circle with a trickster's name. Describe each trickster. Where the circles overlap, write what the tricksters have in common.

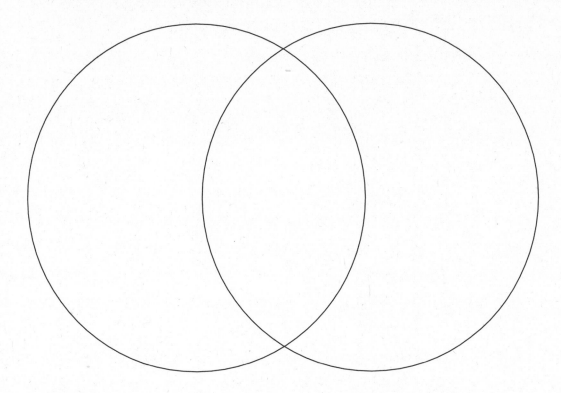

Drafting

Next, write a draft of your essay. Look back at the stories, your Venn diagram, and your trading cards for ideas and information.

Use the guide below to help you organize your paragraphs. Each paragraph should have three or more sentences.

- In the first paragraph, tell your readers what a trickster is. Name the two tricksters you are going to discuss.

- In the second paragraph, describe the first trickster. Support your description with examples of what he says or does.

- In the third paragraph, describe the second trickster. Support your description with examples of what he says or does.

© 2015 K12 Inc. All rights reserved.
Copying or distributing without K12's written consent is prohibited.

- In the fourth paragraph, tell two or more ways the tricksters are alike and two or more ways they are different. When you can, give examples from the stories.

- In the fifth paragraph, tell your readers the most important thing they should know about tricksters.

© 2015 K12 Inc. All rights reserved.
Copying or distributing without K12's written consent is prohibited.

Name _____   Date _____

More Fun with Tricksters

Choose a project and share what you've learned about tricksters.

Think Ahead

Before you start your trickster project, think about what a reader expects to find when he reads a trickster tale. Look back through the stories and discuss the following questions. Make a list of your answers on a separate sheet of paper.

- What do all trickster tales have in common?
- How does a trickster tale begin?
- What happens in the middle of a trickster tale?
- How does a trickster tale end?

Trickster Projects

Complete one or more of the projects listed below.

Write Your Own Trickster Tale

Write an original trickster tale. To get started, make a word web to help you generate ideas for your writing. In the center circle, write the word "Trickster." Then use the questions below to help you generate ideas and details you might want to use in your writing. You may also look back at the stories.

- What kind of animal do you want your trickster to be?
- What characteristics do you want your trickster to have?
- What will your trickster's name be?
- Where does your trickster animal live? In the forest? In the desert? In the sea?
- What kind of animal will the trickster play a trick on?
- What trick do you want your trickster to play?

When you finish, circle or highlight your best ideas and use them to help you write a draft. Then revise, proofread, and publish your story. You may enjoy reading it aloud or acting it out for others.

© 2015 K12 Inc. All rights reserved.
Copying or distributing without K12's written consent is prohibited.

Meet a New Trickster
Research one of the tricksters listed below:

- Coyote
- Iktomi
- Loki
- Leprechauns

Read a story about the trickster you chose. Then do one of the following:

- Write a report that compares and contrasts the trickster to the other tricksters you have learned about.
- Write a letter to the trickster character, describing how he is similar to and different from the other characters.
- Make a poster and write three or more paragraphs that compare and contrast the new trickster to the others. Include an illustration of the new trickster.

Share a Trickster Tale
Read aloud or act out your favorite trickster tale. Think about the following as you choose your story:

- Which story did you think was the funniest?
- Which character did you like best?
- Think about the characters' words and actions. Which would be the most fun to read aloud or act out? Why?

Before you perform the story, practice reading expressively. Here are some questions to think about while you practice:

- How does each character sound?
- How is the character feeling when he or she speaks? Is he excited? Is he frightened? Is he angry?

You may wish to make props and costumes. When you choose them, think about where the story takes place and how the people or animals in the story dress. You may look in the book for ideas and suggestions.

When you're ready, read aloud or perform your story for others.

© 2015 K12 Inc. All rights reserved.
Copying or distributing without K12's written consent is prohibited.

Name _____   Date _____

All Kinds of People

All kinds of people make up the world. In this lesson, you will read four short poems describing some of these different types of people.

First Reading: "Some People"

Vocabulary

You will find this word in the first poem you will read today.

shrivel: (v.) to shrink or dry up
If you leave those apples sitting out in the hot sun, they will *shrivel* up and be no good to eat.

Think Ahead

1. Look through the pages of *Classics for Young Readers*. Use the table of contents to locate the poem "Some People" and turn to that page.
2. Preview the poem and those that follow it by scanning the pages in *Classics for Young Readers*. What do you notice about the structure of these poems? How is the structure of the poems different from the structure of stories and plays you have read?
3. Think of people you know. Are there certain people who always make you feel good when you are with them? Are there others you would rather not be around? Why do you think that is? The poem you are about to read describes different types of people.

Read

Read "Some People" once silently and a second time aloud.

© 2015 K12 Inc. All rights reserved.
Copying or distributing without K12's written consent is prohibited.

Discuss

1. There are two stanzas in this poem. Reread the first stanza. How do the people described in this stanza make us feel? Are these people you would like to spend time with?

2. What do you think it means to have your thoughts "shrivel up like leaves all brown and dried"?

3. The second stanza describes people who affect us in the opposite way. In your own words, how do these people make us feel?

4. When you hear the words "fireflies all shiny in your mind," what image comes to mind? In your own words, how does a person with "thoughts as thick as fireflies" feel?

Second Reading: "Thoughts on Talkers"

Vocabulary
You will find this word in the second poem you will read today.

drawl: (n.) a slow, drawn-out way of speaking
I like the way my aunt from South Carolina speaks with a gentle *drawl.*

Think Ahead
Have you ever been with someone who talks so much you can't slip in any words of your own? Our next poet knows some people like that!

Read
Read "Thoughts on Talkers" once silently and a second time aloud.

Discuss

1. What do you think the poet means in the last two lines of the poem? How can some people talk and "never say anything at all"?

2. In the next-to-last line of the poem, why do you think the poet repeated the words "and talk" so many times?

© 2015 K12 Inc. All rights reserved.
Copying or distributing without K12's written consent is prohibited.

Third Reading: "Ten Kinds"

Vocabulary
You will find these words in the third poem you will read today.

grieve: (v.) to distress or upset
"It *grieves* me to think that you were a bully on the playground today," Teddy's mother told him seriously.

dreary: (adj.) without happiness, gloomy
The sunshine disappeared behind rain clouds, and the sunny day turned dark and *dreary.*

Think Ahead
The next poem uses invented names to describe types of people you might run across in your neighborhood, on your sports team, or even in your family. See if you recognize any of these characters.

Read
Read "Ten Kinds" once silently and a second time aloud.

Discuss
1. Of all the kinds of people described in the poem, which one would you least like to be around, and why?

2. Reread the last two lines of the poem. Of these ten kinds of people, the speaker says it is "easy to choose" which one you would want as a friend. Which one do you think the speaker means? Do you agree?

© 2015 K12 Inc. All rights reserved.
Copying or distributing without K12's written consent is prohibited.

Guidelines for Peer Discussion

Share your thoughts, ideas, questions, and feelings about a text with a peer or others. Listen carefully to what everyone has to say about the text. During your discussion, follow these guidelines.

1. Be prepared to discuss what you think about the text. You should have already read the assignment. Come prepared to discuss your ideas, and use examples from the text to support your thoughts and answers.

2. You will be asked questions about the text. Be ready to answer them, and bring some questions of your own to ask others, such as:

   "Who was your favorite character? Why?"

   "What was your favorite part of the text? Why?"

   "What fact did you enjoy learning? Why do you find this fact interesting?"

   "What question would you ask if you had the chance to meet the author?"

3. Listen if it's not your turn to speak. Pay attention to what others say so that you can add your ideas. Speak clearly and in complete sentences.

4. If you don't understand what someone says, ask a question, such as:

   "What do you mean when you say . . . ?"

   "Can you give an example of . . . ?"

5. If you don't agree with what someone says, explain why.

   "I don't agree with that because . . . "

6. Keep discussions positive! You can disagree, but don't argue. Be respectful.

© 2015 K12 Inc. All rights reserved.
Copying or distributing without K12's written consent is prohibited.

Name _____ Date _____

Your Thoughts

Write your own poem, imitating the structure of "Thoughts on Talkers."

First, read "Thoughts on Talkers" again.

Now, think about other things people do besides talk. For example, they eat, dance, or sing. What other things do people do? Add some verbs here:

_____

_____

_____

_____

Pick one action and use it for a poem with "Thoughts on Talkers" as your model. Here is an example:

Thoughts on Walkers

Some people go out walking all around the town.
And some people go out walking up the roads and down.
Some people walk in a hurry,
And some people slowly stroll.
And some people walk and walk and walk and walk and walk
And never get anywhere at all.

© 2015 K12 Inc. All rights reserved.
Copying or distributing without K12's written consent is prohibited.

Your Thoughts

Use the lines below to write your poem. Your poem does not have to rhyme.

Title: Thoughts on _____

Some people _____

And some people_____.

And some people _____

And some people _____

And some people_____and _____

and_____and _____

And_____.

© 2015 K12 Inc. All rights reserved.
Copying or distributing without K12's written consent is prohibited.

Name _____ Date _____

Such Strange People!

In this lesson, you will read, listen to, and discuss three poems about peculiar people. The characters you will meet in these poems are imaginary, but they might describe someone you know. You might even recognize yourself in one of these poems!

First Reading: "Going Too Far"

Vocabulary

You will find these words in the first poem you will read today.

passion: (n.) a great love
A librarian is thrilled when a child has a *passion* for reading.

rage: (n.) great anger
When the playground in town was torn down to make room for a gas station, the citizens were filled with *rage*.

brew: (v.) to take form
Those dark clouds make me think a storm is starting to *brew* in the west.

whisk: (v.) to take up, carry away
This vacuum cleaner can *whisk* up dirt in the wink of an eye.

Read and Listen

Complete the online activity to read and listen to "Going Too Far."

Discuss

1. What does the character in the poem most like to do? Do you know anyone like this?

2. The actions of the character in the poem are exaggerated, for example, "She scrubbed her doorstep into the ground." Find another example of exaggeration in the poem.

© 2015 K12 Inc. All rights reserved.
Copying or distributing without K12's written consent is prohibited.

3. Look again at the title of the poem. Can you describe two different ways in which the woman is "going to far"?

4. How does the speaker's voice affect your feelings about the poem? How was listening to "Going Too Far" different than reading it?"

Second Reading: "Eat-It-All-Elaine"

Vocabulary
You will find this word in the second poem you will read today.

stir: (n.) excitement, commotion
The quarterback created quite a *stir* when he made the winning touchdown in the last three seconds of the game.

Think Ahead
Have you ever done anything odd or unusual to draw attention to yourself? Well, meet Elaine!

Read
Read "Eat-It-All-Elaine" once silently and a second time aloud.

Discuss
1. Name some of the things Elaine eats that impress her fellow campers.

2. Why do you think Elaine eats the things she does?
3. At the end of the poem the adults give out awards to campers for outstanding achievements. What achievements do you think they might recognize?

4. Reread the last stanza of the poem. Notice that the poet describes certain people at the camp as "thinking." Who are the "thinking" people at the camp?

5. Do you agree with the kids or with the adults? Do you think Elaine's achievements are the "most outstanding"?

© 2015 K12 Inc. All rights reserved.
Copying or distributing without K12's written consent is prohibited.

Third Reading: "Jimmy Jet and His TV Set"

Vocabulary

You will find this expression in the last poem you will read today.

tuning dial: (n.) the knob on older televisions that you turn to locate channels

Rachel turned the *tuning dial* until she found the program she wanted.

Think Ahead

Many people think that watching a lot of television isn't good for you. What do you think?

Read

Read "Jimmy Jet and His TV Set" once silently and a second time aloud.

Discuss

1. What happened to Jimmy Jet? Find lines in the poem that describe how he changes.

2. The second line of the poem says, "And you know what I tell you is true." Why do you think the poet says that?

3. The exaggeration in the poem makes us laugh but it also teaches a lesson. What is the lesson?

© 2015 K12 Inc. All rights reserved.
Copying or distributing without K12's written consent is prohibited.

Name _____   Date _____

Humorous Characters

Have you ever heard the expression, "He's a real *character*"? Well, you're about to meet two imaginary characters who are "real characters"!

First Reading: "Jonathan Bing"

Vocabulary
You will find these words in the first poem you will read today.

Archbishop: (n.) the highest church official in the Church of England
The *Archbishop* arrived at the cathedral to preside over the king's wedding.

court: (n.) the place, such as a palace, where a ruler lives
As he entered the *court,* the knight bowed before his king.

Think Ahead
Have you ever shown up for an event and discovered you were not dressed appropriately? How did you feel? What did you do? Perhaps you can sympathize with the character in the next poem!

Read
Read "Jonathan Bing" once silently and a second time aloud.

Discuss
1. Many songs include a *refrain*—a part that is repeated. "Jonathan Bing" sounds almost like a song because certain lines are repeated. Which lines are repeated in the poem?

2. In each stanza, Jonathan Bing gets a little closer to meeting the king. Where is he in each stanza?

© 2015 K12 Inc. All rights reserved.
Copying or distributing without K12's written consent is prohibited.

3. Why do you think Jonathan Bing says, "For home's the best place for all people like me"?

Second Reading: "The Pirate Don Durk of Dowdee"

Vocabulary

You will find these words in the second poem you will read today.

conscience: (n.) inner feelings and thoughts that tell a person what is right and what is wrong
I told the truth so my *conscience* is clear.

plume: (n.) feather
The actress placed in her hat a turquoise *plume* from a peacock.

crimson: (adj.) a deep red color
The autumn leaves are shades of gold, orange, and *crimson*.

dirk: (n.) a long knife or dagger
Robin Hood had a sharp *dirk* concealed in his cloak.

cuff: (n.) the folded end of a sleeve or pants
The *cuff* on the sleeve of the woman's dress was made of lace.

cutlass: (n.) a short sword
Captain Hook threatened Peter Pan with a *cutlass.*

buccaneer: (n.) a pirate
Peter Pan's lost boys liked to pretend they were *buccaneers.*

© 2015 K12 Inc. All rights reserved.
Copying or distributing without K12's written consent is prohibited.

Think Ahead

The next poem describes an imaginary character who is wicked, frightening—and delightful! See if you can picture him in your imagination as you read the poem.

Read

Read "The Pirate Don Durk of Dowdee" once silently and a second time aloud.

Discuss

1. The poet uses two similes to describe the pirate's conscience. What are they?

2. The poet uses some made-up or unusual words. What do you think a "squizzamaroo" is? (You won't find the word in a dictionary!) Find two other made-up or unusual sounding words.

3. Imagine that you have met the Pirate Don Durk of Dowdee. How would you describe him to a friend?

Activities

Picturing the Pirate

Print the Picturing the Pirate page and follow the directions to complete it. Once you have completed the page, draw a picture of the pirate on a separate sheet of paper. Do your best to make your picture show the pirate as the poem describes him.

Talk About Your Picture

Discuss the picture of the pirate that you drew. Describe how your picture accurately captures the pirate as the text describes him. Use specific examples and details from the poem to support your points.

© 2015 K12 Inc. All rights reserved.
Copying or distributing without K12's written consent is prohibited.

<u>Name</u>   <u>Date</u>

Picturing the Pirate

Examine how the poet uses language to help us picture the pirate in our minds. Use highlighters or colored pencils of three different colors to mark the vivid language in the poem, which is reprinted below.

1. The poet uses many vivid adjectives. The first adjective that describes the pirate is "wicked." Use one color to mark "wicked." Then use the same color to mark the other adjectives that describe the pirate. (Only mark the adjectives that describe the pirate himself.)

2. The poet helps us imagine the pirate by naming many *things* that he wears, keeps, or carries. For example, he has "a floppety plume on his hat." Use another color to mark other things associated with the pirate.

3. We also get to know the pirate through his actions. Use another color to mark the words or lines that show the pirate doing something.

4. If you want to, draw a picture of the pirate. Try to include many of the vivid details that you have marked in the poem.

> Ho, for the Pirate Don Durk of Dowdee!
> He was as wicked as wicked could be,
> But oh, he was perfectly gorgeous to see!
> > The Pirate Don Durk of Dowdee.
>
> His conscience, of course, was black as a
> bat, But he had a floppety plume on his hat
> And when he went walking it jiggled—like that!
> > The plume of the Pirate Dowdee.
>
> His coat it was crimson and cut with a slash,
> And often as ever he twirled his mustache
> Deep down in the ocean the mermaids went splash,
> > Because of Don Durk of Dowdee.

© 2015 K12 Inc. All rights reserved.
Copying or distributing without K12's written consent is prohibited.

Picturing the Pirate

Moreover, Dowdee had a purple tattoo,
And stuck in his belt where he buckled it through
Were a dagger, a dirk and a squizzamaroo,
    For fierce was the Pirate Dowdee.

So fearful he was he would shoot at a puff,
And always at sea when the weather grew rough
He drank from a bottle and wrote on his cuff,
    Did Pirate Don Durk of Dowdee.

Oh, he had a cutlass that swung at his thigh
And he had a parrot called Pepperkin Pye,
And a zigzaggy scar at the end of his eye
    Had Pirate Don Durk of Dowdee.

He kept in a cavern, this buccaneer bold,
A curious chest that was covered with mold,
And all of his pockets were jingly with gold!
    O jing! went the gold of Dowdee.

His conscience, of course, it was crook'd like a squash,
But both of his boots made a slickery slosh,
And he went through the world with a wonderful swash,
    Did Pirate Don Durk of Dowdee.

It's true he was wicked as wicked could be,
His sins they outnumbered a hundred and three,
But oh, he was perfectly gorgeous to see,
    The Pirate Don Durk of Dowdee.

© 2015 K12 Inc. All rights reserved.
Copying or distributing without K12's written consent is prohibited.

Name _____   Date _____

Speaking for Themselves

The poems you will read in this lesson all have speakers who describe different situations and how they feel about these situations. As you read, look for clues that tell us about who the speakers are.

First Reading: "Rhinos Purple, Hippos Green"

Think Ahead
Have you ever been told something you wrote, painted, or performed was "stupid"? The speaker in this poem describes such a situation.

Read
Read "Rhinos Purple, Hippos Green" once silently and a second time aloud.

Discuss
1. Describe the situation in this poem. Who is speaking? What might have happened to lead up to the poem?

2. The sister says that it's "stupid" to color rhinos purple and hippos green because "those are things she's never seen." What does this tell us about the sister?

3. In saying "I don't care what my sister says," and insisting "I will color what I want to," the speaker reveals something about himself or herself. What *adjectives* would you use to describe the speaker?

© 2015 K12 Inc. All rights reserved.
Copying or distributing without K12's written consent is prohibited.

Second Reading: "Since Hanna Moved Away" and "Pete at the Zoo"

Vocabulary

You will find these words in the next two poems you will read today.

halibut: (n.) a type of fish
I usually don't like fish, but the *halibut* my father grilled for dinner was really tasty.

mutt: (n.) a mixed breed dog
Although the puppy we found at the shelter was just a *mutt*, we thought he was cute and brought him home.

note: (v.) to observe or notice
Juan's mother asked him to *note* the time when the package was delivered.

might: (n.) strength or power
The giant showed his *might* by pulling up two huge trees with his bare hands.

hunch: (v.) to arch or push up with your back
We saw the frightened cat *hunch* its back and hiss.

Think Ahead

The speakers in the next two poems are not very happy. As you read, look for the *imagery* that shows what they are feeling.

Imagery is language that creates a mental picture by appealing to the senses. Imagery makes us see, hear, smell, taste, or feel things in our imagination. For example, what do you see when you read "the coal-black night"? What do you feel when you read "the

© 2015 K12 Inc. All rights reserved.
Copying or distributing without K12's written consent is prohibited.

stinging cold"? What do you hear when you read "the rapping and tapping of rain on the roof"?

Read
Read "Since Hanna Moved Away" once silently and a second time aloud.

Discuss
1. The speaker in this poem is sad because her best friend has moved away. Find words in the first and last stanzas of the poem that express the sadness of the speaker.

2. Throughout the poem, the poet uses imagery—language that creates a mental picture by appealing to the senses. What senses do the first two stanzas appeal to?

3. Which phrases in the third stanza appeal to your senses of smell, touch, and sight?

4. Have the bad things that the speaker describes really happened? For example, do the flowers really "smell like halibut"? (Hint: Reread the first stanza.)

5. Why does the speaker describe everything with such unpleasant imagery?

Read
Read "Pete at the Zoo" once silently and a second time aloud.

Discuss
1. Who is the speaker in this poem and where is he? How do you know?

2. What is he wondering?

3. In the last two lines, the speaker compares himself to the elephant. He wonders

> Does he hunch up, as I do,
> Against the dark of night?

What is the speaker saying about his own feelings when night comes?

© 2015 K12 Inc. All rights reserved.
Copying or distributing without K12's written consent is prohibited.

Name _____   Date _____

Speaking for Yourself

Write a poem in which you are the speaker.

Part 1. Review

Think about the poems you read for this lesson. In one, the speaker is a child whose sister calls him or her "stupid" for coloring rhinos purple and hippos green. In another, the speaker feels sad because her best friend has moved away. In another, the speaker thinks about his own loneliness when he sees an elephant at the zoo.

Each of these poems features a speaker who tells us something about himself or herself through the words and images of the poem.

Part 2. Prewriting

Think about a time when you were happy, surprised, angry, sad, or proud—when you felt some strong emotion. What made you feel that way? In one or two sentences, describe the situation that made you feel that way.

_____

_____

_____

_____

_____

_____

© 2015 K12 Inc. All rights reserved.
Copying or distributing without K12's written consent is prohibited.

Speaking for Yourself

Write an image that shows how you felt. Your image should use language that appeals to the senses. (For example, "The sky is grouchy gray"—from "Since Hanna Moved Away.")

_____

_____

Write a simile that expresses how you felt. (For example, "Chocolate ice cream tastes like prunes"—from "Since Hanna Moved Away.")

_____

_____

Part 3. Writing

Write a short poem about the situation you described above and the feelings you had at the time. Speak in your own voice, but be sure to use vivid language. When appropriate, work in the image and simile you wrote above. (Your poem does not have to rhyme.)

_____

_____

_____

_____

_____

© 2015 K12 Inc. All rights reserved.
Copying or distributing without K12's written consent is prohibited.

Name _____   Date _____

Dramatic Reading

Poetry can be great fun to read silently, but did you know that many poems are even more fun to read aloud? In this lesson you will give a dramatic reading for an audience of one poem from this unit. You will also create a visual aid that goes with the poem you choose for your dramatic reading.

Think Ahead

Look over the poems that you have read in this unit. Think about the ones you liked most and the ones that might be fun to read aloud. Then choose one poem to read aloud in front of an audience. If you have trouble choosing a poem, ask yourself the following questions:

- Which poems did I like the most?
- Why was I drawn to them?
- Which poem will be the most fun to read aloud?
- How is the poem I want to read aloud different from the others in the unit?
- What will I do during my reading to bring this poem to life?
- Do I have any ideas about what kind of visual aid I will create to go with this poem? If so, what are they?

Once you've chosen a poem to read aloud, create a visual aid to show while you're reading. The visual aid should be a picture that somehow relates to the poem. The picture might show

- a main character in the poem
- a key event that the poem describes
- a place where the action of the poem takes place
- an emotion that the poem makes you feel

© 2015 K12 Inc. All rights reserved.
Copying or distributing without K12's written consent is prohibited.

Finally, practice reading your poem aloud several times. Each time you read the poem, also practice explaining how your visual aid relates to it. Remember that you will be reading in front of an audience, so

- Speak loudly enough to be heard.
- Speak clearly enough to be understood.
- Capture the rhythm and rhyme scheme of the poem.
- Use your voice to express the mood and emotions of the poem.
- Make eye contact with your audience.

Read Aloud

Read the poem you have chosen aloud in front of an audience and explain to them how your visual aid relates to the poem.

Review

After you have read your poem aloud and explained your visual aid, watch the recording of your dramatic reading. Look for the strengths and weaknesses of your performance. Then answer the following questions:

1. Did you speak loudly and clearly throughout your reading? If not, which parts of the reading could have been better?

_____

_____

_____

_____

2. Did you accurately capture the rhythm and rhyme scheme of the poem? If not, which lines or sections did you have difficulty with?

_____

_____

_____

_____

© 2015 K12 Inc. All rights reserved.
Copying or distributing without K12's written consent is prohibited.

3. What emotions did you attempt to express with your voice during the reading? How did you do so?

_____

_____

_____

_____

4. Could you have have done a better job of expressing the poem's emotions? If so, which parts of the poem would you improve?

_____

_____

_____

_____

5. How well did you explain the connection between the poem and your visual aid? In what ways might you have improved your explanation?

_____

_____

_____

_____

When you have finished answering the questions about your own dramatic reading, gather the Peer Review sheet. Watch a fellow student deliver his or her dramatic reading and complete the Peer Review sheet based on his or her reading.

Finally, consider this question: How was the experience of watching (or reading) a poem aloud different from reading it silently? How does the performance change your experience of the poem and the feelings it creates.

© 2015 K12 Inc. All rights reserved.
Copying or distributing without K12's written consent is prohibited.

Peer Review

Watch another student's dramatic reading of a poem from this unit and answer the questions.

1. Which poem did the student read aloud?

   _____

   _____

2. Did the student speak loudly and clearly throughout the dramatic reading? If not, which parts of the reading could have been improved?

   _____

   _____

   _____

3. Did the student accurately capture the rhythm and rhyme scheme of the poem? If not, which lines or sections did the student have difficulty with?

   _____

   _____

   _____

4. What emotions did the student attempt to express with his or her voice during the reading? How did the student do so?

   _____

   _____

© 2015 K12 Inc. All rights reserved.
Copying or distributing without K12's written consent is prohibited.

5. Could the student have done a better job of expressing the poem's emotions? If so, which parts of the poem could have been improved?

_____

_____

_____

6. How well did the student explain the connection between the poem and the visual aid? In what ways might the student have improved this explanation?

_____

_____

_____

7. Tell about the difference between reading the poem aloud and hearing it performed. How did the experiences differ?

_____

_____

_____

© 2015 K12 Inc. All rights reserved.
Copying or distributing without K12's written consent is prohibited.

Name _____   Date _____

"Noah and the Ark"

Sometimes making the right choice takes great courage.

Vocabulary

You will find these words in today's reading.

jeer: (v.) to mock or make fun of
The jungle animals *jeered* at Anansi because he was small and weak.

hinder: (v.) to slow someone down or get in the way
My little brother tried to *hinder* me from leaving by hanging on
my legs as I walked to the door.

Think Ahead

Today's story is from the Bible. The main character in the story has to
make some very important choices. You make choices every day.
Some are small choices, such as choosing what color shirt to wear or
what to eat for lunch. But some are big, important choices, such as
choosing to tell the truth. Tell about an important choice you have
made. Was it hard to make the choice? Why or why not?

Read

"Noah and the Ark" in *Classics for Young Readers,* Vol. 4A, pages
54-57.

Questions

Answer the following questions in complete sentences in your
Reading Notebook.

1. How were Noah and his family different from their neighbors?
2. What did Noah's neighbors do when they saw him building an ark?
3. Besides his family, what did Noah take aboard the ark?

© 2015 K12 Inc. All rights reserved.
Copying or distributing without K12's written consent is prohibited.

4. How did the animals behave when they were together in the ark?
5. For how long did it rain?
6. Why didn't the dove return when Noah let it out the third time?

Discuss

1. Do you think it took courage for Noah to build the ark when his neighbors laughed at him? Why do you think he kept building?
2. After the flood, what did God promise? What did the rainbow mean to Noah?

Choices and Consequences

In stories, characters make choices. These choices have consequences. Choices and consequences are an important part of a story's plot.

Use details from the story to answer the questions on the Choices and Consequences page.

Bible Character Chart

Keep a chart to help you remember information about the characters in these stories. In the boxes write:

- the main character's name
- the title of the story
- two or three words or phrases to describe the character
- an important choice the character makes
- what matters most to the character in the story

Add Noah to the Bible Character Chart.

© 2015 K12 Inc. All rights reserved.
Copying or distributing without K12's written consent is prohibited.

Name _____   Date _____

Noah: Choices and Consequences

Answer the questions using details from the story.

1. Why did Noah and his family build the ark? What problem did they face
   while they were building it?

   _____

   _____

   _____

2. What did they decide to do?

   _____

   _____

   _____

3. What were the *consequences* of their choice? (What happened to them when
   the rains came?)

   _____

   _____

   _____

© 2015 K12 Inc. All rights reserved.
Copying or distributing without K12's written consent is prohibited.

Noah: Choices and Consequences

4. After the ark settled on Mount Ararat, what did Noah decide to do?

_____

_____

_____

5. After the flood, what did God promise?

_____

_____

_____

© 2015 K12 Inc. All rights reserved.
Copying or distributing without K12's written consent is prohibited.

Name _____

Date _____

Bible Character Chart

In the boxes below, write the character's name, the title of the story, two or three words or phrases that describe the character, an important choice the character made, and what mattered most in the story to the character.

Name	Title	Description	Choice	What Mattered Most

© 2015 K12 Inc. All rights reserved.
Copying or distributing without K12's written consent is prohibited.

Guidelines for Peer Discussion

Share your thoughts, ideas, questions, and feelings about a text with a peer or others. Listen carefully to what everyone has to say about the text. During your discussion, follow these guidelines.

1. Be prepared to discuss what you think about the text. You should have already read the assignment. Come prepared to discuss your ideas, and use examples from the text to support your thoughts and answers.

2. You will be asked questions about the text. Be ready to answer them, and bring some questions of your own to ask others, such as:

   "Who was your favorite character? Why?"

   "What was your favorite part of the text? Why?"

   "What fact did you enjoy learning? Why do you find this fact interesting?"

   "What question would you ask if you had the chance to meet the author?"

3. Listen if it's not your turn to speak. Pay attention to what others say so that you can add your ideas. Speak clearly and in complete sentences.

4. If you don't understand what someone says, ask a question, such as:

   "What do you mean when you say . . . ?"

   "Can you give an example of . . . ?"

5. If you don't agree with what someone says, explain why.

   "I don't agree with that because . . . "

6. Keep discussions positive! You can disagree, but don't argue. Be respectful.

© 2015 K12 Inc. All rights reserved.
Copying or distributing without K12's written consent is prohibited.

Name _____   Date _____

"Joseph and His Brothers": Session 1

In this story, a young man learns to make the best of difficult situations.

Vocabulary
You will find these words in today's reading.

behold: (v.) to look
"Behold," said the man, pointing to the dark clouds in the sky, "a storm approaches."

sheaf: (n.) a bunch of grasses that have been tied together
The boy picked up the fallen wheat and tied it into a *sheaf.*

devour: (v.) to eat up greedily
The hungry dog grabbed the bone and proceeded to *devour* it.

misfortune: (n.) bad luck
I had the *misfortune* to step into a puddle and dirty my new shoes right before the party.

famine: (n.) a time when there is not enough food for everyone
The year it did not rain, no crops grew, and there was a terrible *famine* in the land.

Think Ahead
1. Summarize what you read in "Noah and the Ark." In your summary, tell
   - what Noah built
   - how long it rained
   - how Noah knew it was safe to leave the ark
   - what God promised at the end of the story

© 2015 K12 Inc. All rights reserved.
Copying or distributing without K12's written consent is prohibited.

2. Tell one choice Noah made and the consequences of that choice.
3. What does it mean to be *jealous*? Can you think of a situation where one person might be jealous of another?

Read
Chapters 1-3 of "Joseph and His Brothers" in *Classics for Young Readers,* Vol. 4A, pages 58-66.

Questions
Answer the following questions in complete sentences in your Reading Notebook.
1. Why were Joseph's brothers jealous of him?
2. What did Joseph's brothers decide to do about him first?
3. What did Judah suggest?
4. What happened to Joseph when he first arrived in Egypt?
5. Was Joseph thrown in prison because he committed a crime?

Discuss
1. What did Joseph decide when he arrived in Egypt? Do you think he made a wise choice? Why?
2. Why did Joseph help Pharaoh's servants when they were in prison? Did he have to?
3. What happened when the butler returned to the palace? What were the consequences of Joseph's choice?
4. Why do you think Pharaoh chose Joseph to be the governor over Egypt?

Story Timeline
Use details from the story to answer the questions on the Story Timeline page.

© 2015 K12 Inc. All rights reserved.
Copying or distributing without K12's written consent is prohibited.

Name _____ Date _____

Story Timeline

Use details from the story to answer the questions below.

1. Describe Joseph's first dream. _____

_____

2. What did Joseph's brothers think his dream meant?

_____

_____

3. In the box, draw a symbol to stand for Joseph's dream.

_____

4. Whose dreams did Joseph tell the meaning of next? Where was he when
   he told them?

_____

© 2015 K12 Inc. All rights reserved.
Copying or distributing without K12's written consent is prohibited.

Story Timeline

5. Describe Pharaoh's first dream. _____

_____

_____

6. Describe Pharaoh's second dream. _____

_____

_____

7. Draw a symbol for each of Pharaoh's dreams in the boxes.

© 2015 K12 Inc. All rights reserved.
Copying or distributing without K12's written consent is prohibited.

Story Timeline

8. What did Joseph say the dreams meant? _____

_____

9. What advice did Joseph give Pharaoh? _____

_____

10. What did Pharaoh do? _____

_____

_____

© 2015 K12 Inc. All rights reserved.
Copying or distributing without K12's written consent is prohibited.

Name _____ Date _____

"Joseph and His Brothers" Session 2

Joseph is the governor of Egypt. But will he ever see his family again?

Vocabulary

You will find these words in today's reading.

garments: (n.) clothes

It started raining as I left the library, and by the time I got home, my *garments* were soaked.

hasten: (v.) to hurry

"Come," said the shepherd, "let us *hasten* to the village, for night is falling fast."

Think Ahead

1. Summarize what you have read so far in the story. In your summary, tell
   - the name of Joseph's father
   - what gift Joseph's father gave him that made the other brothers jealous
   - what Joseph's brothers did to him
   - what the seven fat cattle and seven lean cattle meant in Pharaoh's dream

2. Predict what you think will happen next. Explain the reasons for your prediction.

Read

Chapters 4-5 of "Joseph and His Brothers" in *Classics for Young Readers,* Vol. 4A, pages 58-66.

© 2015 K12 Inc. All rights reserved.
Copying or distributing without K12's written consent is prohibited.

Questions

Answer the following questions in complete sentences in your Reading Notebook.

1. Why didn't Joseph's brothers recognize him when they arrived in Egypt?
2. Why didn't Joseph's brothers want to bring Benjamin to Egypt?
3. How did the silver cup get into Benjamin's sack?
4. What did Judah say to the governor when the cup was found in Benjamin's sack?
5. At the end of the story, what did Joseph invite his brothers and their families to do?

Discuss

1. At the beginning of the story, what did Judah suggest the brothers do with Joseph when they found out he was their father's favorite? What does he decide to do when the cup is found in Benjamin's sack? How has Judah changed?

2. Why did Joseph tell his brothers not to be sad or angry with themselves? Think about Joseph's life. What do Joseph's words tell you about the kind of person he is?

From Judah's Perspective

Pretend you are Judah. Retell Chapter 5 from where the brothers leave the governor's palace. For example, you might begin like this:

> What a strange and exciting day it has been! In the morning, my brothers and I packed our sacks and set out for home. We hadn't gone far when the governor's steward came running up to us. He said one of us had taken the governor's silver drinking cup…

When you finish, discuss the following questions:
- What lesson do you think Judah learned?
- Do you think he will act differently in the future? Why?

Bible Character Chart

Add Joseph and Judah to the Bible Character Chart.

© 2015 K12 Inc. All rights reserved.
Copying or distributing without K12's written consent is prohibited.

Name _____ Date _____

"The Story of Moses"

Follow the story of Moses, an Israelite who grew up to save his people.

Vocabulary
You will find these words in today's reading.

bulrushes: (n.) tall, grasslike reeds that grow in wet places
The *bulrushes* grew like enormous blades of grass by the river's edge.

compassion: (n) a desire to help that grows out of feeling someone else's suffering
Everyone felt *compassion* for the people whose home was damaged by the flood, and many people gave them food, clothing, and furniture.

splendid: (adj.) magnificent
He wore a *splendid* jacket woven entirely with silver and gold thread.

Think Ahead
1. You've read "Noah and the Ark" and "Joseph and His Brothers." Who do you think has been the most interesting character you've met so far? Why?

2. Even when you make a wrong choice, you can usually make another choice to make it right. Can you think of a time you made a wrong choice? What did you do to make it right?

Read
"The Story of Moses" in *Classics for Young Readers,* Vol. 4A, pages 67-72.

© 2015 K12 Inc. All rights reserved.
Copying or distributing without K12's written consent is prohibited.

Questions

Answer the following questions in complete sentences in your Reading Notebook.

1. At the beginning of the story, what did Moses' mother do to save him?
2. Who is Miriam? What important thing did she do in the story?
3. Why was Moses sad and troubled while he lived in Pharaoh's palace?
4. What did the voice in the burning bush tell Moses?
5. What happened that made Pharaoh let the Israelites go?
6. What happened when Moses lifted his staff and stretched his hand out over the sea?

Discuss

How does Moses *change* in the story? Think about what he did when he could no longer bear to see how badly the Egyptians were treating the Israelites. Then think about what he did when he heard the voice in the burning bush. Do you think he becomes a braver person and a stronger leader?

A New Word

The departure of the Israelites from Egypt is called the *Exodus*. Say the word aloud and write it in the blanks below:

___ ___ ___ ___ ___ ___

Choices and Consequences

Use details from the story to answer the questions on the Choices and Consequences page.

Bible Character Chart

Add Moses and Pharaoh to the Bible Character Chart.

© 2015 K12 Inc. All rights reserved.
Copying or distributing without K12's written consent is prohibited.

Name _____ Date _____

Moses: Choices and Consequences

In the story of Moses, the characters made important choices, and each choice had important consequences. Write answers to the questions below.

1. What choice did Moses's mother make when she heard that the Egyptians were going to drown the baby boys of the Israelites?

_____

_____

_____

What were the consequences of this choice?

_____

_____

_____

2. What choice did Pharaoh's daughter make when she found the baby in the basket?

_____

_____

_____

© 2015 K12 Inc. All rights reserved.
Copying or distributing without K12's written consent is prohibited.

Moses: Choices and Consequences

What were the consequences of this choice?

_____

_____

_____

3. What choice did Moses make when he could no longer bear to see how badly the Egyptians treated the Israelites?

_____

_____

_____

What were the consequences of this choice?

_____

_____

_____

© 2015 K12 Inc. All rights reserved.
Copying or distributing without K12's written consent is prohibited.

Moses: Choices and Consequences

4. What choice did Pharaoh make when Moses told him, "Let my people go"?

_____

_____

_____

What were the consequences of this choice?

_____

_____

_____

© 2015 K12 Inc. All rights reserved.
Copying or distributing without K12's written consent is prohibited.

Name _____   Date _____

Choices that Matter

Our choices affect what happens to us and others around us. Compare and contrast the characters from the Bible stories and write about the consequences of their choices.

Think Ahead

1. Summarize the story of Moses. In your summary, tell
   - what Moses's mother did to save him
   - his sister's name and how she helped
   - who found baby Moses and what happened because of this
   - why Moses left Egypt
   - what Moses heard that made him go back to Egypt
   - what Moses told Pharaoh, and how Pharaoh responded
   - the special word for the departure of the Israelites from Egypt

2. Choose one character from the Bible Character Chart. What important choice did that character make? How did his or her choice affect others?

Characters and Their Choices

Pick your three favorite characters from the Bible Character Chart. For each, discuss the following questions:

   - What important choice or choices did the character make?
   - Which choices affected others in a positive way? How?
   - Which affected others in a negative way? How?
   - Sometimes one character's choice makes an enormous difference in the way things turn out and in other characters' lives. Choose one character and tell how his or her choice made an enormous difference.

© 2015 K12 Inc. All rights reserved.
Copying or distributing without K12's written consent is prohibited.

Comparing Characters

Divide a poster board into three sections. You may choose any three of the following: Noah, Joseph, Judah, Moses, or Pharaoh. In each space, write:

- the character's name
- two or more sentences that tell about an important choice the character made
- two or more sentences that explain how the character's choice affected other characters
- two or more sentences that tell what kind of person the character is and why you think so.

In each section, draw a symbol of the character. Under the symbol, explain how it stands for the character.

© 2015 K12 Inc. All rights reserved.
Copying or distributing without K12's written consent is prohibited.

Name

Date

Bible Character Chart

In the boxes below, write the character's name, the title of the story, two or three words or phrases that describe the character, an important choice the character made, and what mattered most in the story to the character.

Name	Title	Description	Choice	What Mattered Most

© 2015 K12 Inc. All rights reserved.
Copying or distributing without K12's written consent is prohibited.

Name _____ Date _____

Robinson Crusoe: Chapters 1-6

What would you like to be when you grow up? Read about a young man named Robinson Crusoe who is determined to pursue his dreams, no matter where they take him.

The novel *Robinson Crusoe* was written by British author Daniel Defoe, who lived from 1660-1731. It was published in 1719. Although the book is fiction, it reads as if it were a true story. Defoe based his book on the experiences of a sailor named Alexander Selkirk who was stranded on an island for five years. Defoe used what he had learned about Selkirk and added many of his own ideas to the story of *Robinson Crusoe*.

Vocabulary

You will find these words in today's reading.

gale: (n.) a strong wind
A *gale* blew down the street and popped our umbrellas inside out.

vessel: (n.) a boat
The Regal Eagle was the finest *vessel* that ever sailed the seven seas.

trinkets: (n.) small decorative objects or ornaments
The bedroom shelves were filled with little statues, decorative items, and other *trinkets* the girl collected.

reckon: (v.) to calculate or estimate
I know that the library is five miles from our house, so when we passed it in the car, I *reckoned* that we would be home in about ten minutes.

© 2015 K12 Inc. All rights reserved.
Copying or distributing without K12's written consent is prohibited.

undertake: (v.) to try

This summer, my sister will *undertake* to learn to water-ski.

venture: (n.) a new business, a risk

My friend undertook a *venture*; she opened a store that only sold top hats for turtles.

breakers: (n.) waves

The *breakers* crashed onto the beach, leaving trails of white foam on the sand.

Think Ahead

1. Have you ever read *Treasure Island, Jason and the Argonauts,* or *The Book of Three*? They are *adventure* stories—tales in which the main characters travel to strange places, take risks, and face dangers. Today you are going to begin reading an adventure story from England called *Robinson Crusoe.*

2. Read the first few sentences of the story. Who is the narrator? How is the writing similar to or different from other books you've read?

Read

Chapters 1-6 in *Robinson Crusoe,* pages 4-12

Questions

Answer the following questions in complete sentences in your Reading Notebook.

1. Why does Robinson Crusoe want to be a sailor?
2. Where does Robinson Crusoe grow up?
3. In what country does he live before he is shipwrecked?
4. Where is Robinson Crusoe's ship going?
5. Who else survives the shipwreck?

© 2015 K12 Inc. All rights reserved.
Copying or distributing without K12's written consent is prohibited.

Discuss

1. Robinson Crusoe's mother tells him that a sailor's life is a hard life. Do you think he makes a wise choice in becoming a sailor? Why or why not?

2. In Chapter 2 Robinson Crusoe suffers through a storm. He is very frightened and thinks about going home. "If I live to reach dry land," he said to himself, "I will give up this thought of being a sailor." Why do you think he changes his mind and continues to sail?

Where in the World Is Robinson Crusoe?

The *setting* of a story often affects the plot. Find England, Brazil, the Caribbean Islands, the Atlantic Ocean, and the continent of Africa on your map. Then describe why each place is important in the story.

Trace with your finger the journey Robinson Crusoe planned to take when he left Brazil. Then discuss these questions:

- Where do you think Robinson Crusoe is at the end of Chapter 6?
- Do you think the story takes place long ago or recently? Why?
- Do you think Robinson Crusoe will be rescued quickly?
- What do you think he should do next? Why?

Artifact Sack

Robinson Crusoe is the story of a young man who must build a life for himself and survive after a shipwreck. Remember his adventures with an Artifact Sack.

An *artifact* is a man-made object from the past that helps us understand something about that time. For example, pottery is an artifact that helps us learn something about ancient Greek civilization.

© 2015 K12 Inc. All rights reserved.
Copying or distributing without K12's written consent is prohibited.

Each day after you read, summarize your reading and describe the most important event. Then choose an artifact from the story to represent or remind you of the event.

On the blank side of an index card, draw a picture of the artifact, or attach a small real object. For example, if you read "Cinderella," you might draw a glass slipper or attach a doll's shoe.

On the lined side of the card, write the numbers of the chapters you read. Then write what the artifact is, what it represents, and why it is important.

Keep the artifacts together in a small bag. You may decorate the bag if you wish.

© 2015 K12 Inc. All rights reserved.
Copying or distributing without K12's written consent is prohibited.

Guidelines for Peer Discussion

Share your thoughts, ideas, questions, and feelings about a text with a peer or others. Listen carefully to what everyone has to say about the text. During your discussion, follow these guidelines.

1. Be prepared to discuss what you think about the text. You should have already read the assignment. Come prepared to discuss your ideas, and use examples from the text to support your thoughts and answers.

2. You will be asked questions about the text. Be ready to answer them, and bring some questions of your own to ask others, such as:

   "Who was your favorite character? Why?"

   "What was your favorite part of the text? Why?"

   "What fact did you enjoy learning? Why do you find this fact interesting?"

   "What question would you ask if you had the chance to meet the author?"

3. Listen if it's not your turn to speak. Pay attention to what others say so that you can add your ideas. Speak clearly and in complete sentences.

4. If you don't understand what someone says, ask a question, such as:

   "What do you mean when you say . . . ?"

   "Can you give an example of . . . ?"

5. If you don't agree with what someone says, explain why.

   "I don't agree with that because . . . "

6. Keep discussions positive! You can disagree, but don't argue. Be respectful.

© 2015 K12 Inc. All rights reserved.
Copying or distributing without K12's written consent is prohibited.

Name _____   Date _____

Robinson Crusoe: Chapters 7-11

In today's reading, Robinson Crusoe begins to learn about this strange, empty shore.

Vocabulary

You will find these words in today's reading.

lodging: (n.) a place to stay, usually for a short time
The tired travelers were grateful to find *lodging* at the inn.

wedged: (v.) forced into a narrow space
I *wedged* the block under the door to keep the door open.

rigging: (n.) ropes, chains, and other equipment used to control the sails of a ship
Before you can sail a ship, you must set up the *rigging* so that the sails will fly.

masts: (n.) upright poles used to support a ship's sails and rigging
Before hoisting up the anchor, the sailor checked to be certain the sails were secured to *masts*.

hold: (n.) one of the lower decks of a ship, where goods are stored
He carried the heavy box of salted fish down eight flights of stairs into the ship's dark *hold*.

cove: (n.) a small bay
The *cove* was just large enough for us to sail in our two canoes.

© 2015 K12 Inc. All rights reserved.
Copying or distributing without K12's written consent is prohibited.

Think Ahead

1. Summarize what you read in Chapters 1-6. In your summary, tell:
   - The main character's name
   - What happens during his voyage to Africa
   - Who else survives the shipwreck

2. What do you think Robinson Crusoe should do now that he is on the island? Why?

Read

Chapters 7-11 in *Robinson Crusoe*, pages 12-19

Questions

Answer the following questions in complete sentences in your Reading Notebook.

1. How does Robinson Crusoe feel after he first looks around the shore?
2. Where does Robinson sleep his first night? Why does he choose this spot?
3. List three things he brings back from the ship.
4. How does he transport the goods from the ship back to the island?
5. How does he find out that he is on an island?

Discuss

1. Why do you think Robinson Crusoe works so hard to bring the goods off of the ship?
2. What do you think is the most important thing Robinson rescues from the ship? Why do you believe this item is so valuable?

Problems and Solutions

Divide a page in your Reading Notebook into two columns. Label the columns "Problems" and "Solutions." Then write three problems Robinson Crusoe faces and how he solves them. Look carefully at the problems. What do they have in common?

© 2015 K12 Inc. All rights reserved.
Copying or distributing without K12's written consent is prohibited.

What a character does can tell a reader a lot about the kind of person the character is. Think about the problems Robinson Crusoe faces and how he solves them as you discuss the following questions:

- Are Robinson Crusoe's problems easy to solve or challenging? Are they problems he is used to solving, or are they unusual?
- How does Robinson Crusoe react to his problems?
- How does Robinson solve his problems?
- What words describe him?
- Do you admire him? Why or why not?

Artifact Sack

Add an artifact to your collection. (Hint: Choose something that Robinson makes to solve one of his problems.)

© 2015 K12 Inc. All rights reserved.
Copying or distributing without K12's written consent is prohibited.

Name _____   Date _____

Robinson Crusoe: Chapters 12-18

The island seems peaceful and calm. But is Robinson Crusoe really safe?

Vocabulary
You will find these words in today's reading.

hatchet: (n.) a small axe
She used a *hatchet* to chop small branches off of the fallen tree.

cargo: (n.) items being transported by airplane, truck, train, or ship
The train's *cargo* included crates of oranges and lemons, bunches of grapes, and boxes full of ripe strawberries.

torrent: (n.) a powerful rush of water
The rain came down in *torrents*, even washing people's cars off the roads.

twine: (v.) to twist together
She *twined* the flowers together to make a wreath.

hew: (v.) to cut with heavy blows
Long ago, to make a railroad tunnel through a mountain, the workers had to *hew* through the stone with hammers.

slacken: (v.) to slow
I was running fast, but when I saw that my friend couldn't keep up with me, I *slackened* my pace.

citron: (n.) a lemon-like fruit with a thick rind
Although it looked like a lemon, it was a *citron* growing on the tree.

© 2015 K12 Inc. All rights reserved.
Copying or distributing without K12's written consent is prohibited.

Think Ahead

1. Summarize what you read in Chapters 7-11. In your summary, tell:
   - What Robinson Crusoe does when he awakens
   - How he brings goods back to the beach
   - What some of the goods he chooses to bring with him are
   - How he learns that he is on an island

2. What does Robinson Crusoe need to survive on the island? What do you think he will do first? Why?

Read

Chapters 12-18 in *Robinson Crusoe*, pages 20-30

Questions

Answer the following questions in complete sentences in your Reading Notebook.

1. What happens to Robinson Crusoe's ship?
2. Why does he decide not to build his castle on the beach?
3. Where does he build his castle?
4. What unusual event happens right before the storm?

Discuss

1. What dangers has Robinson Crusoe faced on the island? What has he done about them?
2. What other dangers do you think might await him? Give details from the story to support your opinion.

© 2015 K12 Inc. All rights reserved.
Copying or distributing without K12's written consent is prohibited.

How to Build Crusoe's Castle

How does Robinson Crusoe build a castle all by himself on a deserted island? Reread Chapter 14, "I Build Me a Castle." Then answer the following questions:

- Why does Robinson Crusoe choose the hillside for his castle? What features does it have that make it especially safe and strong?
- What materials does he use? Where does he find them?
- How does he build the castle? What does he do first, next, and last?

In your Reading Notebook, write your own set of instructions for how to build Robinson Crusoe's castle. In five steps or fewer, write instructions for how to build Crusoe's castle wall.
(Hint: Reread the bottom of pages 23-24.)

You may wish to illustrate all of your steps, or draw a diagram of one of the steps and label the parts.

Artifact Sack

Add an artifact to your collection. Choose something that Robinson Crusoe makes himself.

© 2015 K12 Inc. All rights reserved.
Copying or distributing without K12's written consent is prohibited.

Name _____   Date _____

Robinson Crusoe: Chapters 19-24

Can you imagine living in a place with no stores for groceries, clothing, or hardware? On the island, Robinson Crusoe has to make everything he wants or learn to do without it.

Vocabulary

You will find these words in today's reading.

bower: (n.) a shelter made from vines and tree branches
We have a *bower* in the corner of the garden, where the trees' branches and the hanging vines meet and make a roof.

idle: (adj.) not working
It seems like ants are never *idle*; they are always marching, finding food, and carrying crumbs back to their nests.

waterfowl: (n.) birds that swim
Ducks and geese are kinds of *waterfowl*.

sickle: (n.) a tool with a curved blade and short handle that is used for cutting grass or grain
Before there were machines, farmers had to cut all their grain with a hand-held *sickle*.

scythe: (n.) a tool used for mowing grass and cutting grain
To harvest their fields, the colonists used a hand-held tool such as a *scythe* or a sickle.

harrow: (n.) a spiked tool used to break up and smooth soil
The farmer used a *harrow* to break apart clods of dirt until the field was smooth.

© 2015 K12 Inc. All rights reserved.
Copying or distributing without K12's written consent is prohibited.

Think Ahead

1. Summarize what you read in Chapters 12-18. Include the following:
   - What Robinson Crusoe builds on the island
   - What unusual occurrence he survives
   - Two or more things he discovers as he explores the island

2. Think of three or more items you use every day. Choose one and tell how you would make it if you were on Robinson Crusoe's island. Could you build it, or would you have to do without?

Read

Chapters 19-24 in *Robinson Crusoe*, pages 30-43

Questions

Answer the following questions in complete sentences in your Reading Notebook.

1. What are some things Robinson Crusoe finds to eat?
2. List three things Robinson Crusoe makes.
3. Robinson Crusoe makes a calendar. What date does he arrive on the island?

Discuss

1. In Chapter 22, Robinson Crusoe says, "My life was much happier than it had been while I was sailing the seas. I took delight in many things that I had never cared for before." What has he begun to enjoy? Why do you think he is happier?
2. Describe one of the things Robinson Crusoe makes and how he makes it.

Artifact Sack

Add another artifact to your collection.

© 2015 K12 Inc. All rights reserved.
Copying or distributing without K12's written consent is prohibited.

All in Good Time

Before you read, you thought about things you use every day, and you described how you would make or go without one important item if you were on the island. But Robinson Crusoe has to make everything. How does he decide what to do first? Discuss these questions as you think about your answer:

- What are the first two things that Robinson Crusoe does after he reaches the island? (Hint: Look back to Chapters 8, 14, and 15 if you don't remember.)

- Robinson Crusoe's choices tell you something about him. What is important to him? What does he value most?

- Would you make different choices? Why or why not?

Robinson Crusoe's choices are especially important, because his life depends on the consequences. What if he had built the castle before swimming out to the ship? Imagine how different Robinson Crusoe's life would be if the ship had sunk before he retrieved the food, the tools, and the weapons.

Think about these three choices that Robinson Crusoe makes.
- Robinson Crusoe takes the food and the tools off of the ship before he takes the weapons and the money.

- Robinson Crusoe builds his castle on the hillside before he explores the rest of the island.

- Robinson Crusoe hunts for food before he plants seeds.

Go to the Important Decisions page. In the column labeled "Why," write why you think Robinson Crusoe did the tasks in that order. In the column labeled "What If," tell what might have happened if he had done the second task first. Then decide: How did Robinson Crusoe know what to do first?

© 2015 K12 Inc. All rights reserved. Copying or distributing without K12's written consent is prohibited.

Name _____

Date _____

Important Decisions

Read each decision. Then, in the column labeled "Why," write why you think Robinson Crusoe did the tasks in that order. In the column labeled "What If," tell what might have happened if he had done the second task first. Then decide: How did Robinson Crusoe know what to do first?

Decision	Why	What If	How did he know?
Robinson Crusoe takes the food and the tools off of the ship before he takes the weapons and the money.			
Robinson Crusoe builds his castle on the hillside before he explores the rest of the island.			
Robinson Crusoe hunts for food before he plants seeds.			

© 2015 K12 Inc. All rights reserved.
Copying or distributing without K12's written consent is prohibited.

Name _____   Date _____

Robinson Crusoe: Chapters 25-29

Robinson Crusoe makes a boat and hears someone call his name.
Could he be finally going home?

Vocabulary
You will find these words in today's reading.

hewed: (v.) chopped, shaped, or cut with an axe
The boys *hewed* the tree limbs into the right size lumber for
their tree house.

parched: (adj.) dry or dried
After walking through the desert all day without drinking a sip of
water, their lips and tongues were *parched*.

discontented: (adj.) not happy, not satisfied
I stood in line to go on the ride, but the park closed before I
could take my turn, so I went home quite *discontented*.

perilous: (adj.) very dangerous
Mom said, "Move away from that ledge! It is *perilous* to stand in
a place from which you might fall and hurt yourself."

Think Ahead
1. Summarize what you read in Chapters 19-24. Think about the
   new things Robinson Crusoe makes. Include:
   • Two new things Robinson Crusoe makes
   • How he makes one of the things

2. When Robinson Crusoe makes new things, he does not always
   succeed on the first try. Why do you think he keeps trying?

© 2015 K12 Inc. All rights reserved.
Copying or distributing without K12's written consent is prohibited.

Read
Chapters 25-29 in *Robinson Crusoe*, pages 43-54

Questions
Answer the following questions in complete sentences in your Reading Notebook.

1. List three things that Robinson Crusoe makes.
2. Why can't Robinson Crusoe sail in his first canoe?
3. How does Robinson Crusoe get his second canoe into the water?
4. When he returns to the island, Robinson Crusoe hears a voice calling his name. Whose voice is it?

Discuss
1. Robinson Crusoe says that he is always trying to think of ways to escape from the island, but he also says that he is happier than when he had been a sailor. Why do you think he is happier on the island than he was at sea?

2. Robinson Crusoe wishes to escape his island even though he may face dangers trying. What are some of the dangers he fears? Do you think it is worth the risk?

3. When Robinson Crusoe realizes that he cannot move his first canoe into the water he is very upset with himself. Then he returns home and says, "Why should I be unhappy?…I might call myself the king of the island?" Why do you think he feels this way?

Look Before You Leap
Reread Chapter 25, "I Build a Big Canoe." Find the sentence, "The wise man will always look before he leaps." What do you think that saying means? Now complete the Look Before You Leap page. When you finish, review and discuss your answers.

Artifact Sack
Add an artifact to your collection.

© 2015 K12 Inc. All rights reserved.
Copying or distributing without K12's written consent is prohibited.

Name _____   Date _____

Look Before You Leap

Answer the following questions using information from Chapters 25 and 27, "I Build a Big Canoe" and "I Have a Perilous Adventure."

1. What does Robinson Crusoe try to do in Chapter 25?

_____

_____

2. Why does he want to do it?

_____

_____

3. What mistake does he make? How does he not "look before he leaps"?

_____

_____

4. What are the consequences of his mistake?

_____

_____

5. How does he feel about his mistake?

_____

© 2015 K12 Inc. All rights reserved.
Copying or distributing without K12's written consent is prohibited.

Look Before You Leap

6. Read the first two paragraphs of Chapter 27. Do you think Robinson Crusoe's experience with the first canoe and his thoughts and feelings after that experience help him achieve his goal? Why?

_____

_____

7. How long does it take Robinson Crusoe to dig the ditch?

_____

_____

8. Does he ever sail his canoe?

_____

_____

9. Put the phrase "Look before you leap" into your own words.

_____

_____

10. Do you think "Look before you leap" is good advice? Why?

_____

_____

© 2015 K12 Inc. All rights reserved.
Copying or distributing without K12's written consent is prohibited.

Name _____   Date _____

Happy As a King

Explore Robinson Crusoe's island and decide how you would feel if you lived there yourself.

Review

1. Use the objects in your Artifact Sack to summarize what has happened so far in the story.
2. What is your favorite part of the story so far?

Story Map

Make a map of the island. On it, include:

- The beach where Robinson Crusoe is shipwrecked
- His first tent
- The castle
- The bower, Robinson Crusoe's "summer home"
- The river
- The meadows, woods, and orchards
- The big canoe Crusoe has to abandon

Discuss

1. Robinson Crusoe has been on the island for several years. What has he learned? Explain one problem he faces and how he solves it.

2. How does Robinson feel when he first arrives on the island? How has he changed since the shipwreck? Give examples from the story to support your opinion.

3. Does Robinson Crusoe's success surprise you? What do you think the author is trying to say about what a person can accomplish?

© 2015 K12 Inc. All rights reserved.
Copying or distributing without K12's written consent is prohibited.

Message in a Bottle

Would you like to be Robinson Crusoe and have an island of your own? Would you be as happy as a king? As you decide, think about and discuss these questions:

- What would you enjoy most about being alone or only with pets on a deserted island?

- What would you miss?

- Do you think it would be fun or tiresome to build your own house, make your own food, tools, and clothes, and explore the land? Why?

- What kinds of things could you do on the island that you can't do in your home? What kinds of things couldn't you do?

Pretend you are Robinson Crusoe. On the Message in a Bottle page, write a letter to your friends or family, explaining whether or not you are happy and why. You may also color it in, cut it out, roll it up, and place it in a bottle.

© 2015 K12 Inc. All rights reserved.
Copying or distributing without K12's written consent is prohibited.

Name _____   Date _____

Message in a Bottle

Write your letter on the parchment below.

© 2015 K12 Inc. All rights reserved.
Copying or distributing without K12's written consent is prohibited.

Name _____   Date _____

Robinson Crusoe: Chapters 30-33

Perhaps Robinson Crusoe is not alone on the island!

Vocabulary
You will find these words in today's readings.

pursuer: (n.) a person or animal that is chasing another
The hare escaped its *pursuer,* the hound, by hopping into the hollow log.

beckon: (v.) to signal to someone, usually by waving one's hand
When my friends came back from buying their snacks, I *beckoned* to them from my seat to show them where we were sitting in the theater.

Think Ahead
There are 10 chapters left in *Robinson Crusoe.* How do you think the story will end? Do you think Robinson Crusoe will stay on the island, or will he be rescued? Think of two different ways the story could end.

Read
Chapters 30-33 in *Robinson Crusoe,* pages 54-65

Questions
Answer the following questions in complete sentences in your Reading Notebook.

1. What does Robinson Crusoe see in the sand that frightens him?
2. Why does he decide to strengthen his castle?
3. What happens that makes Robinson Crusoe's strange dream even more unusual?

© 2015 K12 Inc. All rights reserved.
Copying or distributing without K12's written consent is prohibited.

4. How does he save the prisoner?
5. What does Robinson Crusoe call the man, and why?

Discuss

1. Do you think Robinson is brave? Why or why not? Give examples from the story to support your opinion.
2. Why does Robinson Crusoe decide to help the prisoner?

Robinson Crusoe and Friday

Compare and contrast Robinson Crusoe and Friday. Divide a page in your Reading Notebook into two columns. Label the left-hand column "Robinson Crusoe." Label the right-hand column "Friday." Underneath each name, write words and phrases that describe each character. You may use the same word for both characters. For example, you might write "determined" for both.

When you finish writing your list, review it. How are the two characters the same? How are they different?

If you wish, complete the Footprint in the Sand page. You may write and illustrate the poem on the page, or you may write and illustrate your own poem on a separate sheet of paper.

Artifact Sack

Add an item to your collection.

© 2015 K12 Inc. All rights reserved.
Copying or distributing without K12's written consent is prohibited.

Name _____   Date _____

Footprint in the Sand

Write a poem about Robinson Crusoe and Friday. You may use this page, or you may write your own poem on a separate sheet of paper.

_____
Title

_____
One way the characters are the same

_____
A second way the characters are the same

_____
A third way the characters are the same

_____
One way the characters are different

_____
A phrase to describe Robinson Crusoe and Friday

© 2015 K12 Inc. All rights reserved.
Copying or distributing without K12's written consent is prohibited.

Name _____ Date _____

Robinson Crusoe: Chapters 34-35

Robinson Crusoe discovers that leaving the island may be more difficult than he thought.

Vocabulary
You will find these words in today's reading.

seaworthy: (adj.) safe to sail
The sailboat was not *seaworthy*: the sails were torn, the mast was broken, and the boat had sprung three leaks.

broth: (n.) a liquid that meat, fish, vegetables, or grain have been cooked in
He boiled the chicken, took out the meat, then fed the rich *broth* to the sick children.

Think Ahead
Summarize what you read in Chapters 30-33. In your summary, tell:
- What Robinson Crusoe first sees that frightens him
- How Friday comes to the island

Read
Chapters 34-35 in *Robinson Crusoe*, pages 66-73

Questions
Answer the following questions in complete sentences in your Reading Notebook.

1. Why is Friday afraid when Robinson Crusoe kills the goat and the bird?
2. What continent does Robinson Crusoe think lies to the west of the island?

© 2015 K12 Inc. All rights reserved.
Copying or distributing without K12's written consent is prohibited.

3. Why does Robinson Crusoe decide to make a new boat?

Discuss

1. Would you want to have Robinson Crusoe as a friend? How about Friday? Why or why not? Give examples from the story to support your opinion.

2. Do you think a person could really have an adventure like Robinson Crusoe's? Why or why not?

Artifact Sack

Add an item to your collection.

The Story Behind the Story

Robinson Crusoe is fiction. But the story is based on a real-life Robinson Crusoe, a man named Alexander Selkirk. From 1704 to 1709, Alexander Selkirk lived alone on tiny Juan Fernandez Island, just west of the South American country of Chile.

Complete The Story Behind the Story page, and find out more about the *real* Robinson Crusoe.

© 2015 K12 Inc. All rights reserved.
Copying or distributing without K12's written consent is prohibited.

Name

Date

The Story Behind the Story

Find facts from the story to compare the real person, Alexander Selkirk, and the fictional character, Robinson Crusoe.

	Alexander Selkirk	Robinson Crusoe
What country was he from?	Scotland	1.
When did he arrive on the	September, 1704	2.
Why did he arrive on the island?	He argued with the captain of his ship and demanded to be let off on the island.	3.
What did he bring onto the island from the ship?	carpenter's tools, clothing, a hatchet, a musket, bullets, gun powder, and a Bible	4.
Where did he live?	First, in a cave near the beach. Then he built two homes in the woods, away from the beach	5.
What did he eat?	fish, turtles, lobster, wild turnips, cabbage, watercress, wild goats	6.
What did he do when his clothes wore out?	He made his clothing and caps out of goatskin.	7.
What pets did he have?	cats and tame kids (baby goats)	8.
Did he have human	no	9.
How long did he stay?	4 years, 4 months	28 years, 2 months, 19 days

© 2015 K12 Inc. All rights reserved.
Copying or distributing without K12's written consent is prohibited.

Name _____   **Date** _____

Robinson Crusoe: Chapters 36-37

The sails of a ship appear on the horizon. But are the crewmen friends or foes?

Vocabulary

You will find these words in today's reading.

companions: (n.) people or animals who spend time together
The dog and cat were great *companions;* they never left each other's sides.

distress: (n.) trouble
The townspeople were in terrible *distress* because the snow was so deep, even the big plows couldn't clear the roads, and no one could enter or leave the town.

venture: (v.) to brave the dangers
We heard a strange noise downstairs, but we were afraid it might be a robber so we did not *venture* down the steps to investigate.

stroll: (v.) to walk in a relaxed or carefree way
We *strolled* through the garden, smelling the flowers and watching the butterflies.

grove: (n.) a group of fruit or nut trees
The trees in our *grove* produced the best peaches and walnuts in our state.

ringleader: (n.) a person who leads others in crime or other activities that are unacceptable
The *ringleader* encouraged the rest of the boys to prevent the girls from playing on the monkey bars and swing set.

© 2015 K12 Inc. All rights reserved.
Copying or distributing without K12's written consent is prohibited.

ruffians: (n.) thugs, gangsters, or tough fellows

"Don't walk down that alley alone in the dark," Dad warned us. "You might be overtaken by *ruffians*."

Think Ahead

1. Is *Robinson Crusoe* fiction or nonfiction?
2. Whose life was the story based on?
3. Do you think that Robinson Crusoe will ever go home? Why or why not?

Read

Chapters 36-37 in *Robinson Crusoe*, pages 73-81

Questions

Answer the following questions in complete sentences in your Reading Notebook.

1. How does Robinson Crusoe decide that the Englishmen have come to the island for no good purpose?

2. Why do most of the sailors rise up against the captain?

3. At first, the sailors are going to kill the captain and the other men. What do they decide to do with the men instead?

4. How does Robinson Crusoe help the captain?

Discuss

1. Why is the captain surprised to see Robinson Crusoe? Tell what the captain says or does in the story that helps you form your opinion.

2. What do you think will happen now that Robinson Crusoe and Friday have rescued the captain? Predict how the other sailors who are still on the ship will react.

© 2015 K12 Inc. All rights reserved.
Copying or distributing without K12's written consent is prohibited.

Artifact Sack
Add an artifact to your collection.

Making Inferences and Drawing Conclusions
Readers learn about characters by paying attention to what they say and do, and what others say about them. But sometimes, to understand a character, we have to go beyond the words in the story. We have to *make inferences.* When we make an inference, or *infer,* we think about the evidence in the story, and then draw conclusions based on that evidence.

What can you infer about Robinson Crusoe from these examples:

- When the prisoners sat down on the beach, Robinson Crusoe says, "I thought then of the time when I had first landed on that shore – how I had no hope, and how I gave myself up for lost. I knew what these men must now have been feeling."

- Later, he says to the captain, "I am an Englishman, and I am ready to help you. I have one servant, and we are well-armed. Tell us what is your case, and how we may serve you."

- Choose an item from your Artifact Sack and tell what you can infer about Robinson Crusoe from what he did.

What conclusions can you draw about Robinson Crusoe from your inferences? In your Reading Notebook, write a paragraph to answer this question: What kind of person is Robinson Crusoe? How do you know?

© 2015 K12 Inc. All rights reserved.
Copying or distributing without K12's written consent is prohibited.

Name _____ Date _____

Robinson Crusoe: Chapters 38-40

Robinson Crusoe must fight for his life and his freedom.

Vocabulary
You will find these words in today's reading.

boatswain: (n.) a ship's officer in charge of the body of the ship
Every day, the *boatswain* carefully checked the body of the ship
for cracks and leaks.

quarter: (n.) mercy
"Give me *quarter*," said the thief to the judge, "and if you do not
punish me, I promise I will never steal again."

dismal: (adj.) gloomy
Inside the dungeon, it was cold and *dismal*.

Think Ahead
1. Summarize what you read in Chapters 36-37. In your summary, tell:
   • What country the sailors come from
   • What the ship captain's problem is
   • Robinson Crusoe's plan to solve the ship captain's problem

2. Does Robinson Crusoe have to help the captain? Why does he?

Read
Chapters 38-40 in *Robinson Crusoe*, pages 81-88

© 2015 K12 Inc. All rights reserved.
Copying or distributing without K12's written consent is prohibited.

Questions

Answer the following questions in complete sentences in your Reading Notebook.

1. Why does Robinson Crusoe teach some of the sailors how to live on his island?

2. Robinson Crusoe goes to England when he finally leaves the island. Why does he go there and why does he leave?

3. Where was Robinson's plantation? What did the man in charge of the plantation send Robinson?

4. Now that Robinson is a rich man, what does he do?

Discuss

1. Reread Chapter 38. Do you think Robinson Crusoe makes the right decision giving the men quarter? Why or why not? What are the consequences of his choice?

2. In Chapter 39, Robinson Crusoe lets the rebel sailors stay on his island instead of going back to face punishment in England. Do you think he makes the right choice? Why or why not?

3. Robinson Crusoe gives the men many of his supplies and explains how he manages his goats. Do you think this is the right choice? What would you have done?

Robinson Crusoe Poster

Make a poster to tell the world about this hardy adventurer!

First, review the objects in your Artifact Sack. Choose three events or three artifacts that remind you of the most important events in the book. Explain why each event is important.

© 2015 K12 Inc. All rights reserved.
Copying or distributing without K12's written consent is prohibited.

Next, write three words that describe Robinson Crusoe.
Then arrange your poster. On it, make sure you have:

- Robinson Crusoe's name
- A drawing of him
- Three words that describe him (Hint: Choose carefully. You will need these three words later.)
- A symbol that represents Robinson Crusoe and one to four sentences explaining what it means

You may also attach your Island Map, your artifacts, and extra illustrations or events.

© 2015 K12 Inc. All rights reserved.
Copying or distributing without K12's written consent is prohibited.

Name _____   Date _____

"Keepers of the Prairie": Session 1

Can you imagine a town with a population bigger than that of the entire United States? Not a town of people, but of prairie dogs?

Vocabulary

You will find these words in today's reading. Look at each word and how it is used in a sentence. You will find any definitions not provided here in the *Feathers, Flippers, and Fur* glossary.

population: (n.)
The *population* of bald eagles has grown and is no longer on the endangered species list.

biologist: (n.)
The *biologists* hope to learn the effects of pollution by studying the plants and animals that live in the area of the oil spill.

densely populated: (adj. phrase) many inhabitants living closely together
The small island is so *densely populated* with seals that it is difficult to see any bare land.

environment: (n.)
The squirrel gathers nuts from its *environment* to save for food for the winter.

predator: (n.) an animal that lives by killing and eating other animals
Foxes are *predators* that hunt rabbits and chickens.

© 2015 K12 Inc. All rights reserved.
Copying or distributing without K12's written consent is prohibited.

endangered: (adj.) in danger of dying out
Many years ago, when pioneers and hunters killed many herds of buffalo, few animals were left alive and the buffalo became *endangered*.

eliminate: (v.)
Because they thought the prairie dogs were eating all the grass their cattle needed, the ranchers decided to *eliminate* them.

exterminate: (v.)
When rats became a problem in Hamlin, the mayor hired the piper to *exterminate* them.

habitat: (n.)
The sea gulls' *habitat* was threatened because of the oil spill.

persecution: (n.)
After people realized that wolves are not harmful to man, they stopped their *persecution* and began protecting the wolves.

Think Ahead

1. What do you think you will learn about as you read the magazine? Do you think the articles are *fiction* or *nonfiction*? Why?
2. Are there any special parts to the magazine? Is the magazine divided into chapters?
3. Look up "Keepers of the Prairie" in the table of contents.

Read

"Keepers of the Prairie."

© 2015 K12 Inc. All rights reserved.
Copying or distributing without K12's written consent is prohibited.

Questions
Answer the following questions in complete sentences in your Reading Notebook.

1. Describe a prairie dog town.
2. Name two animals that benefit from prairie dog towns.
3. How do prairie dogs alert one another when there is danger?
4. Describe why the black-footed ferret is a dangerous enemy to prairie dogs.
5. What happened to other prairie animals when prairie dogs began to disappear?

Discuss
1. Describe how other animals benefit from prairie dog towns.
2. Why do some people view prairie dogs as enemies?
3. Describe the reasons the prairie dog population was getting smaller.

Chain of Events
A cause is the reason why something happens. An effect is the result of, or what happens after, an event. For example, Robinson Crusoe's ship was in a terrible storm and as a result there was a shipwreck, and Crusoe washed up alone on an island. The cause is the storm. The effect is a shipwreck. But the shipwreck causes another effect. It causes Crusoe to be left alone on the island and Crusoe's isolation causes him to build and create many new things.

A cause can create an effect that then becomes the cause of another effect. We call this a chain of events.

The actions of prairie dogs cause many things to happen. One effect of a prairie dog town is that many animals benefit, but there are other effects as well.

© 2015 K12 Inc. All rights reserved.
Copying or distributing without K12's written consent is prohibited.

Use the information in the article "Keepers of the Prairie" to complete the Chain of Events page. You will need to decide the order of the events in the chain. Which causes which? Put the following events in the correct order on the Chain of Events page.

- Prairie dogs clip off all the grass in their towns.
- Scientists realize prairie dogs do more good than harm.
- States require that prairie dogs be exterminated.
- Prairie dogs die or move away.
- The National Wildlife Federation asks the government to protect prairie dogs.
- Cattle have no grass to eat.
- Ferrets die without food and become an endangered species.
- Ranchers poison prairie dogs.
- Animals that benefit from the towns became less common.

Then decide whether you think it is right that the National Wildlife Federation wants to protect the prairie dog.

Listen Up!
Listen carefully as a new paragraph about prairie dogs is read to you. Think about the topic of the paragraph, and then write a summary in your Reading Notebook.

Home on the Range
The photographs in "Keepers of the Prairie" help us see what prairie dogs and some of the other animals that live in or near a prairie dog town look like. But suppose you wanted to add a diagram that shows the inside of a prairie dog burrow. Name some things you would want to show.

Complete the Prairie Dog Town page.

© 2015 K12 Inc. All rights reserved.
Copying or distributing without K12's written consent is prohibited.

- Label the rooms inside the burrow. Most burrows have a nursery where baby prairie dogs stay until they are old enough to take care of themselves. Label the nursery, too.

- Just inside the entrances there is a small dugout area where the prairie dog can slip inside to hide and then turn around in to leave the burrow. Label the two turnarounds.

- Add at least three animals that live in or near a prairie dog town. You may draw pictures of the animals or just write their names and tell what they are doing.

In your Reading Notebook, write a paragraph that tells the things about the burrow that the viewer can't see. Tell what the temperature is like inside the underground burrows.

© 2015 K12 Inc. All rights reserved.
Copying or distributing without K12's written consent is prohibited.

Guidelines for Peer Discussion

Share your thoughts, ideas, questions, and feelings about a text with a peer or others. Listen carefully to what everyone has to say about the text. During your discussion, follow these guidelines.

1. Be prepared to discuss what you think about the text. You should have already read the assignment. Come prepared to discuss your ideas, and use examples from the text to support your thoughts and answers.

2. You will be asked questions about the text. Be ready to answer them, and bring some questions of your own to ask others, such as:

   "Who was your favorite character? Why?"

   "What was your favorite part of the text? Why?"

   "What fact did you enjoy learning? Why do you find this fact interesting?"

   "What question would you ask if you had the chance to meet the author?"

3. Listen if it's not your turn to speak. Pay attention to what others say so that you can add your ideas. Speak clearly and in complete sentences.

4. If you don't understand what someone says, ask a question, such as:

   "What do you mean when you say . . . ?"

   "Can you give an example of . . . ?"

5. If you don't agree with what someone says, explain why.

   "I don't agree with that because . . . "

6. Keep discussions positive! You can disagree, but don't argue. Be respectful.

© 2015 K12 Inc. All rights reserved.
Copying or distributing without K12's written consent is prohibited.

Name _____ Date _____

Parts of a Magazine

Use information in the *Feathers, Flippers, and Fur* magazine to answer the following questions.

1. On what page does the article "Feathers" begin?

_____

2. Where did you find this information?

_____

3. Write the meaning of the word *molting*.

_____

4. Where did you find this definition? _____

_____

5. What is the title of the last article in the magazine? _____

_____

© 2015 K12 Inc. All rights reserved.
Copying or distributing without K12's written consent is prohibited.

Parts of a Magazine

6. Where did you find this information?

_____

7. On which page could you learn more about *blubber*?

_____

8. Where did you find this information?

_____

Think About It!
9. Why are the words in the glossary and the words in the index listed in alphabetical order?

_____

10. Name another book where you will find words listed in alphabetical order.

_____

© 2015 K12 Inc. All rights reserved.
Copying or distributing without K12's written consent is prohibited.

Name

Date

Prairie Dog Town

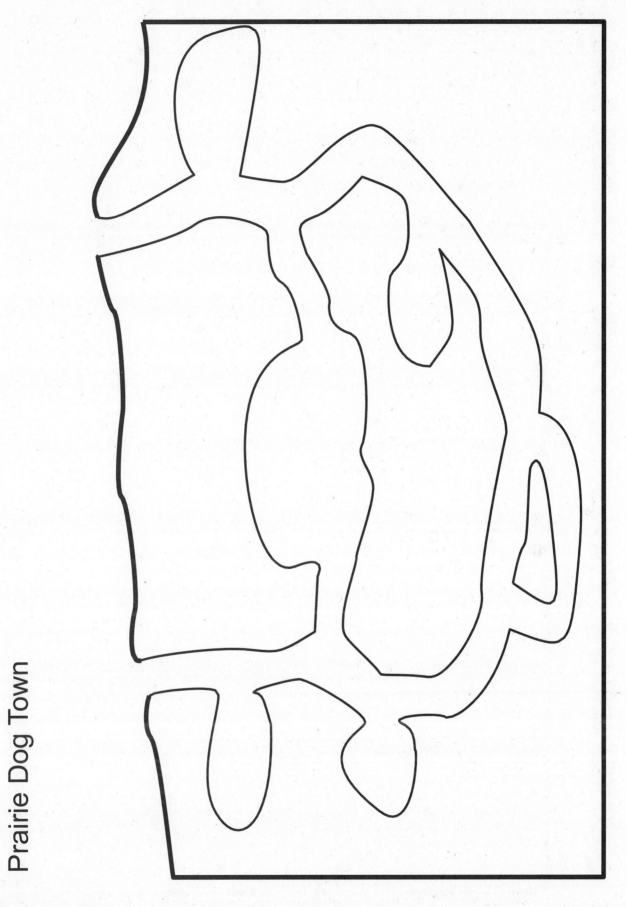

© 2015 K12 Inc. All rights reserved.
Copying or distributing without K12's written consent is prohibited.

Name   Date

Chain of Events

Complete the chain of events by placing the phrases in order on the chain. Decide which cause had which effect and complete the chain. The first cause has been placed for you.

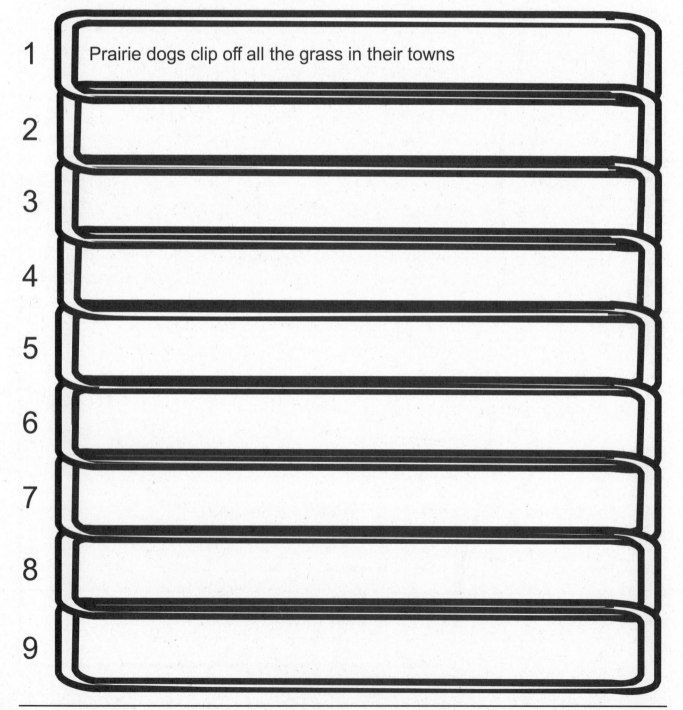

1 Prairie dogs clip off all the grass in their towns

2

3

4

5

6

7

8

9

© 2015 K12 Inc. All rights reserved.
Copying or distributing without K12's written consent is prohibited.

Guidelines for Peer Discussion

Share your thoughts, ideas, questions, and feelings about a text with a peer or others. Listen carefully to what everyone has to say about the text. During your discussion, follow these guidelines.

1. Be prepared to discuss what you think about the text. You should have already read the assignment. Come prepared to discuss your ideas, and use examples from the text to support your thoughts and answers.

2. You will be asked questions about the text. Be ready to answer them, and bring some questions of your own to ask others, such as:

   "Who was your favorite character? Why?"

   "What was your favorite part of the text? Why?"

   "What fact did you enjoy learning? Why do you find this fact interesting?"

   "What question would you ask if you had the chance to meet the author?"

3. Listen if it's not your turn to speak. Pay attention to what others say so that you can add your ideas. Speak clearly and in complete sentences.

4. If you don't understand what someone says, ask a question, such as:

   "What do you mean when you say . . . ?"

   "Can you give an example of . . . ?"

5. If you don't agree with what someone says, explain why.

   "I don't agree with that because . . . "

6. Keep discussions positive! You can disagree, but don't argue. Be respectful.

© 2015 K12 Inc. All rights reserved.
Copying or distributing without K12's written consent is prohibited.

Name _____   Date _____

"Keepers of the Prairie": Session 2

Get the facts. Pretend that YOU are a black-tailed prairie dog and live in a prairie dog town. Answer questions about your home for a reporter from the *Prairie Post* and then give your opinion.

Think Ahead

1. How is a fiction story about prairie dogs different from the article "Keepers of the Prairie"?

2. Where in the magazine would you look to find the pages where *predators* are mentioned?

3. The article says that one prairie dog town took up more land than Connecticut, Massachusetts, New Hampshire, and Rhode Island combined. Look on a map to see just how large an area this is.

4. Do you have an opinion about prairie dogs? Are they friends or foes?

Is That a Fact?

You know that nonfiction is writing about *facts*. Facts are statements that can be proved true. Look at the facts below and tell how you could prove them.

- There are 50 states in the United States.
- Snakes are vertebrates.
- Chocolate is made from cacao nuts.

Give two more facts and explain how you could prove them.

An *opinion* is what a person feels or thinks about something. Opinions are not true or false. People can have different opinions about the same thing without being right or wrong. Look at the opinions below, and then give your opinion about the subject.

© 2015 K12 Inc. All rights reserved.
Copying or distributing without K12's written consent is prohibited.

- Hawaii is a great place to live.
- All snakes are frightening.
- Chocolate ice cream is better than vanilla.

People form opinions based upon their own ideas and experiences, or based on something that they have read or learned. Sometimes an opinion changes when a person learns new information. Read the opinion below.

I thought that all snakes were frightening until I learned that the garter snake is harmless. Now I only believe some snakes are frightening.

Find the paragraph on page 6 that talks about prairie dogs as enemies. Reread the sentence that says, "Because these animals eat grass, ranchers view them as competition for their cattle."

Name a fact that you find in this sentence and write it in your Reading Notebook. Label it *fact*. Then, write a sentence that tells an opinion that ranchers might have about prairie dogs. Label it *opinion*.

Prairie Dog Post

Complete *The Prairie Dog Post* page. Polly Pronghorn from *The Prairie Post* has come to interview you, Peter Prairie Dog, a black-tailed prairie dog. Pretend you are Peter and use information from the article "Keepers of the Prairie" to give Polly the facts about life in the prairie dog town. When Polly asks questions that require you to give an opinion, respond with an opinion that you believe Peter Prairie Dog might have.

© 2015 K12 Inc. All rights reserved.
Copying or distributing without K12's written consent is prohibited.

Name _____   Date _____

The Prairie Dog Post

POLLY PRONGHORN: Good morning Peter! I am Polly Pronghorn with *The Prairie Post*. I'd like you to answer a few questions to help me understand what life is like in your prairie dog town.

PETER PRAIRIE DOG: A prairie dog town may not look like much on the surface but underground, you should see it! Every family has its own set of connected burrows with two or three entrances. There is a large room called a nesting chamber where we sleep and there are side pockets in the burrows where we store our food. Grass is our favorite food. We LOVE to eat grass!

POLLY PRONGHORN: Tell me about life underground. Please describe a burrow.

PETER PRAIRIE DOG: _____

_____

_____

POLLY PRONGHORN: You mentioned that you love to eat grass, but you probably can't eat it all. Why do prairie dogs clip off all the grass in their towns even if they don't plan to eat it?

_____

© 2015 K12 Inc. All rights reserved.
Copying or distributing without K12's written consent is prohibited.

The Prairie Dog Post

PETER PRAIRIE DOG: _____

_____

_____

POLLY PRONGHORN: I understand that clipping and eating all this grass has caused you some problems. How do ranchers feel about prairie dogs eating all the grass?

PETER PRAIRIE DOG: _____

_____

_____

POLLY PRONGHORN: What did the ranchers do and how did the government help them?

PETER PRAIRIE DOG: _____

_____

_____

POLLY PRONGHORN: There are two sides to every story. How do you feel about the ranchers?

PETER PRAIRIE DOG: _____

_____

_____

© 2015 K12 Inc. All rights reserved.
Copying or distributing without K12's written consent is prohibited.

The Prairie Dog Post

POLLY PRONGHORN: But ranchers are not the only dangers to prairie dogs. What else is a danger to prairie dog towns?

PETER PRAIRIE DOG: _____

_____

_____

POLLY PRONGHORN: It's hard to believe that some people see prairie dogs as enemies. Explain how prairie dogs do more good than harm.

PETER PRAIRIE DOG: _____

_____

_____

POLLY PRONGHORN: What other thoughts would you like to tell my audience about prairie dogs?

PETER PRAIRIE DOG: _____

_____

_____

POLLY PRONGHORN: Thank you, Peter. That is all of the time we have. This is Polly Pronghorn with *The Prairie Post* saying keep your eyes open and be safe.

© 2015 K12 Inc. All rights reserved.
Copying or distributing without K12's written consent is prohibited.

Name _____   Date _____

"The Wolf in the Dog": Session 1

A dog is man's best friend, right? But did you know that when you throw a ball for Fido to fetch, he is acting like his relative, the wolf? You might be surprised to find out the many ways in which dogs act like wolves.

Pronunciation
dominant (DOM-uh-nunt)
subordinate (suh-BOR-dun-it)

Vocabulary
You will find these words in today's reading.

instinct: (n.)
Sea lions learn to swim by their *instinct*; they just know how to do it.

snarl: (v.)
The dog shows his teeth and *snarls* at the stranger when he
comes to the door.

prey: (n.) an animal hunted and eaten by another animal
The lion hunted its *prey* almost all night, only to lose it just before dawn.

Think Ahead
1. Review the following common characteristics of nonfiction writing:
   • Provides factual details about a subject
   • Shows that the writer knows information about a subject,
     usually through research
   • Includes visuals such as graphs, maps, tables, timelines, or
     illustrations

2. Ask your student to locate "The Wolf in the Dog" in the magazine
   and predict what the article will be about.

© 2015 K12 Inc. All rights reserved.
Copying or distributing without K12's written consent is prohibited.

Read
"The Wolf in the Dog."

Questions
Answer the following questions in complete sentences in your Reading Notebook.

1. What is a pack?
2. Do all wolf pups grow up to remain in the pack? Explain your answer.
3. What are the responsibilities of the wolf pups to the pack?
4. Describe how dogs behave like wolves in a pack.
5. How does a wolf use its body to show other wolves it is dominant?
6. Where do the collie and Shetland sheepdog get their herding abilities?

Discuss
1. Describe at least three ways in which dogs and wolves are similar.
2. How is this article similar to or different from "Keepers of the Prairie"?

Main Idea
The *main idea* is the most important point that the author makes. Finding the main idea will help you to remember what you have read. There are many ways that you can determine the main idea of what you are reading. Sometimes a main idea is stated at the very beginning of an article. Reread the first paragraph. Do you see the main idea? Which sentence tells you what this article is mostly about?

Write that sentence in your Reading Notebook.

Now go back and look at the article again. What other parts of the article are useful for determining the main idea? (Hint: What does the title tell you? What do the pictures say?) Write these in your Reading Notebook and explain how they help tell the main idea of the article.

© 2015 K12 Inc. All rights reserved.
Copying or distributing without K12's written consent is prohibited.

To tell her readers all about the similarities between dogs and wolves, author Dorothy Hinshaw Patent goes back and forth between dogs and wolves in her writing. Complete the Organization Station page. Identify and write the sentence about dogs that gives similar information to the sentence about wolves.

When you finish, review and discuss your work.

Details

Details give more information about the main idea. The main idea of this article states that dogs are closely related to wolves. You have already found four sentences that contain details that support this main idea.

The author identifies many ways in which dogs and wolves are similar. These are all supporting details. She organizes the article around these details. For example, she explains that both dogs and wolves are pack animals.

The author also gives details about each of the ways in which dogs and wolves are similar. For example, she tells her reader who the members of a wolf pack are and who the alpha is. These are details. She also gives details about the kind of pack the dog lives in. She explains that dogs view their human companions as alphas.

Complete the Wolf in the Dog page. Use information from the article to fill in details and examples for each of the shared behaviors listed in the chart.

When you are finished, discuss how you were able to find this information.

© 2015 K12 Inc. All rights reserved.
Copying or distributing without K12's written consent is prohibited.

Name _____   Date _____

Wolf in the Dog

The main idea of the article is: _____

_____

_____

Dogs	Shared Behaviors	Wolves
Live with a family and consider humans the alpha	Packs	Live with other wolves and have an alpha male and female as head of pack
	Dominant	
	Subordinate	
	Marking	
	Herding	
	Retrieving	

© 2015 K12 Inc. All rights reserved.
Copying or distributing without K12's written consent is prohibited.

Name _____   Date _____

Organization Station

How does Dorothy Hinshaw Patent organize her article? She writes a paragraph about wolf behavior. Then she discusses these same behaviors in dogs in different paragraphs. Read each statement about a wolf. Then find the sentence in the article that tells a similar fact about dogs. Write the sentence in the blank.

Wolf	Dog
Wolves live in family groups called packs. The mother wolf and father wolf head the pack; they are called the alpha female and alpha male, after the first letter of the Greek alphabet.	
When subordinate wolves approach the alphas, they lower their heads and tails and flatten their ears against their heads.	
To mark the boundaries of their territories, wolves urinate on rocks, trees, or other objects along the borders of the area.	
Wolves chase their prey, sometime herding them back toward other members of the pack who are lying in wait.	

© 2015 K12 Inc. All rights reserved.
Copying or distributing without K12's written consent is prohibited.

Name _____   Date _____

What I Know, What I Wonder: Session 1

What are your burning questions about the animals in the articles?

Think Ahead

1. Which article did you like better? Why?
2. What was the most interesting fact that you learned in your reading?
3. What facts surprised you?
4. Why did they surprise you?
5. What else would you like to know about this animal?

Burning Questions

Have you ever had a burning question? A burning question is something that you wonder about when you read or learn new information.

Imagine you are visiting a zoo and you see an exhibit on giant pandas. During your visit, you learn the following facts about giant pandas.

- Giant pandas are an endangered species.
- Giant pandas are vegetarians.
- Most of the physical development of a giant panda occurs after birth.

What questions do you have? Even though you have learned new information, there is more that you wonder about. These are your burning questions. In order to answer them, you would need to do research to find their answers.

© 2015 K12 Inc. All rights reserved.
Copying or distributing without K12's written consent is prohibited.

Now look at your Home on the Range, Prairie Dog Post, Organization Station, and Wolf in the Dog pages. Which animal that you have read about is the most interesting to you?

Choose an animal and write at least five facts that you have learned about it in the "What I Know" column of the Burning Questions: Session 1 page. Then complete the "What I Wonder" column. Think of at least five questions that you still have about this animal and write them down.

Save this page for a later lesson.

© 2015 K12 Inc. All rights reserved.
Copying or distributing without K12's written consent is prohibited.

Name _____ Date _____

Burning Questions: Session 1

Use the chart below to create your list of questions that you would like to learn more about.

What I Know	What I Wonder
1. _____ _____	1. _____ _____
2. _____ _____	2. _____ _____
3. _____ _____	3. _____ _____
4. _____ _____	4. _____ _____
5. _____ _____	5. _____ _____

© 2015 K12 Inc. All rights reserved.
Copying or distributing without K12's written consent is prohibited.

Name _____ Date _____

"Feathers"

Believe it or not, an airplane's wings are designed to be like a bird's. Uncover the mystery of feathers and how they help birds survive in the wild.

Vocabulary

You will find these words in today's reading.

puny: (adj.) small and weak-looking
The baby curled her hands into *puny*, little fists while she slept.

iridescent: (adj.) shining or reflecting light
If you hang a sun catcher or piece of *iridescent* glass in your window, when the sunlight shines on it there will be colors reflected in the room.

blood vessels: (n.)
Because my skin is so fair, you can see my *blood vessels* under my skin.

limbs: (n.)
The tree's *limbs* attach to the trunk of the tree as a human's *limbs* attach to the torso.

molt: (v.)
Snakes *molt* in order to make room for the new skin underneath.

nerves: (n.)
We can't see them on the surface, but underneath a human being's skin *nerves* carry messages from the parts of the body to the brain.

© 2015 K12 Inc. All rights reserved.
Copying or distributing without K12's written consent is prohibited.

Think Ahead

1. How are birds similar to airplanes?
2. Do you think birds can survive without their wings? Why or why not?

Read

"Feathers."

Questions

Answer the following questions in complete sentences in your Reading Notebook.

1. Can birds survive without feathers?
2. What are two reasons feathers are important to birds?
3. What are the four types of bird feathers?
4. How does the color of a bird's feathers help it to live in the wild?
5. What is *molting*?

Discuss

1. How are birds like airplanes?
2. Why do you think female birds do not have brightly colored feathers?
3. Why do you think the author calls feathers a "secret of success"? What does this phrase mean and how does it apply to birds?

© 2015 K12 Inc. All rights reserved.
Copying or distributing without K12's written consent is prohibited.

Classify and Categorize

When we *classify* and *categorize*, we group things according to their likeness or differences. We give these groups names, called *categories.*

The three groups below are classified by what the members have in common. In what way are the members of each group similar?

- Person, cat, dog
- Squirrel, owl, koala
- Shark, lobster, octopus

What names would you give to these categories?

Classification makes it easier to organize information and it helps us to remember details about what we read. Organize what you have learned about feathers by completing the Classification and Categorization page.

Summarize

Summarize what you have learned about feathers. Use the information that you have categorized to write a short paragraph on feathers and how they work. You may illustrate your work by drawing or tracing a bird from the article. Label the four different kinds of feathers on your illustration. Keep this page in your Reading Notebook.

© 2015 K12 Inc. All rights reserved.
Copying or distributing without K12's written consent is prohibited.

Name _____ Date _____

Classify and Categorize

Read the following characteristics. Decide which of the four types of feathers each describes. Then put it into a category. Write flight, outside, inside, or tail. On the line provided.

1. They trap air next to body. _____

2. They are curved feathers on the front edge of the wing. _____

3. They keep the bird warm. _____

4. They help the bird slip through the air when it flies. _____

5. They turn to help steer the bird during flight. _____

6. They are smooth. _____

7. They are strong and cover the wings. _____

8. They spread out and act like a brake when the bird lands. _____

9. They are fluffy. _____

10. They are uneven in shape; some are narrow and stiffer than the others. _____

© 2015 K12 Inc. All rights reserved.
Copying or distributing without K12's written consent is prohibited.

Name _____   Date _____

"Amazing Sea Lions"

Up, down, and around, the sea lion moves with the grace of a gymnast. But how does this underwater acrobat breathe below the waves? Learn about the sea lion's amazing ability to store oxygen and survive underwater.

Vocabulary

You will find these words in today's reading.

protein: (n.)
The man eats meat to get the *protein* he needs to build muscles.

metabolism: (n.)
Because she is so active, her *metabolism* helps her digest her food very quickly.

conserve: (v.) to save
Our neighbors aren't watering the lawns because everyone wants to *conserve* water.

photoreceptor cells: (n.)
Humans do not have enough *photoreceptor cells* in their eyes to capture light, so they cannot see well in the dark.

acrobatics: (n.)
The gymnast performs a routine of *acrobatics* including somersaults and cartwheels.

Think Ahead

1. What do you think you will learn from reading this article?
2. What is a scuba diver?

© 2015 K12 Inc. All rights reserved.
Copying or distributing without K12's written consent is prohibited.

Read
"Amazing Sea Lions."

Questions
Answer the following questions in complete sentences in your Reading Notebook.

1. What parts of the sea lion's body make it well suited for a diving lifestyle?
2. How do the sea lions conserve their energy to remain underwater?
3. How do the sea lions see underwater and avoid getting water in their nostrils?
4. How do sea lions keep warm underwater?

Discuss
Who do you think is the better swimmer—the scuba diver or the sea lion? Give reasons to support your answer.

Compare and Contrast
Author Betsy Shuttle makes an *analogy* between the scuba diver and the sea lion to help explain different characteristics and abilities of the sea lion. An *analogy* is a comparison between two things that are alike or resemble each other in some way. The author carries this analogy through the article to explore the characteristics of sea lions.

Compare and contrast the sea lion to the scuba diver. Remember, when we **compare** two people, places, things or ideas we tell how they are alike. When we **contrast** them we tell how they are different.

Complete the Compare and Contrast page, explaining how the sea lion and the scuba diver share certain characteristics but

© 2015 K12 Inc. All rights reserved.
Copying or distributing without K12's written consent is prohibited.

accomplish them in different ways. Look for signal words in the article to help you identify similarities and differences.

Working with Headings

The author of this article uses headings to separate the sections of "Amazing Sea Lions." The heading of each section gives readers a hint about the information they can expect to find in the paragraphs that follow. Headings are short phrases that tell a main idea or point in a section of a nonfiction article.

Choose one of the other articles from this magazine. Reread the article and think about how the information is organized. Then divide the article into four or five sections. In your Reading Notebook, write your own headings for each of the sections of the article you chose.

© 2015 K12 Inc. All rights reserved.
Copying or distributing without K12's written consent is prohibited.

Name _____   Date _____

Compare and Contrast

Scuba divers and sea lions share many characteristics for underwater swimming, but they don't achieve their goals in the same way. Fill in this chart to compare and contrast the characteristics of sea lions and scuba divers.

Scuba Diver	Characteristics	Sea Lion
Requires a scuba tank filled with oxygen in order to breathe underwater.	BREATHING UNDERWATER	Does not need a scuba tank to breath. Its blood carries extra oxygen.
	ACROBATICS	
	STAYING WARM	
	SEEING IN THE DARKNESS	
	DIVING	
	DIVING EQUIPMENT	
	BACKBONES	

© 2015 K12 Inc. All rights reserved.
Copying or distributing without K12's written consent is prohibited.

Name _____   Date _____

What I Know, What I Wonder: Session 2

What are your burning questions about the animals in the articles?

Think Ahead

1. Which article did you like better? Why?
2. What was the most interesting fact that you learned in your reading?
3. What facts surprised you?
4. Why did they surprise you?
5. What else would you like to know about feathers or sea lions?

Burning Questions

Remember that a burning question is something that you wonder about when you read or learn new information.

You created burning questions that you would like to learn more about after you read "Keepers of the Prairie" and "The Wolf in the Dog."

What questions do you have about feathers and sea lions? Even though you have learned new information, there is more that you wonder about. These are your burning questions. In order to answer them, you would need to do research to find their answers.

Now look at your Classify and Categorize page, Feathers summary, and Compare and Contrast page. What questions do you still have?

Choose an animal and write at least five facts that you have learned about it in the "What I Know" column of the Burning Questions: Session 2 page. Then complete the "What I Wonder" column. Think of at least five questions that you still have about this animal and write them down.

Save this page for a later lesson.

© 2015 K12 Inc. All rights reserved.
Copying or distributing without K12's written consent is prohibited.

Name _____   Date _____

Burning Questions: Session 2

Use the chart below to create your list of questions that you would like to learn more about.

What I Know	What I Wonder
1. _____	1. _____
2. _____	2. _____
3. _____	3. _____
4. _____	4. _____
5. _____	5. _____

© 2015 K12 Inc. All rights reserved.
Copying or distributing without K12's written consent is prohibited.

Name _____ Date _____

Finding the Answers

Answer your own burning questions by doing research.

Think Ahead

What are the best sources of information to answer your burning questions?

Finding the Answers

Gather your two pages of burning questions. Select a set that you would like to research. Reread your questions and consider what they have in common. What kind of information are you seeking? Think about what sources would be the best to find the information to answer your questions. Do you need books, the Internet, encyclopedias, almanacs, or other sources of nonfiction information?

Remember that an encyclopedia is a good place to find general information on a topic, or to get started doing your research. To find more specific information, you will need to consult books or other sources.

Do research to find the answers to each of your burning questions. You may need to ask your librarian for help finding some of the answers you need. Copy each of your questions into your Reading Notebook and write their answers in complete sentences.

If you have time, research the answers to your second set of burning questions.

© 2015 K12 Inc. All rights reserved.
Copying or distributing without K12's written consent is prohibited.

Name _____   Date _____

"Incredible Giraffes"

It is almost impossible to mistake a giraffe for any other animal. But how does a giraffe's unique body help it survive in nature? Learn about the benefits of the giraffe's one-of-a-kind frame.

Vocabulary

You will hear this word in today's reading.

unique: (adj.) special; unusual
One thing that makes Kim *unique* is that she has one green eye and one blue eye.

Think Ahead

1. What do you picture when you hear the word *giraffe*?

2. What do you think you will learn from listening to this article?

Listen

Listen to "Incredible Giraffes" and look at the diagram shown online.

Questions

Answer the following questions in complete sentences in your Reading Notebook.

1. What do giraffes eat?
2. The passage says that the giraffe's great height allows it to spot "predators from far away and thus avoid danger." What is a predator?
3. What do giraffes use their tongues to do?
4. Why do scientists think giraffes have dark tongues?

© 2015 K12 Inc. All rights reserved.
Copying or distributing without K12's written consent is prohibited.

Discuss

1. Remember that the main idea of a piece of nonfiction is the most important point that the author makes. The other details of the passage tell more about the main idea. Think about what you have learned about giraffes from listening to this passage. Then, in one or two sentences, state the passage's main idea.

2. In your own words, restate two details from the passage that support the main idea.

Diagrams

The author of this passage included a diagram. Describe what the diagram shows. Then explain why the diagram is helpful to people listening to the article.

© 2015 K12 Inc. All rights reserved.
Copying or distributing without K12's written consent is prohibited.

Name   Date

Surprises

Today you will read three short poems. Each poem is a *narrative poem*. A narrative poem is a poem that tells a story. Like stories, narrative poems have characters, a plot, and a setting.

When you read a story, what makes it interesting to you? Do you like action, or funny characters, or surprise endings? Complete the following sentence:

I like stories that _____

_____

_____

First Reading: "Daddy Fell Into the Pond"

Vocabulary
You will find these words in the first poem you will read today.

dismal: (adj.) gloomy, dreary
It's windy, cold, and rainy—what a *dismal* day for our picnic!

sheer: (adj.) absolute, complete
I loved the painting for its *sheer* beauty.

duckweed: (n.) tiny free-floating plants that grow on the surface of ponds and slow-moving streams and are eaten by ducks. The *duckweed* looked like a green carpet floating on the pond.

© 2015 K12 Inc. All rights reserved.
Copying or distributing without K12's written consent is prohibited.

daft: (adj.) silly, crazy

As Sally danced in the park with the pigeons, her brother grumbled, "Stop chasing those silly birds; people will think you're *daft*."

Think Ahead

Have you ever been in a really bad mood and then something happens to change that mood? Characters in poems and stories have changes in mood, too.

Read

Read "Daddy Fell Into the Pond" once silently and a second time aloud.

Discuss

1. In a few sentences or less, summarize the plot of the poem. (The plot is what happens; it is the sequence of events.)
2. Which words in the first stanza paint the picture of a terrible mood?
3. Which words or phrases in the second stanza express how the mood has changed?
4. What event in the poem made the mood change? Where does the mood change in the poem?
5. Find the words in the poem that describe a noise being made. (Hint: Look in the second and third stanzas.)

Second Reading: "The Elf and the Dormouse"

Vocabulary

You will find these words in the second poem you will read today. Study each word and how it is used in the sentence.

toadstool: (n.) an umbrella-shaped mushroom

Never eat a *toadstool* you find in your yard because it might be poisonous.

© 2015 K12 Inc. All rights reserved.
Copying or distributing without K12's written consent is prohibited.

gaily: (adv.) happily

After winning a ribbon at the fair, the girl skipped *gaily* home.

lament: (v.) to express oneself sorrowfully

"I've lost my favorite necklace," my mother *lamented.*

Read

Now read the poem once silently and a second time aloud.

Discuss

1. Who are the characters in the poem and how are they described?
2. In a few sentences or less, summarize the plot of the poem. What everyday object does the elf "invent"?
3. Which words in the third stanza describe the elf's fearful mood?
3. Which words in the fourth and fifth stanzas show the elf's change of mood?

Third Reading: "Millions of Strawberries"

Vocabulary

You will find these words in the third poem you will read today. Study each word and how it is used in the sentence.

lust: (n.) strong desire

On a hot, summer day, almost every child feels a *lust* for cold ice cream.

unmatched: (adj.) supreme, unequaled

In completing the race, the swimmer's time was *unmatched.*

Think Ahead

In the blanks below, list your five senses.

_____   _____   _____

_____   _____

© 2015 K12 Inc. All rights reserved.
Copying or distributing without K12's written consent is prohibited.

When a poet uses language that appeals to the senses, that language is called *imagery*. As you read the next poem, be aware of language that creates sights, sounds, smells, tastes, or feelings in your imagination.

Read
Read "Millions of Strawberries" once silently and a second time aloud.

Discuss
1. Who are the two characters in this poem? What are they doing? What do you think they were supposed to bring home, and what did they do instead?

2. The phrases "over the curve" and "way down" suggest the place where the friends in the poem are eating their strawberries. The words "hot day" and "late gold" suggest the time of day. In your own words describe this *setting*. (The setting is where and when a story takes place.)

3. This poem is rich in imagery. Find words in the poem that appeal to your senses of touch, sight, and hearing.

4. In line 6 of the poem, the poet describes a day that is so hot that it faints from its own heat! This description, "the hot day fainted," is an example of *personification*, because the day is described in human terms. A day doesn't really faint, but a person can. The poet also uses a simile to describe how much the friends are enjoying their romp through the berries. (A simile compares two things, using the words *like* or *as*.) Can you find this simile?

Activity

Inventions of Imagery
Complete the Inventions of Imagery page.

© 2015 K12 Inc. All rights reserved.
Copying or distributing without K12's written consent is prohibited.

Name _____   Date _____

Inventions of Imagery

Language that appeals to the senses—sight, hearing, taste, smell, touch—is called *imagery*.

A. Write phrases or sentences full of imagery for any two of the items listed below. You do not have to fill in the blank for every sense, but fill in as many as you can. Note that a simile can be part of the imagery.

Example:

cotton candy

    sight: bright pink, like a small puffy cloud

    hearing:

    smell: warm, strong, like the sweetest flower

    taste: super-sweet

    touch: sticky, light as a feather, melts on my tongue

Pick any two of these words:

seaweed	rainbow	mud	roses
hamburger	pine cone	peanut butter	old shoe
ice cube	blanket	kitten	puppy

First Word: _____

    sight: _____

    hearing: _____

    smell: _____

    taste: _____

    touch: _____

© 2015 K12 Inc. All rights reserved.
Copying or distributing without K12's written consent is prohibited.

Inventions of Imagery

Second Word: _____

sight: _____

hearing: _____

smell: _____

taste: _____

touch: _____

B. Optional: From Imagery to Poem
If you want to, turn your imagery into a short poem. For example, here's the imagery about cotton candy, followed by a poem that uses the imagery:

sight: bright pink, like a small puffy cloud
hearing:
smell: strong, like the sweetest flower
taste: super-sweet
touch: sticky, light as a feather, melts on my tongue

Cotton Candy
Like a bright pink small puffy cloud
Smelling sweeter than the sweetest flower
Light as a feather
Sticking to my sweaty fingers
Melting on my tongue
Mmmmmmmm!

© 2015 K12 Inc. All rights reserved.
Copying or distributing without K12's written consent is prohibited.

Name _____   Date _____

The Little Hero of Holland

Complete this sentence:
A narrative poem is a poem that _____

_____.

Today you will read "The Leak in the Dike," a narrative poem that tells a story you might already know.

Vocabulary
You will find these words in the poem you will read today.

sluice: (n.) a canal for water to flow through
On farms *sluices* can be used to bring water to fields.

turf: (n.) a mat of grass and roots, which, when dried, can be used for fuel
The farmer lit the *turf* in the fireplace, and soon the room was warm.

trudge: (v.) to walk tiredly
The miner *trudged* home from a long, hard day of work.

prattle: (n.) chatter
While the mother drove the car, she listened to the *prattle* of the children in the back seat.

fret: (v.) to worry
The boy started to *fret* when he couldn't find his wallet.

chafe: (v.) to rub against and wear away; to irritate
Year after year, as the waves *chafed* at the sand dune, the dune got smaller and smaller.

© 2015 K12 Inc. All rights reserved.
Copying or distributing without K12's written consent is prohibited.

succor: (n.) help, relief
The kind villagers gave *succor* to the wounded soldier.

perish (v.) to die
"My goldfish *perished*," my brother said tearfully.

astir: (adv.) up out of bed, moving
At the break of dawn, the rooster is the first animal *astir* in the barnyard.

stricken: (adj.) deeply upset or distressed
The *stricken* parents carried their son to the hospital.

valiant: (adj.) brave
All alone, the *valiant* knight rode forth to battle the terrible dragon.

Think Ahead
Today's poem is set in Holland. Find Holland on a map or globe. Holland is also called The Netherlands.

The main character in today's poem is sometimes called "the little hero of Holland." Can you name a hero you admire? When you think of the word *hero,* what adjectives come to mind? In the spaces below, write two or more adjectives that describe a hero.

_____ _____ _____ _____

Read
Now read "The Leak in the Dike" once silently and a second time aloud. Since the poem is long, you might want to share reading the stanzas aloud with another person. Remember to read with expression.

© 2015 K12 Inc. All rights reserved.
Copying or distributing without K12's written consent is prohibited.

Discuss

1. Briefly summarize the story the poem tells.

2. How is Peter described at the beginning of the poem? Point to specific words and phrases in the third and fourth stanzas.

3. How is Peter described later while he is holding back the leak in the dike? Look at stanzas 8 and 9. Is he afraid? Does he know he is in danger?

4. At the end of stanza 9, the poet says of Peter,
    But he never thinks he can leave the place
    Where duty holds him fast.

    What is the "duty" that holds him? What do these two lines tell us about Peter?

5. In the last two stanzas, what words does the poet use to describe Peter as a hero? According to the poem, can you be afraid and still be a hero?

6. Look at stanzas 6 and 7. The poet uses *personification* to describe the sea. What words describe the sea in human terms?

7. *Suspense* is a feeling of excitement and uncertainty about what is going to happen. Can you think of a story or movie that is full of suspense? In "The Leak in the Dike," how does the poet build suspense in stanza 11?

© 2015 K12 Inc. All rights reserved.
Copying or distributing without K12's written consent is prohibited.

Activities

Tribute to a Hero

The people of Peter's village are gathering to celebrate Peter's heroic deed. You have been asked to speak for the children of the village.

Write a short speech to honor Peter and his heroic action. Your speech should tell *why* Peter is a hero. If you want to, write your speech as a poem. In your speech, you may use ideas and details from "The Leak in the Dike."

Optional: A Dramatic Presentation

Tell aloud in your own words the story of what happened to Peter in "The Leak in the Dike," and follow this with a dramatic reading or recitation of the final two stanzas of the poem. Try to memorize the stanzas if possible, and recite them with real expression and feeling.

© 2015 K12 Inc. All rights reserved.
Copying or distributing without K12's written consent is prohibited.

Name _____ Date _____

Troublesome Doctors and Terrible Cooks

The poems you will read today are humorous. They describe silly events to make us laugh.

First Reading: "Adventures of Isabel"

Vocabulary

You will find these words in the first poem you will read today.

ravenous: (adj.) very hungry
The campers missed breakfast and then hiked up a mountain, so by lunchtime they were *ravenous.*

cavernous: (adj.) hollow like a cave
The empty gym felt *cavernous* to the lonely boy who was shooting baskets.

pitch: (n.) tar
The Highway Department covered the road with *pitch*.

rancor: (n.) hate or spite
My grandmother says, "Never speak in *rancor*, for you might say something you will regret."

hideous: (adj.) very ugly, shocking
To play the pirate, Tyler wore some *hideous* makeup, including several fake scars and a fake nose the size of a squash.

self-reliant: (adj.) self-confident
After she turned 16, Margaret seemed much more *self-reliant*.

zwieback: (n.) a kind of dry, crisp, usually sweet bread
Babies love to gnaw on *zwieback* when they are teething.

© 2015 K12 Inc. All rights reserved.
Copying or distributing without K12's written consent is prohibited.

satchel: (n.) small suitcase or bag for carrying things
The professor carried her books in a black *satchel*.

concoct: (v.) to mix up from various materials; to invent
My sister loves to throw together lots of ingredients to *concoct*
new recipes, though we don't always like to eat the results!

Think Ahead
What do you expect when you see the word "Adventures" in the
title of a book or movie?

The poem you are about to read is called "Adventures of Isabel." It was
written by a poet named Ogden Nash. He had two daughters, and one
was named Isabel. Do you think this poem will be about a *real* little
girl's *real* adventures? You'll see before you get very far into the poem!

Read
Read "Adventures of Isabel" once silently and a second time aloud.

Discuss
1. As you can see, Isabel's adventures are not real at all. Did the
   adventures in this poem turn out to be what you expected?
   Which of Isabel's encounters is the funniest to you?

2. Identify the four characters Isabel meets, and identify adjectives in
   the poem that describe each of these characters or their features.

3. Two lines are repeated in every stanza of the poem:

   Isabel, Isabel, didn't worry,
   Isabel didn't scream or scurry.

   What do those lines tell you about Isabel? What adjectives
   would you use to describe her?

4. A group of two lines in a poem is called a *couplet*. Sometimes
   the two lines rhyme, and sometimes they don't. When they do,
   then the two lines are called a *rhyming couplet*. "Adventures of

© 2015 K12 Inc. All rights reserved.
Copying or distributing without K12's written consent is prohibited.

Isabel" is written in rhyming couplets. Some of the rhymes use common words, such as:

> Isabel met an enormous <u>bear</u>,
> Isabel, Isabel, didn't <u>care</u>.

Other rhymes are funny, surprising, or unusual, such as:

> She showed no rage and she showed no <u>rancor</u>,
> But she turned the witch into milk and <u>drank her</u>.

Go back through the poem and find three more funny, surprising, or unusual rhymes. Write them in the spaces below. Which is your favorite?

_____	_____	_____
_____	_____	_____

Second Reading: "Mummy Slept Late and Daddy Fixed Breakfast"

Pronunciation
bituminous (bih-TYOO-muh-nus)
anthracite (AN-thruh-site)

Vocabulary
You will find these words in the next poem you will read today.

bituminous (adj.) and **anthracite** (n.): two kinds of coal
Bituminous coal is softer than *anthracite*.

hack-saw: (n.) a saw used for cutting metal
My father had to use a *hack-saw* to cut the padlock off the old trunk he found in the attic.

© 2015 K12 Inc. All rights reserved.
Copying or distributing without K12's written consent is prohibited.

Think Ahead

Have you, or has an adult you know, ever cooked or baked something that didn't turn out the way it was supposed to?

Read

Read "Mummy Slept Late and Daddy Fixed Breakfast" once silently and a second time aloud.

Discuss

1. To *narrate* means to tell a story. In a story or narrative poem, *the narrator* is the person who tells the story. Who is the narrator of this poem?

2. The narrator uses the *simile* "like gravel pudding" to describe the waffles Daddy fixes. Can you find another simile the narrator uses to describe the waffles? (Look in the third stanza.)

3. Do you know what it means to *exaggerate?* If you're cold and you say something like, "I'm frozen solid!" then you're exaggerating. In "Mummy Slept Late and Daddy Fixed Breakfast," exaggeration is used for humor. Identify at least two examples of humorous exaggeration in the poem.

Activities

Rhyme Schemes

Complete the Rhyme Schemes page.

Optional: One More Adventure for Isabel

Add a stanza to "Adventures of Isabel." If you want to, you can have Isabel meet someone or something *nice* for a change! For more suggestions, see the end of the Rhyme Schemes page.

© 2015 K12 Inc. All rights reserved.
Copying or distributing without K12's written consent is prohibited.

Name _____ Date _____

Rhyme Schemes

A rhyme scheme is the pattern of rhymes in a poem. You use a different letter of the alphabet to stand for each new rhyme. For example, here is how you mark the rhyme scheme of a poem you might know. (The rhyming words or syllables are underlined.)

There once were two cats of Kil<u>kenny</u>,	**a**
Each thought there was one cat too <u>many</u>,	**a**
So they fought and they <u>fit</u>,	**b**
And they scratched and they <u>bit</u>,	**b**
Till, excepting their <u>nails</u>	**c**
And the tips of their <u>tails</u>,	**c**
Instead of two cats, there weren't <u>any</u>.	**a**

Do you see how the last line ends with "any," which rhymes with the first two lines? That's why you use the letter **a** again for "any."

1. In the example above, the first two lines rhyme, then the next two lines rhyme, then the next two lines rhyme. In poetry, what is the special name for two rhyming lines in a row?

_____

2. Here is the first stanza of "Adventures of Isabel." Fill in the rhyme scheme.

Isabel met an enormous bear,	_____
Isabel, Isabel, didn't care;	_____
The bear was hungry, the bear was ravenous,	_____
The bear's big mouth was cruel and cavernous.	_____
The bear said, Isabel, glad to meet you,	_____
How do, Isabel, now I'll eat you!	_____
Isabel, Isabel, didn't worry,	_____
Isabel didn't scream or scurry.	_____
She washed her hands and she straightened her hair up,	_____
Then Isabel quietly ate the bear up.	_____

© 2015 K12 Inc. All rights reserved.
Copying or distributing without K12's written consent is prohibited.

Rhyme Schemes

3. Here are the first two stanzas of "Mummy Slept Late and Daddy Fixed Breakfast." Fill in the rhyme scheme. (In the second stanza, start over with **a**.)

Daddy fixed breakfast. _____

He made us each a waffle. _____

It looked like gravel pudding. _____

It tasted something awful. _____

"Ha, ha," he said, "I'll try again. _____

This time I'll get it right." _____

But what *I* got was in between _____

Bituminous and anthracite. _____

4. Optional: One More Adventure for Isabel
Write a new stanza to add to "Adventures of Isabel." Try to follow the rhyme scheme of the poem. Also, in the seventh and eighth lines of your stanza, use the lines repeated in all the other stanzas:
Isabel, Isabel, didn't worry,
Isabel didn't scream or scurry.

You can choose one of these lines to get you started or make up your own. Also, in your stanza, maybe Isabel will meet someone or something nice!

• Isabel met a nasty gnome.
• Isabel met a talking fish.
• Isabel met a fat orange cat.
• Isabel met a wandering knight.
• Isabel met a lost little boy.

© 2015 K12 Inc. All rights reserved.
Copying or distributing without K12's written consent is prohibited.

Name _____   Date _____

Through the Eyes of a Child

Do you know this little poem?

> There was a little girl, she had a little curl
>   Right in the middle of her forehead;
> And when she was good, she was very, very good,
>   And when she was bad, she was horrid.

That poem was written by one of the most popular and best-loved American poets of all time, Henry Wadsworth Longfellow. Today you will read part of a long narrative poem called *The Song of Hiawatha*, published by Longfellow in 1855.

Reading: "Hiawatha's Childhood"

Pronunciation
Hiawatha (HIE-uh-WAH-thuh)
Gitche Gumee (GITCH-ee GOOM-ee)
Nokomis (nuh-KOH-mis)

Vocabulary
You will find these words in today's reading.

brake: (n.) an area overgrown with briers and vines
The rabbit escaped from the fox by darting into the thick *brake*.

linden: (n.) a tall tree that grows mainly in the forests of the eastern and central United States; (adj.) made from a linden tree
The *linden* chest has been in our family for years.

plumes: (n.) feathers or a group of feathers, especially large and bright ones
The marching band wore caps with bright gold *plumes*.

© 2015 K12 Inc. All rights reserved.
Copying or distributing without K12's written consent is prohibited.

rushes: (n.) plants that usually grow in wet places
The *rushes* growing on the shore provided a hiding place for the small birds.

sinews: (n.) tendons; in animals, the tough, fiber-like tissues that connect muscles to bones
The Plains Indians used the *sinews* of buffalos to sew together the buffalo hides.

tresses: (n.) long locks of hair
Rapunzel let her long golden *tresses* fall from the tower window to the prince on the ground far below.

Think Ahead

In this brief selection from "The Song of Hiawatha," you will meet Hiawatha as a child, when he is being raised by his grandmother, Nokomis. The Hiawatha in this poem is a fictional character and a member of the Ojibwa tribe. There was a real Hiawatha. He was a leader of one of the Iroquois nations in the late 1500s, and he helped make peace between warring peoples.

The first lines of the poem refer to "Gitche Gumee," the "Big-Sea-Water," which we know as one of the five Great Lakes, Lake Superior. Find Lake Superior on a map of the United States.

Read

Now read "Hiawatha's Childhood" once silently and then a second time aloud. Because the poem is long, you might want to share reading the stanzas aloud with another person.

© 2015 K12 Inc. All rights reserved.
Copying or distributing without K12's written consent is prohibited.

Discuss

1. Reread the first stanza and find the words and phrases that describe the setting of the poem. Which of your senses (hearing, taste, sight, touch, or smell) do these descriptions appeal to?

2. Reread the second stanza. What words or phrases describe Nokomis? What can you tell about her from the way she treats the baby Hiawatha?

3. Sounds are very important in the poem. In the fourth stanza, Hiawatha listens to sounds. What sounds does he hear?

4. As Hiawatha grows up, Nokomis teaches him many things. In the sixth, seventh, and eighth stanzas, Hiawatha asks Nokomis the same question three times: "What is that, Nokomis?" What things is he asking about? How does Nokomis answer his questions?

5. Reread stanzas 9 and 10. Describe the relationship between Hiawatha and the animals.

Activities

Metaphor

You know that a *simile* uses the words *like* or *as* to compare two unlike things, for example, "My old blanket is soft as a puffy cloud." A *metaphor* also compares one thing to another, but does not use *like* or *as*. For example:

The cat's eyes were emeralds shining in the night.

That metaphor compares a cat's eyes to emeralds. It does not say that the cat's eyes are *like* emeralds. It says they *are* emeralds. You could explain the metaphor this way:

cat's eyes = emeralds

© 2015 K12 Inc. All rights reserved.
Copying or distributing without K12's written consent is prohibited.

What things are being compared in these metaphors?

- His mind is a storm of ideas, blowing this way and that.

  _____=_____

- Time is a river that flows ever onward.

  _____=_____

- Her cheeks are ripe peaches, and her hair is shining silk.

  _____=_____

  _____=_____

Now reread stanza 7 in "Hiawatha's Childhood." What metaphor does Nokomis use to explain what a rainbow is?

rainbow = _____

Reading with Rhythm
Complete the activity on the Reading with Rhythm page.

© 2015 K12 Inc. All rights reserved.
Copying or distributing without K12's written consent is prohibited.

Name _____   Date _____

Reading with Rhythm

Do a dramatic reading of the first stanza of "Hiawatha's Childhood." For an extra challenge, memorize and recite it.

Before you read, think about the *rhythm* of the poem. Like music, poems have rhythm. Rhythm is the regular "beat" of the sounds of the words. It's the pattern of strong and soft sounds in the lines of the poem.

When you read poetry aloud, you emphasize, or *stress*, some words and syllables more than others. Listen for these stresses as you read aloud the first two lines of "Hiawatha's Childhood." To help emphasize the rhythm, read slowly and clap as you say each underlined word or syllable.

> <u>By </u>the <u>shores </u>of <u>Gitch</u>e <u>Gum</u>ee,
> <u>By </u>the <u>shin</u>ing <u>Big</u>-Sea-<u>Wa</u>ter

Do you notice the pattern—how one stressed sound is followed by a softer sound? Did you hear the rhythm? It is very steady and regular, like a boat rocking in the water, or like gently beating drums.

Now, look at the next two lines. Underline the words or syllables that you would stress in reading them aloud.

> Stood the wigwam of Nokomis,
> Daughter of the Moon,
> Nokomis

© 2015 K12 Inc. All rights reserved.
Copying or distributing without K12's written consent is prohibited.

Reading with Rhythm

Now it's time to prepare for your reading. Read the stanza carefully and think about how each line should sound. Practice on your own before you read (or recite from memory) to an audience. Speak clearly and with expression.

By the shores of Gitche Gumee,
By the shining Big-Sea-Water,
Stood the wigwam of Nokomis,
Daughter of the Moon, Nokomis,
Dark behind it rose the forest,
Rose the black and gloomy pine-
trees, Rose the firs with cones upon
them; Bright before it beat the water.
Beat the clear and sunny water.
Beat the shining Big-Sea-Water.

© 2015 K12 Inc. All rights reserved.
Copying or distributing without K12's written consent is prohibited.

Name _____   Date _____

"Louis Pasteur: Battle with Death": Session 1

Meet Louis Pasteur, a man who helped make our lives a little safer through his discoveries.

Vocabulary

You will find these words in today's reading.

rabies: (n.) a disease, often transmitted by animals, that makes muscles tighten and twitch. It can lead to paralysis and death. We always make sure that our dog gets his *rabies* shots because we don't want him to get sick if he gets bitten by another animal.

vaccinate: (v.) to inject a vaccine (a form of medicine) that will prevent a certain disease
Doctors *vaccinate* their patients to prevent diseases such as small pox, polio, and even the flu.

saliva: (n.) a watery liquid produced by the mouth
My mouth is so dry; there is not a drop of *saliva.*

immune: (adj.) to be protected from a disease
The doctor gave me a shot so that I will be *immune* to chicken pox and not catch them.

resistance: (n.) the ability to fight or work against
My grandmother once told me that getting plenty of sleep and drinking plenty of liquids can help build my *resistance* to getting sick.

Think Ahead

1. The stories in this unit are about real people who made important contributions to medicine. The stories are based on fact; however,

© 2015 K12 Inc. All rights reserved.
Copying or distributing without K12's written consent is prohibited.

they contain parts that are fiction. When real events from history are mixed with fictional events, we call this type of story *historical fiction*. As you read, see if you can find the facts.

2. Louis Pasteur was a famous scientist who was born in 1822 and died in 1895. He was inducted into the National Inventor's Hall of Fame in 1978 for his work—83 years after he died!

3. Have you ever thought of Louis Pasteur when drinking a glass of milk? You should. He is responsible for many discoveries that we benefit from each day. Read to learn more about this great scientist.

Read
"Louis Pasteur: Battle with Death" in *Classics for Young Readers*, Vol. 4A, pages 74-79

Questions
Answer the following questions in complete sentences in your Reading Notebook.

1. What scene did Louis Pasteur remember most from his childhood?
2. What was the cure for rabies when Pasteur was a little boy?
3. How did the scientist cure cows that were sick from anthrax?
4. What did Pasteur do that prevented people from becoming ill from the milk of sick cows?
5. What was Pasteur's idea for curing rabies? How did it work?
6. How did Louis Pasteur discover that his rabies vaccination would be safe for humans?

Discuss
1. How do Louis Pasteur's discoveries make our lives safer?
2. Why do you think the mother of the nine-year-old boy asked to use Pasteur's cure on her son even though it hadn't been tested on humans?
3. Which of Louis Pasteur's discoveries do you think was the most important? Why?

© 2015 K12 Inc. All rights reserved.
Copying or distributing without K12's written consent is prohibited.

Book About Louis Pasteur

Louis Pasteur was a great scientist. His contributions make people's lives better. Create a book telling about the scientist.

Choose three events from Pasteur's life that are important. On three separate pieces of paper, write about the three events from his life. On each page, write at least three sentences that describe the event and tell why it was important. Place the events in the order in which they occurred. Make a cover for your book. Illustrate the pages if time permits.

The Fact Detective

"Louis Pasteur: Battle with Death" is a historical fiction story. That means that the story contains real events, or *facts,* mixed with fictional details. *Facts* are real details usually found through research. *Fiction* is when the story contains ideas that are made up from the imagination.

Read the paragraph below.

> Prince Edward VI of England was born on October 12, 1537. He was the child of King Henry VIII and his third wife, Jane Seymour. For more than 25 years, King Henry had wanted a son to be the next king of England. There was great rejoicing when Edward was born. As Prince Edward was growing up, his sisters Princess Elizabeth and Princess Mary often thought, "Edward is a good brother, but I don't see what is so special about him. I could rule England just as well as he."

Which sentences contain facts? Which do you believe are fictional?

Go back to the story and find factual details about Louis Pasteur's life. Write the facts on your Fact Detective page. Identify at least five facts.

© 2015 K12 Inc. All rights reserved.
Copying or distributing without K12's written consent is prohibited.

Name _____   Date _____

The Fact Detective

Look back in the story and identify at least five facts. Write each fact in the magnifying glass.

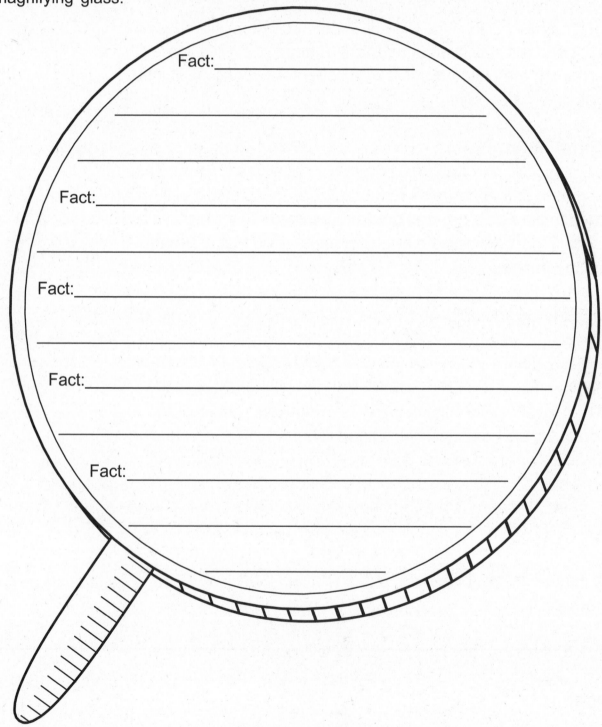

Fact:_____

_____

_____

Fact:_____

_____

Fact:_____

_____

Fact:_____

_____

Fact:_____

_____

© 2015 K12 Inc. All rights reserved.
Copying or distributing without K12's written consent is prohibited.

Guidelines for Peer Discussion

Share your thoughts, ideas, questions, and feelings about a text with a peer or others. Listen carefully to what everyone has to say about the text. During your discussion, follow these guidelines.

1. Be prepared to discuss what you think about the text. You should have already read the assignment. Come prepared to discuss your ideas, and use examples from the text to support your thoughts and answers.

2. You will be asked questions about the text. Be ready to answer them, and bring some questions of your own to ask others, such as:

   "Who was your favorite character? Why?"

   "What was your favorite part of the text? Why?"

   "What fact did you enjoy learning? Why do you find this fact interesting?"

   "What question would you ask if you had the chance to meet the author?"

3. Listen if it's not your turn to speak. Pay attention to what others say so that you can add your ideas. Speak clearly and in complete sentences.

4. If you don't understand what someone says, ask a question, such as:

   "What do you mean when you say . . . ?"

   "Can you give an example of . . . ?"

5. If you don't agree with what someone says, explain why.

   "I don't agree with that because . . . "

6. Keep discussions positive! You can disagree, but don't argue. Be respectful.

© 2015 K12 Inc. All rights reserved.
Copying or distributing without K12's written consent is prohibited.

Name _____ Date _____

"Louis Pasteur: Battle with Death": Session 2

Can you imagine being someone famous? Here's your chance. Respond to the interview questions as though you were Dr. Louis Pasteur.

Think Ahead

1. If you could meet Louis Pasteur, what would you want to ask him?
2. What things would you tell him about the medical discoveries since his death?
3. What kind of personality do you think he would have?

An Interview with Louis Pasteur

An interview is a meeting with a person to answer questions or talk about something. Often, researchers use interviews to collect facts for their stories or articles. Pretend you are Dr. Louis Pasteur and that Dr. I.M. Fine for the *Medical Monthly Journal* is interviewing you. Answer the questions using facts from the story. When Dr. Fine asks you a question that you can't answer with facts, make up your own historical fiction. Answer the question the way you think Louis Pasteur might.

Complete the Interview with Dr. Pasteur page. When you are finished, you may wish to act out the interview with another person.

© 2015 K12 Inc. All rights reserved.
Copying or distributing without K12's written consent is prohibited.

Name _____ Date _____

An Interview with Dr. Pasteur

Pretend you are Dr. Louis Pasteur and respond to this interview with Dr. I.M. Fine of the *Medical Monthly Journal*.

Dr. Fine: Thank you so much for being here today, Dr. Pasteur. How did you first come to be interested in the disease, rabies?

Dr. Pasteur: _____

_____

_____

Dr. Fine: I see. What was the treatment for rabies when you were a boy?

Dr. Pasteur: _____

_____

_____

Dr. Fine: Wow! That must have hurt. I can see why this experience interested you in science. Did you always know you would be a scientist or did you have other interests?

Dr. Pasteur: _____

_____

_____

© 2015 K12 Inc. All rights reserved.
Copying or distributing without K12's written consent is prohibited.

An Interview with Dr. Pasteur

Dr. Fine: But you went on to study science. What subjects did you study?

Dr. Pasteur: _____

_____

_____

Dr. Fine: Now when you went to school, you didn't know that germs cause viruses. Yet you were able to cure anthrax in cattle and rabies in humans. Please explain how you worked with healthy and sick animals.

Dr. Pasteur: _____

_____

_____

Dr. Fine: What did you do once you had caused the disease in the healthy animals?

Dr. Pasteur: _____

_____

_____

Dr. Fine: So that's how you were able to make the dogs immune to the disease. That was quite a breakthrough. When did you decide to test your method on humans?

Dr. Pasteur: _____

_____

_____

© 2015 K12 Inc. All rights reserved.
Copying or distributing without K12's written consent is prohibited.

An Interview with Dr. Pasteur

Dr. Fine: That must have been a scary test. Were you afraid to test the vaccine on Joseph? How did you feel about it? What went through your mind?

Dr. Pasteur: _____

_____

_____

Dr. Fine: How did you feel when Joseph got better?

Dr. Pasteur: _____

_____

_____

Dr. Fine: You have a lot to be proud of, Dr. Pasteur. You belong in the Hall of Fame. What discovery are you most proud of?

Dr. Pasteur: _____

_____

_____

© 2015 K12 Inc. All rights reserved.
Copying or distributing without K12's written consent is prohibited.

Name _____   Date _____

"Elizabeth Blackwell: A Pioneering Physician": Session 1

Can you imagine a time when women were not allowed to be doctors, lawyers, or bankers or to go to good schools? A young girl named Elizabeth Blackwell lived during this time in history. Learn why she was a pioneering physician.

Vocabulary
You will find these words in today's reading.

steerage: (n.) a section of poor living quarters on a passenger ship
Many men, women, and children in *steerage* died from illness on their journey to America.

cholera: (n.) a highly contagious disease of humans and animals that causes severe stomach and digestive symptoms
Cholera is extremely contagious and spreads rapidly when people are confined in small spaces.

indigent: (adj.) very poor or needy
The doctor could have practiced medicine anywhere and chose to work with the *indigent* people of the town because they needed the most care.

Think Ahead
1. Elizabeth Blackwell was born in Bristol, England in 1821 and died in London in 1910. She is remembered for her accomplishments in the National Women's Hall of Fame in Seneca Falls, New York.

2. What does it mean to be a pioneer? Do you know anyone today you could call a pioneer?

© 2015 K12 Inc. All rights reserved.
Copying or distributing without K12's written consent is prohibited.

Read

"Elizabeth Blackwell: A Pioneering Physician" in *Classics for Young Readers,* Vol. 4A, pages 80-86

Questions

Answer the following questions in complete sentences in your Reading Notebook.

1. What concerned Elizabeth Blackwell on her journey from England to America?

2. How did her father feel about her dream to be a doctor?

3. What did Elizabeth Blackwell do to prepare herself to be a doctor?

4. How did the people at the school treat Elizabeth Blackwell?

5. What was Elizabeth Blackwell the first woman to do? How did she feel about her accomplishment?

6. Where did Dr. Blackwell practice medicine and whom did she treat?

Discuss

1. What did Elizabeth Blackwell's father do that may have helped her reach her goals?

2. Why do you think people believed women could not become doctors?

3. Elizabeth Blackwell believed in preventative medicine. Describe what that is and how it is similar to or different from what we do today. Do you think Dr. Blackwell's beliefs were common at the time?

4. Why do you think Dr. Blackwell chose to set up her clinic in a poor neighborhood and to take care of women and children?

© 2015 K12 Inc. All rights reserved.
Copying or distributing without K12's written consent is prohibited.

Elizabeth Blackwell's Diary

Dr. Blackwell had to overcome many obstacles to become a doctor. It was not easy for her to do, but she was very determined. How do you think Dr. Blackwell felt? Pretend that you are Dr. Elizabeth Blackwell. Write an entry in your diary about a day in your life. In a diary, people write what they did, what they felt, or what they thought during a period of time.

You may choose a day in medical school or a day when you were taking care of people in your clinic.

Be sure to include facts or events from the story to tell how you spent your day. Include details about what happened. Then use your imagination and tell how you felt about the events of the day.

Write your diary entry in your Reading Notebook.

© 2015 K12 Inc. All rights reserved.
Copying or distributing without K12's written consent is prohibited.

Name _____   Date _____

"Elizabeth Blackwell: A Pioneering Physician": Session 2

Dr. Elizabeth Blackwell was the first woman to graduate from medical school and become a doctor. She went on to accomplish many great things in her lifetime. What advice would she give about dreams?

Think Ahead

1. How do you think Elizabeth Blackwell felt when people called her names and teased her in medical school?
2. Why do you think she continued pursuing her dream even though others didn't believe she could do it?
3. What advice do you think Elizabeth Blackwell would give other people?

Dear Dr. Blackwell

If Dr. Elizabeth Blackwell had an advice column in a newspaper, what kinds of letters would she receive? How would she answer them? Complete the Dear Dr. Blackwell page. Pretend you are Dr. Elizabeth Blackwell and you received the two letters asking you for advice. What advice would you give the writers? Write notes back to them giving them advice on their problems as if you were Elizabeth Blackwell. Use details from Blackwell's life to support your responses.

© 2015 K12 Inc. All rights reserved.
Copying or distributing without K12's written consent is prohibited.

Name _____ **Date** _____

Dear Dr. Blackwell

Pretend you are Dr. Elizabeth Blackwell. How would you advise these letter writers?

Dear Dr. Blackwell,

    I really want to be a soccer player when I grow up, but everyone is telling me that girls can't play professional soccer. My friends think it is a dumb idea and a lot of them are making fun of me. I want to play on a team in my town, but the boys who are on it don't want to play with me. What should I do? I know I could be a great goalie if I try.

Signed,

Best Foot Forward

Dear Best Foot Forward,

_____

_____

_____

_____

_____

_____

_____

_____

_____

_____

_____

© 2015 K12 Inc. All rights reserved.
Copying or distributing without K12's written consent is prohibited.

Dear Dr. Blackwell

Dear Dr. Blackwell,

    I have studied and worked very hard to be a chef. I have worked in many restaurants, but I would like to do something that helps people. I know how to cook good, nutritious meals. What advice do you have?

    Signed,

    Waiting to Serve

Dear Waiting to Serve,

_____

_____

_____

_____

_____

_____

_____

_____

_____

_____

_____

© 2015 K12 Inc. All rights reserved.
Copying or distributing without K12's written consent is prohibited.

Name _____

Date _____

"Sir Alexander Fleming: The Accident That Changed the World": Session 1

Sometimes amazing discoveries happen when you least expect it. This is exactly what happened to a scientist named Sir Alexander Fleming.

Vocabulary

You will find these words in today's reading.

spore: (n.) a tiny cell produced by certain plants that can grow into a new plant
The bread must have gotten damp because there were green mold *spores* growing on it.

organism: (n.) any living thing
Plants, animals, and bacteria are examples of *organisms*.

colony: (n.) a group of plants living or growing together
The scientist looked under his microscope to see the *colony* of spores in the Petri dish.

Think Ahead

1. Alexander Fleming was born in 1881 in Lochfield, Scotland. He died in 1955. He was famous for discovering something that would help sick people get well. For his discovery, he was knighted in 1944 and was called Sir Alexander Fleming from then on. He was awarded the Nobel Prize in 1945.

2. Sir Alexander Fleming once said, "One sometimes finds what one is not looking for." Has this ever happened to you?

© 2015 K12 Inc. All rights reserved.
Copying or distributing without K12's written consent is prohibited.

Read

"Alexander Fleming: The Accident That Changed the World" in *Classics for Young Readers,* Vol. 4A, pages 87–92

Questions

Answer the following questions in complete sentences in your Reading Notebook.

1. How did the mold spore get into the Petri dish?
2. What was Alexander Fleming's profession?
3. Describe what the scientist saw when he took the cover off of the Petri dish for the first time.
4. Why was the spot of mold with the ring around it so important to Alexander Fleming?
5. Explain how Dr. Fleming tested the mold. What did he do and what did he find?
6. Where did the yellow fluid come from?
7. What happened to the sick animals once they were injected with the yellow fluid?

Discuss

1. About his discovery Sir Alexander Fleming once said, "It all started as something of an accident. After that it was a question of patience and work—good, satisfying work!" Why did his work take so much patience?

2. Why do you think penicillin was such an important discovery? How does it help people today?

3. Compare and contrast the discoveries made by Louis Pasteur and Sir Alexander Fleming.

© 2015 K12 Inc. All rights reserved.
Copying or distributing without K12's written consent is prohibited.

Extra! Extra! Read All About It!

You are a reporter for a newspaper. Imagine you were there the day that Alexander Fleming made his accidental discovery. What would you include in your article?

A news article contains facts and events. It starts with an interesting sentence or hook to catch the reader's attention. The rest of the story is written in chronological order and explains what happened and why the event is newsworthy. Create a newspaper article that summarizes what you read in the book about Sir Alexander Fleming and the discovery of penicillin. First, answer the following questions:

- *Who* is the story about?
- *What* happened in the story?
- *Where* does the story take place?
- *When* does the story take place?
- *Why* is the event important?
- *How* did the event occur?

Use the Who? What? Where? When? Why? and How? page to plan your article. Once your thoughts are organized, write your article about Alexander Fleming's discovery in your Reading Notebook.

Here is an example of an article written about Louis Pasteur:

Scientist Saves Young Boy's Life

Today in France a scientist named Louis Pasteur saved a young boy's life. The unfortunate nine-year-old boy had been bitten 14 times by a rabid animal. His death seemed certain.

Sources report that on July 16, 1885, the boy's terrified mother, Madame Meister, rushed to Dr. Pasteur's laboratory. She had heard about Pasteur's rabies

© 2015 K12 Inc. All rights reserved.
Copying or distributing without K12's written consent is prohibited.

vaccine and how it saved animals. She begged the scientist to give the medicine to her son. Louis Pasteur was unsure since the medicine had never been tested on humans. The frantic mother begged the doctor to try because she knew the boy had no other hope of survival. The mother believed it was the only way to save her son.

Pasteur began the treatment on the young boy. Every day he injected the boy with increasingly strong doses of the rabies vaccine. The trick was to build the body's immunity to the disease.

On the day after the last dose of medicine, Madame Meister again went to the scientist and told him to hurry back to her home. Louis Pasteur feared the worst. He was wrong! The nine-year-old boy was saved thanks to the scientist's vaccine. Louis Pasteur will no doubt go down in history as a great inventor.

© 2015 K12 Inc. All rights reserved.
Copying or distributing without K12's written consent is prohibited.

Name _____   Date _____

Who? What? Where? When? Why? How?

Fill in the boxes with information from the text.

Who is the story about?	**What** happens in the story?	**Where** does the story take place?
When does the story take place?	**Why** does an important event occur?	**How** does an important event occur?

© 2015 K12 Inc. All rights reserved.
Copying or distributing without K12's written consent is prohibited.

Name _____ Date _____

"Sir Alexander Fleming: The Accident That Changed the World": Session 2

Sir Alexander Fleming's accidental discovery made a great contribution to medicine. Why isn't he in the National Inventors Hall of Fame?

Think Ahead

1. The Nobel Prize is an award that is given yearly. It is a very important honor that is awarded to people for achievements in physics, chemistry, medicine, literature, and peace. Winners of the prize receive a medal, a personal diploma, and a prize amount. In 1945 Sir Alexander Fleming earned the Nobel Prize in Medicine for his work. Why do you think he earned that award?

2. How do you think people felt when they heard the news of the scientist's discovery? What effect might it have had on their lives?

3. Andrew J. Moyer was inducted into the National Inventors Hall of Fame in 1987 for his work in mass-producing penicillin. Alexander Fleming is not a part of the Hall of Fame for his discovery of penicillin. Why do you think that is?

National Inventors Hall of Fame

The National Inventors Hall of Fame honors the women and men responsible for the technological advances that make human, social, and economic progress possible. Alexander Fleming was knighted and won the Nobel Prize for discovering penicillin and how it could be used to cure illnesses. But he has not been inducted into the National Inventors Hall of Fame in Akron, Ohio as Louis Pasteur was. Did Alexander Fleming "invent" anything? Is there a difference between "inventing" something and "discovering" something?

© 2015 K12 Inc. All rights reserved.
Copying or distributing without K12's written consent is prohibited.

Writing to Persuade

When you write to persuade, you try to convince someone to think or feel how you do about a subject. Persuasive writing expresses an opinion and backs it up with facts, personal experiences, and explanations.

Read the paragraph below. Find the facts and the opinions.

> I think dogs make better pets than birds. Dogs are friendly and like to be around people. Birds sit in a cage all day and do not really do much of anything. If you like to play catch and run around, then a dog is the perfect animal for you. Most dogs can play games for hours. Dogs can go for a long walk on a sunny day, but birds can't. A dog makes a better pet because you can do more things with it than a bird. In my opinion, everyone should have a dog.

Writing a Persuasive Letter

Write a persuasive letter either to encourage or discourage Sir Alexander Fleming's induction into the museum. Choose a side and give reasons why you think Alexander Fleming should or should not be a part of the museum, and include facts from the story to back up your opinion. Complete this assignment in your Reading Notebook.

© 2015 K12 Inc. All rights reserved.
Copying or distributing without K12's written consent is prohibited.

Name _____   Date _____

Looking Back

Compare and contrast the lives and accomplishments of Louis Pasteur, Elizabeth Blackwell, and Sir Alexander Fleming.

Think Ahead

1. Who do you think made the most important contribution to medicine—Louis Pasteur, Elizabeth Blackwell, or Sir Alexander Fleming? Why?

2. Which person would you have liked to meet? Why?

Activities

Choose one of the following activities to complete.

Notable People Museum

You have been selected to be a part of creating an exhibit for the Notable People Museum. Your exhibit will feature one of the following people who made important contributions to the world of medicine—Louis Pasteur, Elizabeth Blackwell, or Sir Alexander Fleming. Create a poster board exhibit that includes the following:

- A picture or sketch of the person
- Four sentences describing the important facts about the person (on an index card)
- Four sentences describing their discovery (on an index card)
- Four sentences describing how people are affected by their discovery (on an index card)
- Four sentences describing one event in the person's life that you thought was interesting (on an index card)

You may choose to do the layout of your exhibit any way you choose. Feel free to add other details to it. Show your exhibit to someone and explain why this person is in the Notable People Museum.

© 2015 K12 Inc. All rights reserved.
Copying or distributing without K12's written consent is prohibited.

Compare and Contrast Notable People

Divide your poster board into three columns. Label the top of each column with one name: Louis Pasteur, Sir Alexander Fleming, and Elizabeth Blackwell. In each person's space, write at least four sentences describing the person and his or her accomplishments. Draw a symbol that stands for something that this person accomplished. Then write a sentence under each symbol to explain why you think it stands for something the person did.

When you have completed this, answer the following questions in your Reading Notebook:

- How are these people similar?
- How are these people different?
- What contributions did each person make to how people live today?
- Which person is the most important? Why?

© 2015 K12 Inc. All rights reserved.
Copying or distributing without K12's written consent is prohibited.

Name _____   Date _____

Semester Review

Review the skills you've learned and the stories you've read this semester.

Mix and Match

This semester, you've learned words that describe parts of stories and poems. For example, the word *plot* describes what happens in a story.

Play a Mix and Match game to help you review the words you've learned. First, cut out the Mix and Match cards. Then shuffle them and lay them face down. For each turn, you may turn over two cards. If the word and definition match, you may take the pair. If they do not match, turn them face down and choose again.

Act It Out!

Choose one or more of the poems below to read aloud or act out.
After you finish:

- Tell what the poem is about, who the speaker is, and describe the setting.
- Write the rhyme scheme.
- Find a simile or metaphor. If there isn't one, make up an example that could fit in the poem.
- Find an example of imagery in the poem. Explain which senses it appeals to.
- Show where there is alliteration in the poem. If there is no alliteration, make up a line that alliterates that could fit in or after the poem.

Poems:
"Some People"
"Going Too Far"
"The Pirate Don Durk of Dowdee"
"Since Hanna Moved Away"
"Millions of Strawberries"

© 2015 K12 Inc. All rights reserved.
Copying or distributing without K12's written consent is prohibited.

Next, choose one or more stories from the Life Stories unit to read aloud or act out. After you finish:

- Tell three important facts from the story.
- Describe an important choice the person made, why he or she made it, and the consequences of the choice.
- Give your opinion about the person. What advice do you think that person might give people today?

Life Stories:
"Louis Pasteur: Battle with Death"
"Alexander Fleming: The Accident That Changed the World"
"Elizabeth Blackwell: A Pioneering Physician"

Fast Facts
This semester, you've met some well-known authors and story characters. Test your memory on the Fast Facts page.

Discuss
Discuss the questions to compare and contrast Robinson Crusoe with one of the characters in the list below.

Characters:
Genghis Khan from "The King and His Hawk"
The Tinker from "The Green Glass Ball"
Anansi from "From Tiger to Anansi"
Brer Rabbit from "Brer Rabbit Goes Back to Mr. Man's Garden"
Noah from "Noah and the Ark"
Moses from "The Story of Moses"

- Describe an important choice each character makes. Why do you think the character makes that choice?
- What words describe each character? Why?
- Compare and contrast the characters. Describe the most important way they are alike and the most important way they are different.

© 2015 K12 Inc. All rights reserved.
Copying or distributing without K12's written consent is prohibited.

- What can you learn from these two characters? Can you think of other stories in this unit that have a similar message?

What a Character!

Choose a character from the unit about whom you feel strongly. For example, you could choose a character you admire, dislike, or think is funny or unusual. Summarize the character's story.

Describe the character. Look at what the character says and does. Notice what choices the character makes and why he or she makes them. What conclusions can you draw about the character? Do you like him or her? Why or why not?

Next, write a list of words and phrases that describe the character. Include the following things in your list:
- One or more similes or metaphors
- One or more phrases in which you use alliteration
- One or more phrases in which you use hyperbole

If you wish, you may write a poem about the character or write and illustrate your descriptive phrases on a blank piece of paper.

All About Nonfiction

Look back through the magazine you read and projects you completed during the *Feathers, Flippers, and Fur* unit. Then do the following things:

- Describe three ways you can find information quickly in the magazine.
- Explain how to use a glossary.
- Define *chain of events* and give an example.
- Present one article. In your presentation, tell the main idea and give two details.

© 2015 K12 Inc. All rights reserved.
Copying or distributing without K12's written consent is prohibited.

Name _____ Date _____

Fast Facts

Choose the best answer. You may look back to the stories for help.

Part 1: Trickster Tales

1. In a trickster tale, a trickster
   ⓐ always gets tricked.
   ⓑ never gets tricked.
   ⓒ helps other characters solve their problems.
   ⓓ plays a trick on another character.

2. Trickster characters
   ⓐ are usually bigger or stronger than the other characters.
   ⓑ never get caught in their stories.
   ⓒ are usually weaker or smaller than the other characters.
   ⓓ always get caught in their stories.

3. Trickster tales come from
   ⓐ the Western coast of Europe.
   ⓑ small African countries.
   ⓒ North and South America.
   ⓓ all around the world.

Part 2: Stories from the Bible

4. Besides his family, what did Noah put into the ark?
   ⓐ two of each kind of animal
   ⓑ two of each kind of plant
   ⓒ two plants and two animals
   ⓓ all the animals in the world

© 2015 K12 Inc. All rights reserved.
Copying or distributing without K12's written consent is prohibited.

Fast Facts

5. How long did it rain?
   ⓐ 40 days and 40 nights
   ⓑ 7 days and 6 nights
   ⓒ 30 days and 30 nights
   ⓓ 15 days and 14 nights

6. What sign did God give as a promise not to send such a flood again?
   ⓐ a dove
   ⓑ an olive branch
   ⓒ a rainbow
   ⓓ an ark

7. What gift did Joseph's father give him that made the other sons jealous?
   ⓐ a golden coat
   ⓑ a coat of many colors
   ⓒ a silver coat
   ⓓ a scarf of many colors

8. At first Joseph's brothers plotted to kill him, but what did they do instead?
   ⓐ They brought him home.
   ⓑ They had dreams about him.
   ⓒ They sold him as a slave.
   ⓓ They let the wild animals eat him.

9. What did Joseph say that the seven fat cattle and seven lean cattle meant in Pharaoh's dream?
   ⓐ seven years of famine followed by seven years of plenty
   ⓑ seven years of plenty followed by seven years of famine
   ⓒ seven years of plagues followed by seven years with no plagues
   ⓓ seven fat cows would come to Egypt, then seven thin cows

10. Who found the baby Moses in the bulrushes (the reeds by the water)?
    ⓐ Miriam
    ⓑ Moses' mother
    ⓒ Pharaoh's daughter
    ⓓ Pharaoh

© 2015 K12 Inc. All rights reserved.
Copying or distributing without K12's written consent is prohibited.

Fast Facts

11. After Moses left Egypt, he heard the voice of God speaking to him. Where did this voice come from?
    - (a) a telephone
    - (b) a burning bush
    - (c) a burning house
    - (d) a rainbow

Part 3: Robinson Crusoe

12. What do you expect to find in an adventure story like *Robinson Crusoe*?
    - (a) The main character travels to strange places, takes risks, and faces danger.
    - (b) The main character tricks other characters.
    - (c) The main character solves a mystery.
    - (d) The main character falls in love with another character.

13. What country did the author live in when he wrote *Robinson Crusoe*?
    - (a) Germany
    - (b) England
    - (c) France
    - (d) South America

14. How did Robinson Crusoe arrive on the island?
    - (a) He sailed there.
    - (b) He swam there from South America.
    - (c) He was shipwrecked.
    - (d) He flew on an airplane from Egypt.

15. What did Robinson Crusoe see on the beach that frightened him?
    - (a) a wild animal
    - (b) a human footprint
    - (c) a parrot
    - (d) a sea monster

© 2015 K12 Inc. All rights reserved.
Copying or distributing without K12's written consent is prohibited.

Fast Facts

16. How did Friday come to the island?
    - ⓐ He paddled there in a canoe.
    - ⓑ He brought prisoners to the island.
    - ⓒ He was brought to the island as a prisoner.
    - ⓓ He arrived by plane.

17. How did Robinson Crusoe get off the island?
    - ⓐ He helped a ship's captain take back his ship from rebels.
    - ⓑ He helped rebels take over the captain's ship.
    - ⓒ He attacked a ship sailing close to the island.
    - ⓓ He built a canoe and paddled away.

© 2015 K12 Inc. All rights reserved.
Copying or distributing without K12's written consent is prohibited.

Name _____ Date _____

Mix and Match

plot	what happens in a story	narrative poem	a poem that tells a story
imagery	language that creates a mental picture by appealing to the senses	setting	where and when a story takes place
simile	compares one thing to another, using use like or as	metaphor	compares one thing to another, but does not use like or as
rhyming couplets	two lines, one right after the other, that rhyme	alliteration	use of words with the same or similar beginning sounds
hyperbole	a figure of speech that uses exaggeration, often for comic effect	narrator	the character who tells the story

© 2015 K12 Inc. All rights reserved.
Copying or distributing without K12's written consent is prohibited.

Name _____   Date _____

"The Hodja Speaks"

How much would you be willing to lose in order to win a contest?

Pronunciation
Hodja (HOHD-jah)
kavuk (kuh-VOOK)
learned (LUHR-nuhd)

Vocabulary
You will find these words in today's reading.

legendary: (adj.) a person, place, or event from an old, well-known story
Merlin is a *legendary* character from the stories of King Arthur and the Knights of the Round Table.

learned: (adj.) well-educated
They read many books and studied their lessons so that they would become *learned* and wise.

indicate: (v.) to point or refer to something
When my mother tapped her watch, she was *indicating* that it was time to leave.

exasperated: (adj.) annoyed
Dad became *exasperated* when my sister and I continued to argue about who should feed the dog.

warily: (adv.) in a careful, mistrustful way
The sheepdog looked *warily* at the trees and watched for signs of the wolf.

© 2015 K12 Inc. All rights reserved.
Copying or distributing without K12's written consent is prohibited.

emphatically: (adv.) in a forceful way

"<u>Never </u>chase a ball into the street," she said *emphatically,* "because you could get hurt."

Think Ahead

1. Have you ever read "Brer Rabbit and Brer Fox" or "Paul Bunyan"? These stories are American *folktales.* A folktale is a story that is passed down from one generation to the next.

2. The stories in this unit are folktales from around the world. Today's folktale is from Turkey. Find Turkey on a map or globe.

3. A man named Nasreddin Hodja lived more than 800 years ago in Turkey. He was a clever teacher, and people told stories about the things he said and did. As time passed, people told, retold, and added to the stories. Today the "Hodja" is a legendary character, the hero *and* trickster of countless Turkish folktales, including the one you will read today.

4. Find "The Hodja Speaks" in the table of contents and turn to it in the book. How does this play look different on the page from the other stories you have been reading?

5. Who are some of the characters in the play?

6. Just as books are sometimes divided into chapters, plays are sometimes divided into *scenes.* Identify the setting (the time and place of the action) of Scene 1.

7. Today you will be reading a *script* of a play. The script shows the written words that the actors say on stage. The script also gives *stage directions,* which give the actors information about where to go on stage or how to say a particular line. Stage directions are usually written in parentheses. They are not read aloud. Find the stage directions in the following lines. How should the characters speak their lines?

> WIFE (*Indignantly*): But I have other things to do. Besides, when have you cooked the meals (*Indicating right*) or cleaned the house?
> HODJA (*Calmly*): I cannot remember.

© 2015 K12 Inc. All rights reserved.
Copying or distributing without K12's written consent is prohibited.

You will see some stage directions with the word *Aside,* like this:

> THIEF: Do you not forgive me? *(Pause. Looks at audience and shrugs. Aside)* The Hodja appears to have lost his voice.

In an aside, the actor speaks words that are heard by the audience but not by the other actors on stage. Sometimes an actor will address an aside directly to the audience. In the example above, the Thief would look at the audience and say, "The Hodja appears to have lost his voice."

Read

"The Hodja Speaks" in *Classics for Young Readers,* Vol. 4B, pages 6-10.

Questions

Answer the following questions in complete sentences in your Reading Notebook.

1. What do the Hodja and his wife argue about?
2. Describe the contest the Hodja and his wife have.
3. How does the Hodja try to trick his wife into speaking first?
4. What happens while the Hodja is napping?
5. What does the thief say when the Hodja wakes up?
6. Why doesn't the Hodja forgive the thief?
7. At the end of the story, who wins the contest?

Discuss

1. Have you ever heard someone say, "A penny saved is a penny earned," or, "Don't judge a book by its cover"? Well-known statements like these are called *sayings*. Sometimes these kinds of sayings are called *adages* or *proverbs*. Adages and proverbs are short, familiar statements that tell about something most people think is true.

© 2015 K12 Inc. All rights reserved.
Copying or distributing without K12's written consent is prohibited.

What do you think the saying "Two heads are better than one" means? Why do you think people believe this saying is true?

Another kind of saying is called an *idiom*. An idiom is an expression that can't be understood by the meaning of the words themselves. A popular idiom is to say that people have "spilled the beans" when they accidentally tell a secret. Did you ever hear a person say that something cost an "arm and a leg"? This idiom means that someone paid a lot of money to buy something—so much money that it was like giving up "an arm and a leg." Idioms make our language more colorful and descriptive.

What do you think is the meaning of the idiom in the sentence, "It's raining cats and dogs"? How did you figure that out?

2. At the beginning of the play, the Narrator says, "The Hodja was not always as wise as he thought, but neither was he the fool that many considered him." What does this saying mean? Another saying about wise men and fools is "I'd rather lose an argument to a wise man than win one to a fool." Does this saying apply to the Hodja? Why or why not?

3. Give one example of a time when you think the Hodja was wise and one example of when he was not. Then tell whether you agree or disagree with the Narrator's statement about the Hodja.

4. Do you admire the Hodja? Why or why not? Use examples from the play to support your answer.

Wisdom from Around the World

On the Wisdom from Around the World page, write the title of the story, the setting, and a short summary of the plot. In your summary tell only the main, or most important, story events.

The *plot* is what happens in a story. The *theme* of a story is the author's message or "big idea." It is what the author wants you to know or think about after reading the story.

© 2015 K12 Inc. All rights reserved.
Copying or distributing without K12's written consent is prohibited.

The *theme* of a story is similar to the moral of a fable. Both a theme and a moral tell the main message of a story. One difference is that a moral is almost always written in a sentence at the end of a fable, but a theme is not. Readers must pay careful attention and make inferences from the evidence in the story to discover the theme.

One important clue in your search for a story's theme is what happens to the characters at the end of the story. What lesson do you think the Hodja learns? What can a reader learn from "The Hodja Speaks"?

Write the theme of the story on the Wisdom from Around the World page.

© 2015 K12 Inc. All rights reserved.
Copying or distributing without K12's written consent is prohibited.

Guidelines for Peer Discussion

Share your thoughts, ideas, questions, and feelings about a text with a peer or others. Listen carefully to what everyone has to say about the text. During your discussion, follow these guidelines.

1. Be prepared to discuss what you think about the text. You should have already read the assignment. Come prepared to discuss your ideas, and use examples from the text to support your thoughts and answers.

2. You will be asked questions about the text. Be ready to answer them, and bring some questions of your own to ask others, such as:

   "Who was your favorite character? Why?"

   "What was your favorite part of the text? Why?"

   "What fact did you enjoy learning? Why do you find this fact interesting?"

   "What question would you ask if you had the chance to meet the author?"

3. Listen if it's not your turn to speak. Pay attention to what others say so that you can add your ideas. Speak clearly and in complete sentences.

4. If you don't understand what someone says, ask a question, such as:

   "What do you mean when you say . . . ?"

   "Can you give an example of . . . ?"

5. If you don't agree with what someone says, explain why.

   "I don't agree with that because . . . "

6. Keep discussions positive! You can disagree, but don't argue. Be respectful.

© 2015 K12 Inc. All rights reserved.
Copying or distributing without K12's written consent is prohibited.

Name _____ Date _____

Wisdom from Around the World

Use details from the story to fill in the lines below.

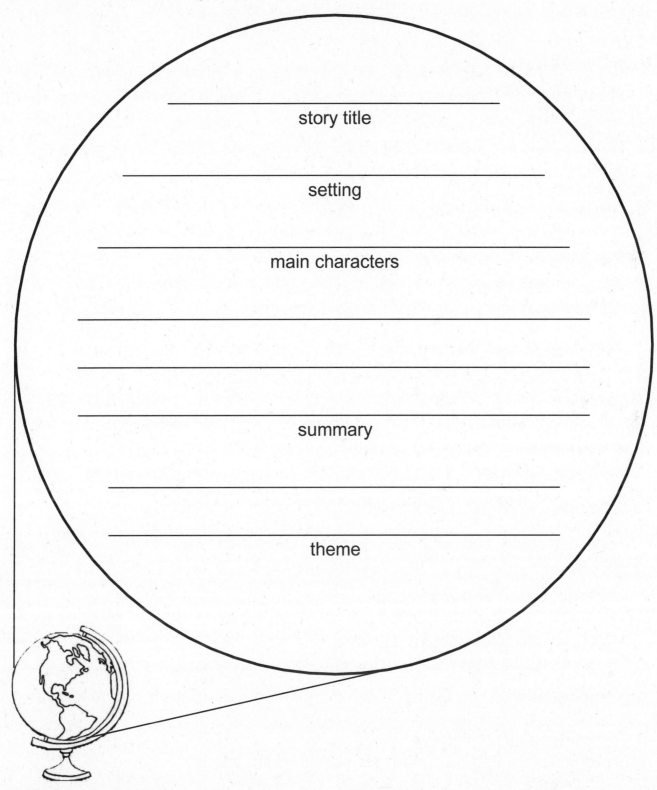

story title

setting

main characters

summary

theme

© 2015 K12 Inc. All rights reserved.
Copying or distributing without K12's written consent is prohibited.

Name _____   Date _____

"Younde Goes to Town"

Enjoy this funny story about a young man's first visit to a big city.

Pronunciation
Younde (YOON-day)
Akim (ah-KIM)
Accra (AH-kruh)

Vocabulary
You will find these words in today's reading.

impress: (v.) to be deeply affected in a positive way
My father was so *impressed* by the young man's good manners that he immediately offered him a job in his shop.

tremendous: (adj.) huge, great
That *tremendous* ocean wave must have been more than 20 feet high!

to do justice: an expression meaning to appreciate something the way it deserves
Her painting needs a gold frame *to do justice* to its beauty.

personage: (n.) a person, often of great importance or power
We wanted to see the royal *personage* in the parade, so we looked for the person with a crown.

swarm: (v.) to move as part of a crowd
The moment the gates opened, the children *swarmed* into the amusement park.

transact: (v.) to complete
My mom *transacted* her banking business by telephone.

© 2015 K12 Inc. All rights reserved.
Copying or distributing without K12's written consent is prohibited.

mourn: (v.) to express grief or sorrow

My sister and I still *mourn* the death of our dog Misty.

Think Ahead

1. Summarize "The Hodja Speaks." What do you think the Hodja learned?

2. As you read this next story, think about how the story is like and unlike "The Hodja Speaks."

3. Today's folktale is from West Africa. West Africa is the part of Africa between the Sahara, the Gulf of Guinea, and Lake Chad. Find West Africa on a map or globe.

Read

"Younde Goes to Town" in *Classics for Young Readers,* Vol. 4B, pages 11-14

Questions

Answer the following questions in complete sentences in your Reading Notebook.

1. Why does Younde go to Accra?
2. Who or what is Minu?
3. Why does Younde cry at the end of the story?
4. What is Younde's mistake?

Discuss

1. We learn about characters by what they say and do and what others say about them. Using evidence from the story to support your ideas, describe Younde.

2. Think back to "The Hodja Speaks." Tell two ways the stories are alike and different.

© 2015 K12 Inc. All rights reserved.
Copying or distributing without K12's written consent is prohibited.

Wisdom from Around the World

On the Wisdom from Around the World page, write the title of the story, the setting, the main character, and a short summary of the plot.

Next, think about the *theme*. The theme of a story is the author's message or "big idea." Remember that the theme is not written out in the story. You must think about the story events and what happens to the characters to discover it.

One way you can find the theme is to compare the events of the story to your own life. Think about "Younde Goes to Town." Have *you* ever gone somewhere new by yourself: to a camp, a new friend's house, or a new music class or sports practice? Describe your experience and tell how it was like or different from Younde's.

Discuss or think about these questions. They can help you decide on a theme.

- What do you think the phrase "Don't jump to conclusions" means? How does it apply to this story?
- What advice would you give Younde? Why?
- What do you think a reader can learn from this story?

Now write the theme of the story on the Wisdom from Around the World page.

How Characters Change

In almost all stories, characters change. It might be a change we expect, like Wilbur from *Charlotte's Web* growing from a baby to a young pig. It might even be a change we do not expect, like King Midas discovering that he loves his daughter more than all of the gold in the world.

Following are some of the things characters in a story may change:

- How they look
- What they say and think
- How they act

© 2015 K12 Inc. All rights reserved.
Copying or distributing without K12's written consent is prohibited.

Describe the Hodja and Younde at the beginning and end of their stories. How does each character change? What does the character see, do, or have happen to him that causes him to change? Does the Hodja or Younde change more? Explain.

In your Reading Notebook write a sentence that explains how each character changes. Then draw a symbol to stand for one of the characters. Write one or more sentences to explain why the symbol stands for the character.

© 2015 K12 Inc. All rights reserved.
Copying or distributing without K12's written consent is prohibited.

Name _____ Date _____

Wisdom from Around the World

Use details from the story to fill in the lines below.

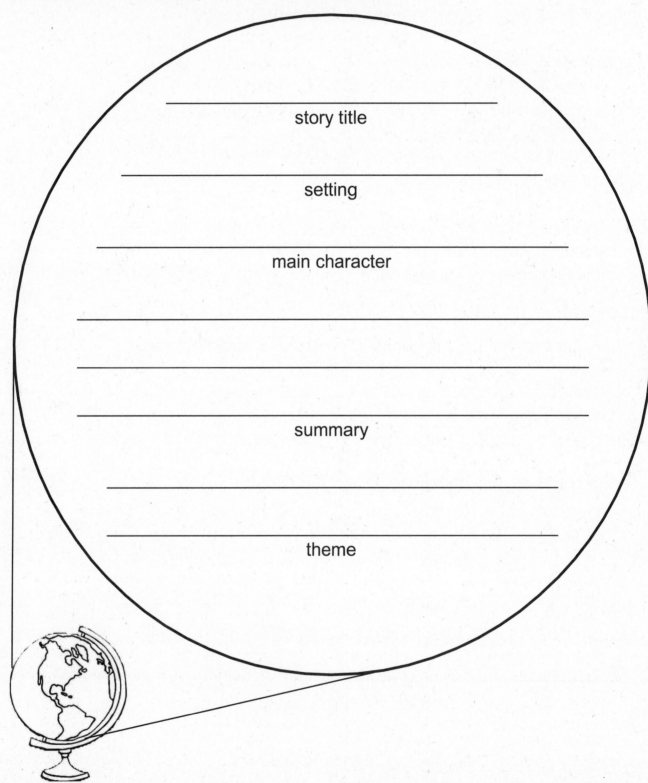

_____

story title

_____

setting

_____

main character

_____

_____

_____

summary

_____

theme

© 2015 K12 Inc. All rights reserved.
Copying or distributing without K12's written consent is prohibited.

Name _____   Date _____

"The Little Smoke Thief"

Can you catch the thief in this folktale? Read on and find out!

Vocabulary

You will find these words in today's reading.

prosperous: (adj.) successful in one's work
Last year, the harvest was so good that the farmers went from being poor to being *prosperous*.

ready: (v.) to make ready
The sailors were sweeping the decks, raising the sails, and *readying* the ship for the voyage.

clutch: (v.) to hold on tightly
She *clutched* the ticket in her hand so that she would not lose it.

aroma: (n.) smell
When the *aroma* of Grandma's cookies floats past my nose, I drop what I am doing and run to the kitchen.

fragrant: (adj.) having a noticeable scent
The meadow was so *fragrant* with clover that hundreds of bees visited it each day.

impulse: (n.) an inspiration or motivation that causes an action
It's not a good idea to buy a pet on an *impulse* because pets are a responsibility and require a long-term commitment.

defiantly: (adv.) boldly, in a way that shows one is willing to fight or argue
"I won't," he shouted *defiantly*, "and you can't make me!"

© 2015 K12 Inc. All rights reserved.
Copying or distributing without K12's written consent is prohibited.

unfolding: (adj.) currently taking place
At first the outdoor play did not seem interesting, but soon a crowd had gathered to watch the *unfolding* events.

proclamation: (n.) a formal announcement
The king made a *proclamation* that any of his subjects could go to the castle and receive help from him.

Think Ahead
1. Read the title of the story. Predict what the story will be about. Give reasons for your prediction.
2. Today's folktale comes from France. Find France on a map or globe.

Read
"The Little Smoke Thief" in *Classics for Young Readers,* Vol. 4B, pages 15-18

Questions
Answer the following questions in complete sentences in your Reading Notebook.

1. Why does the baker give René a loaf of bread?
2. What does the meat seller want René to pay for?
3. How does the baker settle the case?
4. Was your prediction about the story correct? Why or why not?

Discuss
1. Why do you think René trusted the baker to settle the case?
2. Do you think the baker settled the case fairly? Why or why not?
3. Why does the meat seller try to make René pay for the smoke? Do you think he would have tried to do the same thing with an adult? Why or why not?

© 2015 K12 Inc. All rights reserved.
Copying or distributing without K12's written consent is prohibited.

The Baker's Letter

You know that we learn about characters by what they say and do and what others say about them. Remember that to understand a character, we have to go beyond the words in the story and make an inference. When we make an inference, or *infer,* we think about the evidence in the story. Then we draw conclusions based on that evidence.

For example, why do you think at the end of the story the baker asked René to be a helper in his shop? We know that René had asked the baker if he could help unload the cart. Re-read the description of what René does after the baker agrees to let him help:

> René wasted no time. He snatched up bags of flour and piled them in the baker's shop. Soon the cart was empty.

René asked to help. He did his work quickly and well. You know that people like hard workers. Based on the evidence in the story and what you already know, you can make an inference. You can infer that one reason the baker asked René to be a helper in his shop was that René is a hard worker.

Pretend you are the baker. Write a letter to a friend. Explain why you asked René to be a helper in your shop. Give two or more reasons. Support each reason with what you know and with evidence from the text.

Wisdom from Around the World

On the Wisdom from Around the World page, write the title of the story, the setting, the main characters, and a short summary of the plot.

Next, think about the theme. The theme is the story's main message. Sometimes the theme of a story is about "big ideas," such as what it means to be fair, honest, or brave. Think about the characters' choices and actions. They can help you decide what the main message of the story is.

© 2015 K12 Inc. All rights reserved.
Copying or distributing without K12's written consent is prohibited.

Discuss these questions. They can help lead you to the theme.

- Do you think René is brave to ask the baker for work? Do you think he is brave to stand up to the meat seller? Why?
- Why do you think the baker decides to help René solve the problem with the meat seller?
- What do you think is the most important thing that happens in the story? Why? What do you think a reader can learn from it?

Now write the theme of the story on the Wisdom from Around the World page.

© 2015 K12 Inc. All rights reserved.
Copying or distributing without K12's written consent is prohibited.

Name _____ Date _____

Wisdom from Around the World

Use details from the story to fill in the lines below.

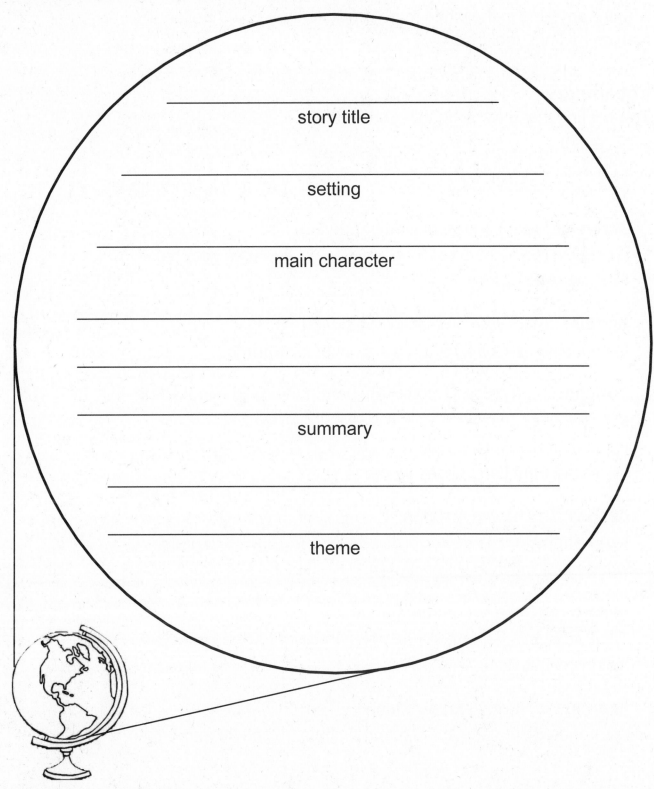

_____
story title

_____
setting

_____
main character

_____

_____

_____
summary

_____

_____
theme

© 2015 K12 Inc. All rights reserved.
Copying or distributing without K12's written consent is prohibited.

Name _____   Date _____

"The Gold Coin"

Is there anything in the world more valuable than gold? Follow one man as he finds real treasure.

Vocabulary

You will find these words in today's reading.

sickly: (adj.) due to or showing sickness
The *sickly* puppy had a runny nose, a dull coat, and a drooping tail.

shriveled: (adj.) to be wrinkled or dried up
If I stay in the bathtub too long, my fingers and toes become like *shriveled* prunes.

huddle: (v.) to wrap oneself in something
He *huddled* himself tightly in his blanket for warmth.

poncho: (n.) a piece of cloth with a slit in the middle, pulled on over the head and worn as a sleeveless garment
I pulled on my *poncho* over my head and crossed my arms under the front flap to keep warm.

despair: (n.) having no hope
I was happy that it was Saturday, but my joy turned to *despair* when I saw my long list of chores.

desert: (v.) to be left or abandoned
The house had been *deserted* when the roof fell in, and no one had lived in it since.

hoarse: (adj.) with a rough sound
We shouted so much at the game that our voices were *hoarse*.

© 2015 K12 Inc. All rights reserved.
Copying or distributing without K12's written consent is prohibited.

tensely: (adv.) in a way that shows stress or strain
"Please hold the other end of this box," he said *tensely.* "It is so heavy that I am about to drop it."

lumber: (v.) to move slowly
The oxen *lumbered* along the road, pulling the heavy cart behind them.

ransacked: (adj.) something that is disarranged or messy because it has been searched
I looked at my *ransacked* room with clothes thrown everywhere, drawers pulled out, and my mattress overturned, but I had finally found my missing red sock!

Think Ahead

1. Are there things in life more important than money? If so, what are they?
2. As you read this story, think about what the main character learns about the importance of money.
3. Today's tale takes place in Central America. Central America is the area between Mexico and South America. With your finger, trace Central America on a map or globe.

Read

"The Gold Coin" in *Classics for Young Readers,* Vol. 4B, pages 19-27

Questions

Answer the following questions in complete sentences in your Reading Notebook.

1. How many gold coins does Juan think Doña Josefa has?
2. Why does Juan follow Doña Josefa?
3. Why does Doña Josefa travel from place to place?

4. Give one example of how Juan helps someone else on his journey.
5. How many coins does Doña Josefa actually have?
6. What does Juan do when Doña Josefa offers him the gold coin?

Discuss

1. At the beginning of the story, who damages Doña Josefa's roof? At the end of the story, what does Juan offer to do? Why is this important?
2. What does Juan give up at the end of the story? Why do you think he does this?
3. How does helping other people help change Juan?

Juan's Journey

In many stories the main character changes. We learn about how a character changes by comparing and contrasting how the character looks, what he says or thinks, or what he does at different points in the story.

Read the two paragraphs from "The Gold Coin" below. The first paragraph is from the beginning of the story. The second paragraph is near the end.

> Juan had been a thief for many years. Because he did his stealing by night, his skin had become pale and sickly. Because he spent his time either hiding or sneaking about, his body had become shriveled and bent. And because he had neither friend nor relative to make him smile, his face was always twisted into an angry frown.

> So Juan spent yet another long day in the fields. Working beneath the summer sun, Juan noticed that his skin had begun to tan. And although he had to stoop down to pick the squash, he found that he could now stretch his body. His back had begun to straighten, too.

© 2015 K12 Inc. All rights reserved.
Copying or distributing without K12's written consent is prohibited.

Discuss:

- In your own words, describe what Juan looks like in the first paragraph.
- How has Juan changed in the second paragraph?
- What did Juan do that caused the changes?
- Find the paragraph in the story that tells when and why Juan smiled. What is the importance of Juan's smile?

Use details from the story to complete Juan's Journey page.

Wisdom from Around the World

On the Wisdom from Around the World page, write the title of the story, the setting, the main character, and a short summary of the plot.

Next, think about the theme. Remember that the theme is the story's main message. One way to find the theme is to think about how and why the main character changes in the story.

Discuss these questions to help you discover the theme.

- Do you think Juan is surprised when Doña Josefa gives him the coin? Why or why not?
- At the end of the story, what is more important to Juan than the gold coin?
- How does Juan change throughout the story?
- In your opinion, what is the most important way Juan changes? Why?
- What do you think a reader can learn from Juan?

Now write the theme of the story on the Wisdom from Around the World page.

© 2015 K12 Inc. All rights reserved.
Copying or distributing without K12's written consent is prohibited.

Name _____   Date _____

Juan's Journey

Use details from the story to answer the questions. When you finish, draw pictures of Juan at the beginning and end of the story in the boxes.

At the beginning of the story…   At the end of the story…
Juan looks like: _____   Juan looks like: _____

_____   _____

_____   _____

Juan says or thinks: _____   Juan says or thinks: _____

_____   _____

_____   _____

Juan does: _____   Juan does: _____

_____   _____

_____   _____

© 2015 K12 Inc. All rights reserved.
Copying or distributing without K12's written consent is prohibited.

Juan's Journey

What do you think makes Juan change?

_____

_____

_____

_____

_____

_____

_____

_____

_____

_____

_____

_____

© 2015 K12 Inc. All rights reserved.
Copying or distributing without K12's written consent is prohibited.

Name _____   Date _____

Wisdom from Around the World

Use details from the story to fill in the lines below.

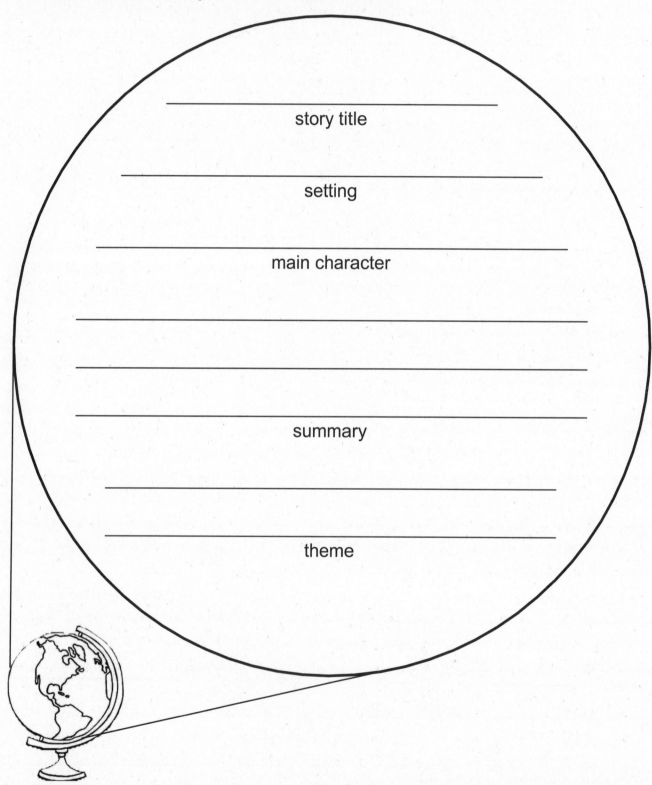

_____
story title

_____
setting

_____
main character

_____

_____

_____
summary

_____

_____
theme

© 2015 K12 Inc. All rights reserved.
Copying or distributing without K12's written consent is prohibited.

Name _____   Date _____

"The Grateful Stork"

How many ways can you think of to say "thank you" to someone you care about?

Pronunciation
gomen (goh-MEHN)
kudasai (koo-dah-siy)
hibachi (hih-BAH-chee)
Ojii-san (oh-JEE-sahn)
Obaa-san (oh-BAH-sahn)

Vocabulary
You will find these words in today's reading.

kindling: (n.) small pieces of wood used to start a fire
Slender, dry branches make good *kindling* because they catch fire and burn easily.

churn: (v.) to stir up
He was moving his hands back and forth in the dishwater and *churning* up little soapy waves.

anxious: (adj.) worried and impatient
I was so *anxious* to find out whether I got a part in the play that I checked the board twice each day for the cast list!

omen: (n.) an event that gives clues about what will happen in the future; a sign
Might a rainbow be considered an *omen* of good weather?

venture: (v.) to take a risk, to leave
No one *ventured* out of the house until the blizzard ended.

© 2015 K12 Inc. All rights reserved.
Copying or distributing without K12's written consent is prohibited.

scarcely: (adv.) hardly, barely

We had so little rain this summer that the crops *scarcely* grew higher than my ankle.

brocade: (n.) a fabric woven with raised designs, often made with gold or silver thread

Over her light silk gown, she wore a heavy *brocade* robe with designs in silver and gold.

Think Ahead

1. What does the word *grateful* mean?
2. How do you show others that you are grateful?
3. Today's folktale comes from Japan. Find Japan on a map or globe.

Read

"The Grateful Stork" in *Classics for Young Readers,* Vol. 4B, pages 28-37

Questions

Answer the following questions in complete sentences in your Reading Notebook.

1. At the beginning of the story, how does the old man help the stork?
2. Describe the old man and old woman's life before the girl comes to their home.
3. How does the girl help the old man and woman?
4. Why does the girl leave?
5. Who was the girl?

Discuss

1. How does the girl change the lives of the old man and the old woman?
2. Why is the girl so upset that the old woman has looked behind the screen?

© 2015 K12 Inc. All rights reserved.
Copying or distributing without K12's written consent is prohibited.

3. At the end of the story, the old woman apologizes to the girl, but the girl still leaves. Do you think the girl was right to leave or should she have stayed? Why?

© 2015 K12 Inc. All rights reserved.
Copying or distributing without K12's written consent is prohibited.

Compare and Contrast Characters

On the bottom half of a piece of paper, draw a Venn diagram. Next, draw a *third* circle that overlaps both of the circles you drew. Label the circles "the old man," "the old woman," and "the girl."

In each circle, write two or more words that describe the character. Where two circles overlap, write one or more words that describe *both* characters. Where all three circles overlap, write one word that describes *all three* characters.

Then discuss this question:

> What do you think is the most important difference among the characters? Why?

Wisdom from Around the World

On the Wisdom from Around the World page, write the title of the story, the setting, and a short summary of the plot.

Next, think about the theme. The theme is the story's main message. Sometimes the theme of a story asks us to think about "big ideas," such as what it means to be responsible, grateful, or honest. By looking at the characters' choices—and the consequences of their choices—you can decide what you think is the main message of the story.

Discuss these questions to help you decide on a theme.
- The old man did not have to help the stork. Why do you think he did?
- How does the girl show gratitude to the old man and woman? How do the old man and woman show gratitude to the girl?
- Why do you think the old woman looked behind the screen?
- Why was the old man upset by what she had done?
- What do you think the old woman would change if she had a chance? The old man? The girl?

Think about your answers to the questions. Now write the theme on the Wisdom from Around the World page.

© 2015 K12 Inc. All rights reserved.
Copying or distributing without K12's written consent is prohibited.

Name _____ Date _____

Wisdom from Around the World

Use details from the story to fill in the lines below.

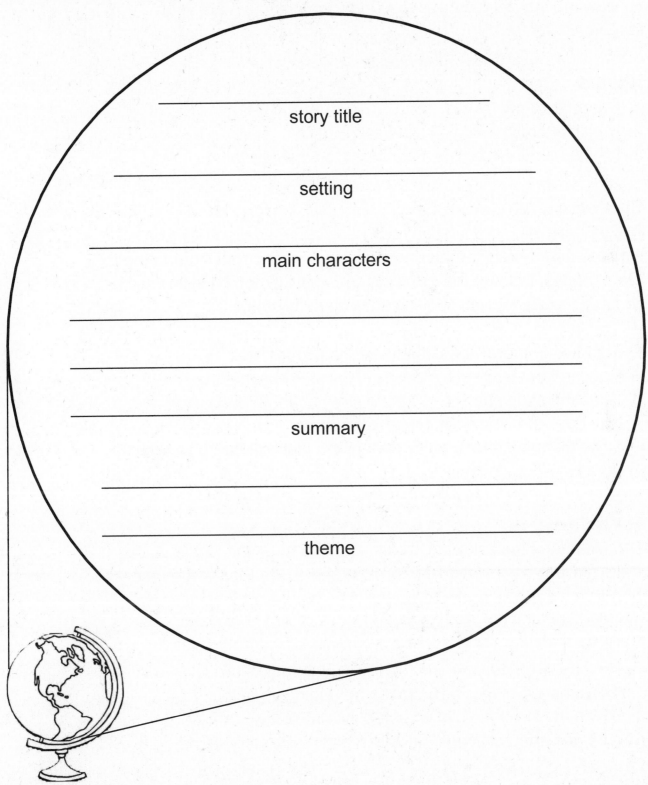

_____
story title

_____
setting

_____
main characters

_____

_____

_____
summary

_____

_____
theme

© 2015 K12 Inc. All rights reserved.
Copying or distributing without K12's written consent is prohibited.

Name _____   Date _____

Review and Reflect

Review the stories you have read in this unit and act out your favorite character.

Review

1. Summarize each story.
2. Which character did you like best? Why?
3. Which theme was most meaningful to you? Explain.

Compare and Contrast

To compare and contrast two or more things means to tell how they are alike and different. Review your Wisdom from Around the World pages. Discuss the following questions to compare and contrast the stories you have read so far in this unit.

- Find two or more stories that have similar themes.
- How are these two stories alike? How are they different?
- Does the main character in each story change? If so, how and why does the character change?
- Does the main character in each of the stories learn a lesson or not? How do you know?

Act It Out!

Choose one of the following characters to act out: the Hodja, Juan, or the old woman. Pretend you are the character. Plan, write, and then give a speech in which you tell how the events in your story changed you. In your speech, include:

- The character's name and the title and author of story,
- A description of the character at the beginning of the story,
- Which events in the plot changed the character,
- What the character was like at the end of the story, and

© 2015 K12 Inc. All rights reserved.
Copying or distributing without K12's written consent is prohibited.

- What the character learned and why it is important for others to know.

After you finish writing, revise and proofread your speech. Then practice and present it. If you want, you may dress, speak, and have props like the character would.

© 2015 K12 Inc. All rights reserved.
Copying or distributing without K12's written consent is prohibited.

<u>Name</u>   <u>Date</u>

"Rikki-Tikki-Tavi": Session 1

What has four legs, red eyes, and a tail like a bottlebrush? A mongoose!
What's a mongoose? Read on to find out!

Vocabulary
You will find these words in today's reading.

bungalow: (n.) a one-story house with a low roof
The *bungalow* was a bright spot of pink beneath the tall palm trees.

mongoose: (n.) a furry grey or brown carnivore (meat eater) with a
pointed nose, small ears, short legs, and a long tail
Some *mongooses* use their powerful legs and strong jaws to hunt
and kill poisonous snakes.

revive: (v.) to become conscious and active after suffering an injury
or shock
When the dog *revived*, it got up unsteadily and gave a weak bark.

veranda: (n.) a porch with a roof
When it started raining, we moved our picnic from the grass to the
veranda.

kerosene: (n.) a kind of oil that burns, used for fuel
Before people discovered how to use electricity, lamps were
sometimes made with a wick resting in a small pool of *kerosene*.

cultivated: (adj.) prepared for the growing of crops
Most of the meadow grows wild, but we have a *cultivated* patch of
peas, beans, and squash in one corner.

providence: (n.) a blessing
It was *providence* that the sun came out just in time for our picnic.

© 2015 K12 Inc. All rights reserved.
Copying or distributing without K12's written consent is prohibited.

Think Ahead

"Rikki-Tikki-Tavi" was written by British author Rudyard Kipling, who lived from 1865 to 1936. The story is part of a larger collection of Rudyard Kipling's stories called *The Jungle Book.* "Rikki-Tikki-Tavi" and the other stories in *The Jungle Book* take place in India. Find India on a map or globe.

Read

Part 1 of "Rikki-Tikki-Tavi" in *Classics for Young Readers,* Vol. 4B, pages 38-45

Questions

Answer the following questions in complete sentences in your Reading Notebook.

1. How does Rikki-Tikki-Tavi become part of Teddy's family?
2. Who is Darzee? Why are he and his wife unhappy?
3. Who and what are Nag and Nagaina?
4. How does Darzee help Rikki-Tikki-Tavi?
5. How does Rikki-Tikki-Tavi save Teddy's life?

Discuss

1. Why doesn't Rikki-Tikki-Tavi follow Nag and Nagaina after they disappeared into the grass? Do you think he was wise? Why or why not?

2. The author says that Rikki-Tikki is "rather amused at all the fuss" that Teddy's family makes over him after he kills the snake. Why is he amused?

Making Inferences and Drawing Conclusions

We learn about characters by paying attention to what they say and do and what others say about them. Sometimes to understand a character, we have to go beyond the words in the story. We have to *make inferences.* When we make an inference, or *infer,* we think about the

© 2015 K12 Inc. All rights reserved.
Copying or distributing without K12's written consent is prohibited.

evidence in the story and what we know from our own experience. Then we draw conclusions based on evidence.

For example, what can you infer about Rikki-Tikki from the paragraph below?

> But [Rikki-Tikki] was a restless companion, because he had to get up and attend to every noise all through the night, and find out what made it. Teddy's mother and father came in, the last thing, to look at their boy, and Rikki-Tikki was awake on the pillow.

The author says that Rikki-Tikki gets up and investigates every noise. We know that a person or animal that does that is curious about what made the noise. Even though the author describes Rikki-Tikki as "restless," he always comes back and sits awake by Teddy on his pillow. Since he always comes back, he is loyal. Based on evidence, we can infer that Rikki-Tikki is both curious and loyal, since he goes to investigate every noise but always returns to Teddy.

Complete the Making Inferences and Drawing Conclusions page. When you finish, review and discuss your work.

A True Mongoose

In Part 1, Rudyard Kipling calls Rikki-Tikki-Tavi a "true mongoose." Find the quotation in the story and describe in your own words what a "true mongoose" is. Then write a paragraph in your Reading Notebook that gives two or more reasons why Rikki-Tikki is a "true mongoose."

When you finish, you may illustrate your paragraph.

© 2015 K12 Inc. All rights reserved.
Copying or distributing without K12's written consent is prohibited.

Name _____ Date _____

Making Inferences and Drawing Conclusions

What can you infer about Rikki-Tikki-Tavi from each paragraph? Write your responses in complete sentences.

1. [Nag] spread out his hood more than ever, and Rikki-tikki saw the spectacle-mark on the back of it that looks exactly like the eye part of a hook-and-eye fastening. He was afraid for the minute, but it is impossible for a mongoose to stay frightened for any length of time. And, though Rikki-tikki had never met a live cobra before, his mother had fed him on dead ones. He knew that a grown mongoose's business in life was to fight and eat snakes. Nag knew that too and, at the bottom of his cold heart, he was afraid.

_____

_____

_____

_____

2. That night at dinner, walking to and fro among the glasses on the table, [Rikki-Tikki] might have stuffed himself with nice things. But he remembered Nag and Nagaina, and though it was very pleasant to be patted and petted by Teddy's mother, and to sit on Teddy's shoulder, his eyes would get red from time to time, and he would go off into his long war cry of *"Rikk-tikk-tikki-tikki-tchk!"*

_____

_____

_____

_____

© 2015 K12 Inc. All rights reserved.
Copying or distributing without K12's written consent is prohibited.

Name _____   Date _____

"Rikki-Tikki-Tavi": Session 2

Will young Rikki-Tikki-Tavi win the battle against the cobras?

Vocabulary
You will find these words in today's reading.

sluice: (n.) a pipe or trough for water, usually with a gate
We have a *sluice* instead of a hose to bring water to our garden.

worthwhile: (adj.) important, a good use of a person's time
It is *worthwhile* to study hard, because if you stick to your lessons, your lessons will stick to you!

lame: (adj.) injured, unable to move freely
The horse bruised its leg so badly it was *lame* for a week.

consolation: (n.) something that cheers up a person who is sad or disappointed
Even though he didn't win, it was a *consolation* to him that he had played his best.

lilt: (n.) a cheerful song
They played a merry *lilt* on their flutes.

Think Ahead
1. Summarize what you have read so far in the story.
2. Predict what you think will happen next. Give reasons for your prediction.

Read
Part 2 of "Rikki-Tikki-Tavi" in *Classics for Young Readers,* Vol. 4B, pages 45-58

© 2015 K12 Inc. All rights reserved.
Copying or distributing without K12's written consent is prohibited.

Questions

Answer the following questions in complete sentences in your
Reading Notebook.

1. Why do Nag and Nagaina want to kill Teddy and his family?
2. Why does Nag hide in the water jar?
3. How does Darzee's wife help Rikki-Tikki-Tavi?
4. How does Rikki-Tikki use Nagaina's last egg?
5. Was your prediction correct? Explain.

Discuss

1. Look back to Part 1 and your writing about Rikki-Tikki-Tavi from
   yesterday. How does Rikki-Tikki-Tavi change over the course of
   the story? How can you tell?

2. Why is it so important for Rikki-Tikki-Tavi to kill the snakes?
   Why doesn't he just leave the garden?

Compare and Contrast Characters

Choose one character from each column to compare and contrast.

Column 1	Column 2
Rikki-Tikki-Tavi	Darzee
Nag	Darzee's wife
Nagaina	Chuchundra
	Teddy's father
	Teddy's mother

Discuss:
- Tell one important trait the characters share. How does each
  character show that trait?
- Tell the most important difference between the characters. Why
  is that difference important?
- What effect does the difference have on what happens to each
  character?

In your Reading Notebook, draw a symbol for each character.
Then write a sentence that describes the meaning of the symbol.

© 2015 K12 Inc. All rights reserved.
Copying or distributing without K12's written consent is prohibited.

Compare and Contrast Versions

It's your choice! Enjoy "Rikki-Tikki-Tavi" in another way: through a song, a cartoon, audio recording, or e-book.

Discuss:

- How are the two versions alike? How are they different?
- What did the new version add to the story that your book did not have? Which version did you like best? Why?
- If you looked at new pictures, how did seeing the story unfold help you better understand the plot, characters, and setting?
- If you heard the story through a recording or song, how did hearing the voices help you understand the traits, mood, or feelings?

Wisdom from Around the World

On the Wisdom from Around the World page, write the title of the story, the setting, and a short summary of the plot.

Next, think about the theme. The theme is the story's main message. Sometimes the theme of a story asks us to think about "big ideas," such as what it means to be brave, to be responsible, or to be a good friend. Look at the characters' choices and actions and then decide what you think is the main message of the story.

Discuss these questions. Then write the theme of the story on the Wisdom from Around the World page.

- Do you think Rikki-Tikki is brave? Why or why not?
- Would you want Rikki-Tikki as a friend? Why or why not?
- Why does Rikki-Tikki help Teddy and his family?
- What do you think is the most important thing that happens in the story? Why? What do you think a reader can learn from it?

When you finish, gather all six Wisdom from Around the World pages. Cut out the circles carefully. Fold each circle in half. Bring

© 2015 K12 Inc. All rights reserved.
Copying or distributing without K12's written consent is prohibited.

the left edge over to the right edge and crease the paper down the middle.

Next, take two of the folded circles. Glue or tape the back of the right-hand side of one circle to the back of left-hand side of the other circle. Attach the rest of the circles the same way. For the last circle, attach the back of the right-hand side to the back of the left-hand side of the first circle.

When you finish, you may color in and hang up the sphere if you wish. What does the sphere represent?

© 2015 K12 Inc. All rights reserved.
Copying or distributing without K12's written consent is prohibited.

Name _____ **Date** _____

Wisdom from Around the World

Use details from the story to fill in the lines below.

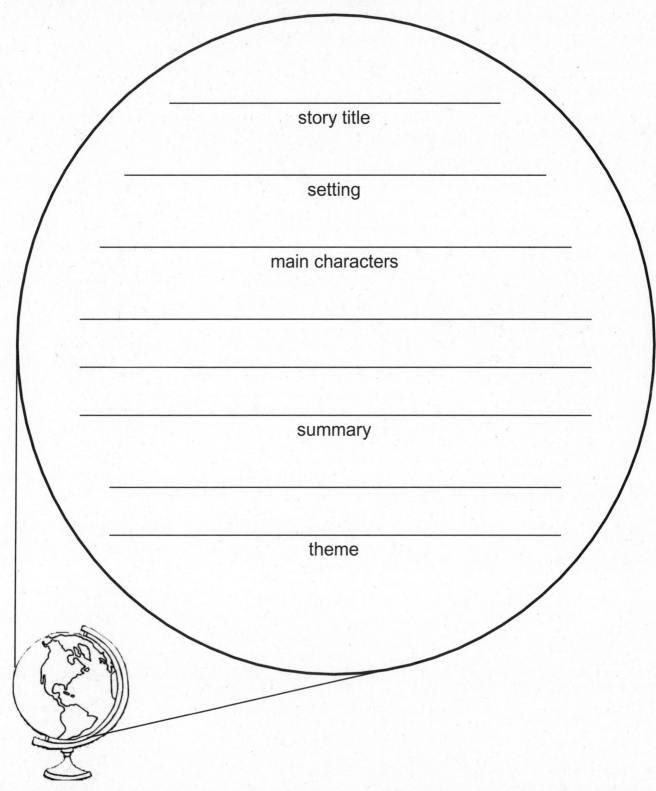

_____
story title

_____
setting

_____
main characters

_____

_____

_____
summary

_____

_____
theme

© 2015 K12 Inc. All rights reserved.
Copying or distributing without K12's written consent is prohibited.

Name   Date

"What Good Is a Forest Fire?"

Can a forest fire ever be good thing? Find out why some natural fires are good, and even necessary, to a forest.

Vocabulary

You will find these words in today's reading. Where the definition is not written, look it up in the *glossary* in your book.

thrive: (v.) to grow very well
Some flowers will grow indoors, but most need to be planted outside to *thrive*.

embers: (n.) glowing, still-warm coals from a fire
After the flames died out, we baked our potatoes in the glowing red *embers* at the bottom of the fire-pit.

adapt: (v.)
I *adapted* my wardrobe for summer by changing my sweaters and coats for t-shirts and shorts.

ignite: (v.)
I used a match to *ignite* the kindling.

life cycle: (n.)
There are four stages in the *life cycle* of a butterfly: egg, larva, pupa, and adult.

Think Ahead

1. What do you think you will learn about as you read the magazine? Do you think the articles are *fiction* or *nonfiction*? Why?

© 2015 K12 Inc. All rights reserved.
Copying or distributing without K12's written consent is prohibited.

2. You have read other nonfiction articles, such as the ones in the magazine *Feathers, Flippers, and Fur.* What are some of the characteristics of nonfiction?

3. Look through the magazine. Remember that many forms of nonfiction have features to help you find information easily. These include:
   - The table of contents that tells you the page on which each article begins
   - The glossary, which is a dictionary containing meanings of some key words
   - The index, which is the last part of the book and contains key words and concepts with page numbers next to each

4. Look up "What Good Is a Forest Fire?" in the table of contents.

5. Today's article begins in Yellowstone National Park, the oldest national park in the world. The park is located mainly in the northwest corner of Wyoming. Find Yellowstone National Park on a map.

6. Brainstorm a list of ways that a forest fire can start.

Read
"What Good Is a Forest Fire?" in *Nature's Way*

Questions
Answer the following questions in complete sentences in your Reading Notebook.

1. What causes a natural forest fire?
2. How are redwoods and ponderosa pines protected from burning?
3. Why does a hundred-year-old lodgepole pine forest contain little life?
4. Write two changes that take place in a lodgepole pine forest after a natural fire.

© 2015 K12 Inc. All rights reserved.
Copying or distributing without K12's written consent is prohibited.

5. Describe a *mosaic* left behind by a natural fire. What does it look like and why is it useful? (Hint: Who or what lives there?)

Discuss

1. Why can natural fires be good for a forest?
2. A *cycle* is a series of events that repeats. How are forest fires part of the life cycle of a forest? Describe the steps in the cycle.

Main Idea and Details

Each article in this magazine is two or more pages long. That's a lot of information! Finding the *main idea* will help you remember the most important information in an article.

The main idea is the most important point the author makes. In many articles, one sentence in the first paragraph tells the main idea. Look for the *main idea* in the paragraph below.

Have you ever seen the letter "S" move? If you do, watch out. It's probably a sidewinder. Sidewinders are small, pale-colored rattlesnakes that live in the deserts of the southwestern United States. A sidewinder forms its body into an "S" shape. Then it pushes parts of the "S" against the ground, throws its body to one side, and drags the rest of its body forward. It keeps repeating this throwing and dragging motion until it reaches its destination. Sidewinders move in an unusual way.

Discuss:
- What point is the author trying to make about sidewinders?
- Underline the sentence that gives the *main idea*.

Details give more information about the main idea. Discuss the following questions about details:
- What reasons does the author state for her main idea?
- Circle three *details* that give more information about the main idea.

© 2015 K12 Inc. All rights reserved.
Copying or distributing without K12's written consent is prohibited.

Complete the Main Idea and Details page. When you finish, review and discuss your work.

Adaptation Cube

The word *adapt* means to change in order to fit new conditions. Plants and animals *adapt* to face challenges in their environments. Think about this example of plant adaptation:

> Broad leaves form a canopy high above the floor of a rainforest. That's good for the tall trees, whose leaves are soaking up all the sunlight. But it's not so good for small plants, because the canopy keeps sunlight from reaching the rainforest floor. One small plant, a vine called a *liana*, adapted to this environment. It sinks its roots into the ground, and then grows up and around the trees, climbing all the way into the tree canopy—and the sunlight.

Discuss:
- How has the liana adapted so that it can reach the sunlight?
- Would the liana be able to survive without that adaptation? Why or why not?

Some plants in Yellowstone National Park have adapted to survive forest fires. Look back through the article and find two examples of plant *adaptations*. Describe each adaptation.

Discuss:
- How does each plant's adaptation help it survive in Yellowstone National Park?
- Would the adaptation help it survive if it were in another place, like the North Pole? Why or why not?

Choose your favorite example. Then draw the plant, write its name, and describe its adaptation in one of the squares of the Adaptation Cube. Save the page to use in future lessons.

© 2015 K12 Inc. All rights reserved.
Copying or distributing without K12's written consent is prohibited.

Name _____   Date _____

Adaptation Cube

In each square of the Adaptation Cube on the next page, draw the plant or animal, write its name, and describe its adaptation. Below is a sample of how you should enter information in the cube.

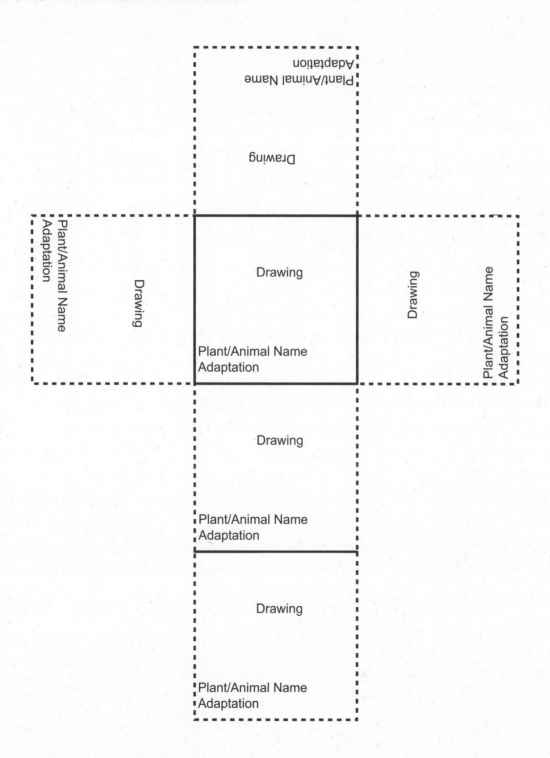

© 2015 K12 Inc. All rights reserved.
Copying or distributing without K12's written consent is prohibited.

Adaptation Cube

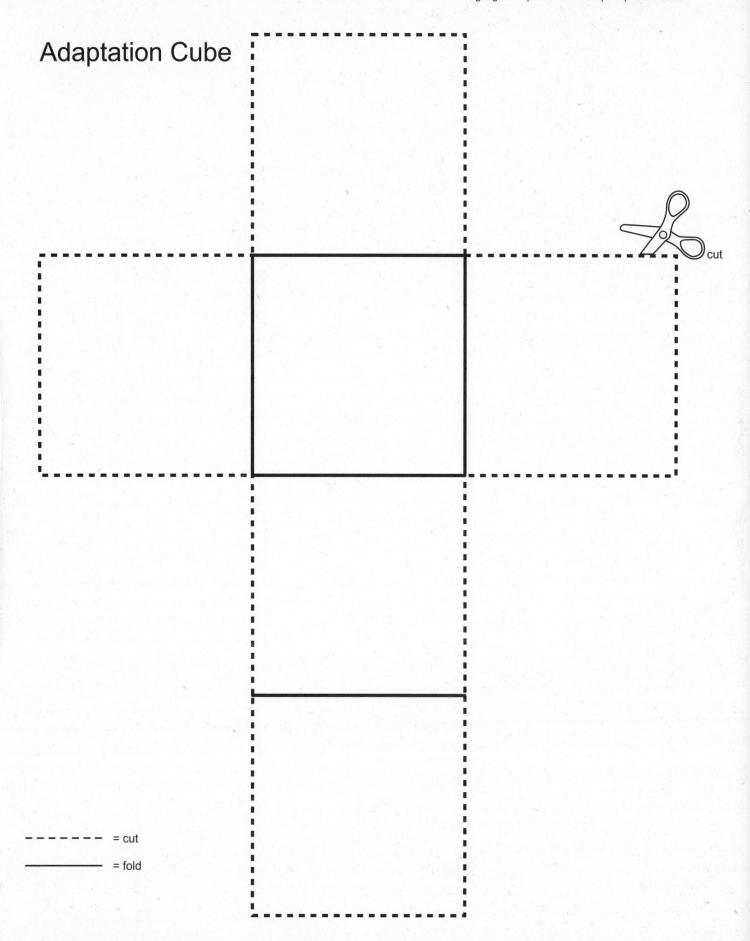

- - - - - = cut

——— = fold

© 2015 K12 Inc. All rights reserved.
Copying or distributing without K12's written consent is prohibited.

Name _____   Date _____

Main Idea and Details

Answer the questions using information from the article.

1. Which sentence from "What Good Is a Forest Fire?" states the main idea of the article?

   ⓐ But the following spring, green grass and wildflowers thrived among the blackened trunks.

   ⓑ In fact, natural fires are a necessary part of the life cycle of most forests.

   ⓒ Lightning is a common cause of fire: one strike can splinter a tree and send hundreds of sparks and embers flying.

   ⓓ Another tree, the lodgepole pine, has some cones that only open when they come in contact with extreme heat.

2. Which two sentences below are details that support the main idea?

   ⓐ After a fire, a lodgepole pine forest is not what it used to be, but it has much more life than before.

   ⓑ In 1988, fires swept through parts of Yellowstone National Park, located in Wyoming, Montana, and Idaho.

   ⓒ A mosaic is a mixture of burned and unburned areas.

   ⓓ Forest managers now realize how good natural fires can be for a forest.

3. Answer the question asked in the title of the article: What good is a forest fire? Give at least two details from the article that support the idea that a forest fire is a good thing.

   _____

   _____

   _____

   _____

   _____

© 2015 K12 Inc. All rights reserved.
Copying or distributing without K12's written consent is prohibited.

Guidelines for Peer Discussion

Share your thoughts, ideas, questions, and feelings about a text with a peer or others. Listen carefully to what everyone has to say about the text. During your discussion, follow these guidelines.

1. Be prepared to discuss what you think about the text. You should have already read the assignment. Come prepared to discuss your ideas, and use examples from the text to support your thoughts and answers.

2. You will be asked questions about the text. Be ready to answer them, and bring some questions of your own to ask others, such as:

   "Who was your favorite character? Why?"

   "What was your favorite part of the text? Why?"

   "What fact did you enjoy learning? Why do you find this fact interesting?"

   "What question would you ask if you had the chance to meet the author?"

3. Listen if it's not your turn to speak. Pay attention to what others say so that you can add your ideas. Speak clearly and in complete sentences.

4. If you don't understand what someone says, ask a question, such as:

   "What do you mean when you say . . . ?"

   "Can you give an example of . . . ?"

5. If you don't agree with what someone says, explain why.

   "I don't agree with that because . . . "

6. Keep discussions positive! You can disagree, but don't argue. Be respectful.

© 2015 K12 Inc. All rights reserved.
Copying or distributing without K12's written consent is prohibited.

Name _____   Date _____

"Frogs on Ice"

Have you ever been so cold that you said, "I'm *freezing*"? Today, meet one amphibian that really means it!

Vocabulary

You will find these words in today's reading. Where the definition is not written, look it up in the *glossary* in your book.

amphibian: (n.)
Frogs and toads are two kinds of *amphibians*.

antifreeze: (n.)
She put *antifreeze* in the car so that the liquid in the engine wouldn't freeze during the winter.

glucose: (n.)
Glucose is a kind of sugar that people's and animals' bodies use to make energy.

Think Ahead

1. Read the title of the article. What do you think the article will be about?

2. In this article, you'll hear about the only North American frog that can survive the freezing temperatures of the Arctic Circle. Find the Arctic Circle on a globe.

3. You've learned that the *main idea* of an article is the author's most important point. What are your strategies for finding the main idea of an article?

© 2015 K12 Inc. All rights reserved.
Copying or distributing without K12's written consent is prohibited.

Take Note!

Take notes on "Frogs on Ice." When you *take notes*, you write down the most important pieces of information from something you read or hear.

Listen as the article is read aloud. You will hear the section twice. Write down your notes on the Take Note! page. You do *not* have to write in complete sentences.

Questions

Answer the following questions in complete sentences in your Reading Notebook.

1. How does the wood frog survive the winter?

2. What do the wood frog's cells flood with when it gets ready to freeze?

Discuss

1. Look at your notes. What is the *main idea* of the article? What makes the wood frog unusual?

2. Give two details from the article that support, or give more information about, the main idea.

3. A process is a series of steps needed to accomplish a goal. What are the steps in the wood frog's freezing process? Describe them in order. (Hint: Reread page 10.)

Adaptation Cube

In "What Good Is a Forest Fire?" you read how some plants in Yellowstone National Park adapt to survive forest fires. In "Frogs on Ice," you read about an animal that adapts to face a challenge in its environment.

© 2015 K12 Inc. All rights reserved.
Copying or distributing without K12's written consent is prohibited.

Look back through your notes and describe the wood frog's adaptation. Discuss:

- How does the wood frog's adaptation help it survive in the Arctic Circle?

- Would the adaptation help it survive if it were in another place, like the desert? Why or why not?

- Read the pull-out box on page 11. Does the wood frog's adaptation help it face *all* of the challenges in its environment?

Add the wood frog to your Adaptation Cube. Draw a picture of it, write its name, and describe its adaptation.

© 2015 K12 Inc. All rights reserved.
Copying or distributing without K12's written consent is prohibited.

Name _____ Date _____

Take Note!

Listen as "Frogs on Ice" is read to you. Write down the important information from the selection. You do not have to write in complete sentences.

Kind of frog:_____

Where the frog lives:_____

What unusual thing the frog does:_____

When the frog does it:_____

How the frog does it:_____

Why the frog does it:_____

What other animals do at this time:_____

Other important information:

_____

_____

_____

_____

_____

_____

_____

© 2015 K12 Inc. All rights reserved.
Copying or distributing without K12's written consent is prohibited.

Name _____ Date _____

"Desert Home"

Picture the hottest desert in the United States. What could live there? Read on and find out.

Pronunciations
Sonoran (suh-NOHR-uhn)
saguaro (suh-WAHR-uh)

Vocabulary
You will find this word in today's reading. Look up the definition in the *glossary* in your book.

humidity: (n.)
The temperature and *humidity* were so high that walking outside felt like walking through steam.

Think Ahead
1. Think back to "What Good Is a Forest Fire?" and "Frogs on Ice." In which part of the world does each article take place? Describe each climate.

2. Today's article will take you far from the ice fields of the Arctic and the pine forests of Yellowstone. Travel south on your map from Yellowstone to the Sonoran Desert. The Sonoran Desert covers parts of *southwestern* Arizona, *southeastern* California, and *northwestern* Mexico. Find the Sonoran Desert on a map or globe.

3. Imagine a desert. Describe the climate. Are there plants and animals? If so, what kinds?

Read
"Desert Home" in *Nature's Way*, pages 12-16

© 2015 K12 Inc. All rights reserved.
Copying or distributing without K12's written consent is prohibited.

Questions

Answer the following questions in complete sentences in your Reading Notebook.

1. Is the Sonoran Desert the hottest desert in the United States, the largest desert in the United States, or the driest desert in the United States?

2. What does the Sonoran Desert have more of than any other American desert?

3. How many rainy seasons does the Sonoran Desert have?

4. How is that different from other deserts?

5. What do you think is the connection between the extra rainy season in the Sonoran Desert and the amount of plant and animal life?

Discuss

1. A *cause* is the reason why something happens. An *effect* is the result of, or what happens after, the cause. The climate of the Sonoran desert causes many effects for the plants and animals that live there. Name some of the effects of the heat and lack of water in this desert.

2. One plant you will find only in the Sonoran Desert is the giant saguaro cactus. Describe the giant saguaro. How does it use its pleats to survive? Why do you think giant saguaros grow so slowly?

3. Why do you think the author calls cacti the "champions of desert plants"?

Surprises, Surprises

The main idea is the most important point of an article. Because the main idea is so important, the author will often write it in a sentence in the first paragraph.

© 2015 K12 Inc. All rights reserved.
Copying or distributing without K12's written consent is prohibited.

Another way an author can draw a reader's attention to a main idea is to state an idea or opinion many people believe is true, and then give a surprising fact about it. Discuss the following example:

> Some people think that because elephants are so large, they must make a lot of noise stomping through the forests. But the elephants' feet are so soft and wide, an entire herd can pass by almost silently, leaving hardly any tracks behind.

Discuss:
- What does the author say about elephants that people might believe to be true?
- What surprising facts does the author give?

Review the main ideas of "What Good Is a Forest Fire?" and "Frogs on Ice." Then complete the Surprises, Surprises page. When you finish, review and discuss your answers.

Adaptation Cube

Add one plant and one animal *or* two animals from the Sonoran Desert to your Adaptation Cube. For each plant or animal, draw a picture, write its name, and describe its adaptation. How does each adaptation help the animal survive in the hot, dry Sonoran Desert?

© 2015 K12 Inc. All rights reserved.
Copying or distributing without K12's written consent is prohibited.

Name _____   Date _____

Surprises, Surprises

Answer the questions using information from the articles.

1. In "What Good Is a Forest Fire?" what common opinion does the author give about the forest fires that swept through parts of Yellowstone National Park?

_____

_____

2. What surprising fact does the author give about forest fires?

_____

_____

3. In "Frogs on Ice," what does the author say most animals do to survive the winter?

_____

_____

4. What surprising fact does she give about how the wood frog survives the winter?

_____

_____

© 2015 K12 Inc. All rights reserved.
Copying or distributing without K12's written consent is prohibited.

Surprises, Surprises

5. In "Desert Home," what does the author expect you will think of when you picture a desert?

_____

_____

6. What surprising fact does she give about what the Sonoran Desert is really like?

_____

_____

7. What is the main idea of "Desert Home"?

_____

_____

8. Do you think stating a common opinion and then writing a surprising fact helps a reader remember the main idea? Why or why not?

_____

_____

© 2015 K12 Inc. All rights reserved.
Copying or distributing without K12's written consent is prohibited.

Name _____   Date _____

"Seed Travel"

Swimmers, jumpers, and marathon runners: do they sound like Olympic athletes? Surprise! They are seeds that go to the extreme to travel from place to place.

Pronunciations

Mediterranean   (meh-duh-tuh-RAY-nee-uhn)
anisoptera (an-ih-SAHP-tuh-ruh)
alsomitra (ahl-soh-MIY-truh)
cocklebur (KAH-kuhl-buhr)

Vocabulary

You will find these words in today's reading. Where the definition is missing, look it up in the *glossary* in your magazine.

expand: (v.) to become bigger
The balloon's skin *expanded* when I blew into it.

fertilizer: (n.)
We put a layer of *fertilizer* over our garden so the plants would have the nutrients they need to grow.

Think Ahead

Look back at your Adaptation Cube. Describe two of the plant or animal adaptations, and how each helps the plant or animal survive in its climate.

Read

"Seed Travel" in *Nature's Way,* pages 17-21

© 2015 K12 Inc. All rights reserved.
Copying or distributing without K12's written consent is prohibited.

Questions

Answer the following questions in complete sentences in your Reading Notebook.

1. Give two reasons why seeds need to travel.
2. List three or more ways seeds can travel.

Discuss

When we *classify* and *categorize*, we group things according to their likeness or differences. When we have grouped similar objects, words, or ideas, we can give the group a name called a *category*. How would you classify the seeds in this article? What categories would you create?

What's the Main Idea?

The main idea is the most important point in an article. But sometimes finding the main idea requires a little detective work. In many articles, one sentence in the first paragraph tells the main idea. But in other articles, the main idea is unstated. *Unstated* means "not said." When the main idea is unstated, no one sentence in the paragraph tells the main idea.

To find an *unstated main idea*, read all the sentences in a paragraph, and decide what the facts have in common. That will help you uncover the hidden or unstated main idea.

Find the unstated main idea in the paragraph below. First, read the sentences. Tell three facts the paragraph gives about nuts. Then decide what the facts have in common.

Nuts are a good source of protein, vitamins, and minerals. Many people who do not eat meat add nuts to their meals to create a healthy diet. Many people enjoy nuts eaten alone as a snack. Nuts are also found in cakes, breads, muffins, and even soups because they add a lot of flavor.

© 2015 K12 Inc. All rights reserved.
Copying or distributing without K12's written consent is prohibited.

Think about three facts that are stated. Why do people eat nuts? What is the main idea?

Now find the unstated main idea in the first paragraph of "Seed Travel." First, read the sentences. Tell three facts the paragraph gives about seeds, such as, "Some seeds travel like rockets."

Decide what the facts have in common. Then choose the unstated main idea of the paragraph from the sentences below.

1. Seeds travel to get away from their parent plants.
2. Some seeds travel like rockets, parachutes, gliders, and helicopters.
3. Seeds are interesting.

Adaptation Cube

Add two seeds to your Adaptation Cube. For each seed, draw a picture, write its name, and describe its adaptation.

Discuss:
- How do the adaptations help the seeds travel to a new living space?
- Why do you think a seed like a coconut would float instead of hitchhiking?

© 2015 K12 Inc. All rights reserved.
Copying or distributing without K12's written consent is prohibited.

Name _____   Date _____

Analyze a Presentation and Choose Your Topic

Watch and explore a model presentation to learn what a presentation should include, how it should be organized, and how to deliver it effectively to an audience. Then choose a topic for your own presentation.

Analyze a Model Presentation for Content
Watch and study one student's presentation about a famous scientist. Examine the information that the student includes in the presentation and how that information is organized.

Analyze a Model Presentation for Delivery
Watch and study one student's presentation on a famous scientist again. This time, examine how the student's delivery affects the presentation.

Choose a Topic for Your Presentation
Now it's time to choose a topic for your presentation. Your presentation will be about an animal or plant with adaptations that help it to survive. Review all the topic choices before choosing the one that interests you most. Write your choice of topic on the line.

Possible Topics

Animal/Plant	Adaptation
arctic fox	thick fur that changes from brown (in summer) to white (in winter)
chameleon	skin that can change color to match its environment
blowfish	a body that can puff up to twice its normal size
cactus	stems that can store water and a large root system
Venus fly trap	leaves that close to trap insects and small spiders

© 2015 K12 Inc. All rights reserved.
Copying or distributing without K12's written consent is prohibited.

My Topic: _____

© 2015 K12 Inc. All rights reserved.
Copying or distributing without K12's written consent is prohibited.

Name _____ Date _____

Research a Topic and Organize a Presentation

Examine the steps that one student took to research a topic
and organize information for a presentation. Then begin to
research your topic and organize the information you find.

Analyze the First Steps of Creating a Model Presentation

Explore how one student developed a plan for a presentation by doing research,
filling out a graphic organizer, and completing an outline. These tools—a graphic
organizer and an outline—can help you take notes and organize your thoughts.

Research a Topic and Organize Information

Now it's time to begin to research the topic of your presentation.

First, find at least two trustworthy sources of information on your topic. Remember
that trustworthy sources are those whose information can be proven to be true and
accurate.

Offline, some trustworthy sources are

- Books
- Newspaper and magazine articles
- Encyclopedia entries

Online, some trustworthy sources are
- Websites created by people and organizations with recognized expertise on
  the subject
- Websites with URLs that end in .gov, .edu, or .org.

NOTE: Wikipedia.org and other websites that allow users to freely add information
are **not** trustworthy.

When it comes to learning about the animals and plants you had to choose from,
some useful offline resources are books written about the plant or animal, and
magazines such as *National Geographic* and *Smithsonian*.

© 2015 K12 Inc. All rights reserved.
Copying or distributing without K12's written consent is prohibited.

Online, look for web sites maintained by zoos, museums, conservation groups, and universities.

Once you have found **two** trustworthy sources of information, use them to learn the answers to the following questions about your topic. You will need to answer all of these questions for your presentation.

- What animal or plant will your presentation be about?

- Where do s this animal or plant live?

- What a e the conditions like where this animal or plant lives?

- Wh dangers does this animal or plant face?

- V ich adaptations or abilities help this animal or plant to survive?

- How do the adaptations or abilities improve the animal's or plant's chances of survival?

- Why might an animal or plant without these adaptations or abilities struggle to survive?

- What other interesting facts did you learn about this animal or plant? Next, write your topic in the center circle below and in the surrounding circles fill in the most important information you found during your research. Remember that you do not have to write in complete sentences. List your sources on the lines at the bottom.

© 2015 K12 Inc. All rights reserved.
Copying or distributing without K12's written consent is prohibited.

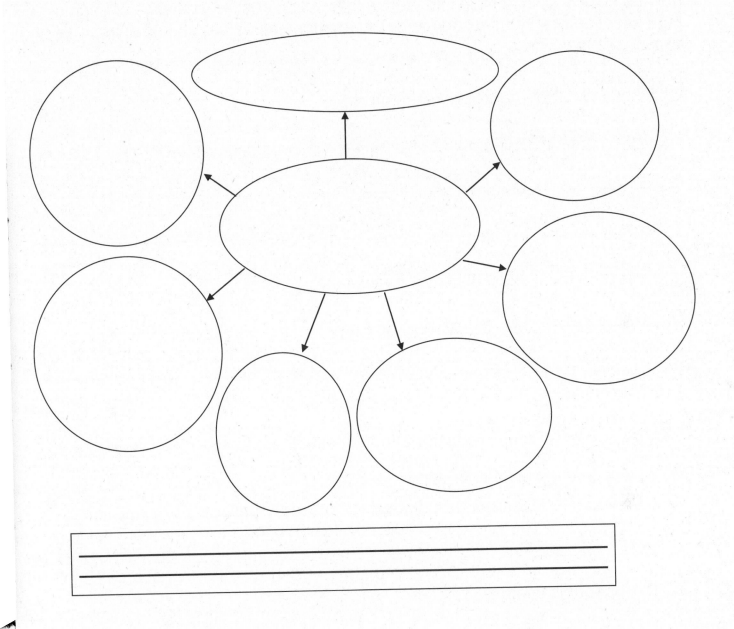

© 2015 K12 Inc. All rights reserved.
Copying or distributing without K12's written consent is prohibited.

After you have completed your research and filled in the graphic organizer, organize the information into an outline. Complete the outline below. Remember that the hook should contain information that will interest an audience or capture their attention and that the supporting information and details should help prove or explain the main idea.

I. INTRODUCTION

    A. Hook:

    _____

    _____

    B. Statement of topic and main idea:

    _____

    _____

II. BODY

    A. Supporting information/detail:

    _____

    _____

    B. Supporting information/detail:

    _____

    _____

    C. Supporting information/detail:

    _____

© 2015 K12 Inc. All rights reserved.
Copying or distributing without K12's written consent is prohibited.

D. Supporting information/detail:

_____

_____

III. CONCLUSION

A. Wrap-up:

_____

_____

B. Restatement of main idea:

_____

_____

© 2015 K12 Inc. All rights reserved.
Copying or distributing without K12's written consent is prohibited.

Name _____   Date _____

Create a Presentation

See how one student prepared for a presentation by creating
note cards and selecting the appropriate media to accompany
the information in the presentation. Then prepare for your
own presentation by creating note cards and selecting
appropriate media.

Analyze the Creation of a Model Presentation

Explore the steps one student took when transferring information from an outline
to note cards to create a presentation. Remember that the order of the facts and
the way the ideas fit together is important.

Analyze How Media Is Chosen for a Model Presentation

Appropriate media—sound, visuals, and videos—can make a presentation much
better. Learn how to choose media that is appropriate to a topic by examining how
one student chose media for the model presentation.

Create Your Presentation and Choose Media

Fill out note cards to use during your presentation and choose media that is
appropriate for your presentation.

Create Notecards

First, gather the outline you created and several note cards.

On the top of each note card, write a heading—Introduction, Body, Conclusion—to
match a heading from the outline. Note that you may wish to make more than one
Body note card.

In the middle of each note card, write the proper subheadings from your outline.
For example, the Introduction note card should have these subheadings: Hook,
Statement of Topic and Main Idea.

Finally, fill the note cards with information from the outline. It is not necessary to
write in complete sentences. But, you may wish to expand on some details or

© 2015 K12 Inc. All rights reserved.
Copying or distributing without K12's written consent is prohibited.

change the language to make it easier for you to say. Remember that you will use the note cards when you are giving your presentation, so be sure that what you write is clear to *you*.

When you have finished creating your note cards, put them in order according to the same pattern of organization as the outline.

Choose Media

There are many different kinds of media. Pictures, videos, maps, diagrams, charts, graphs, models, and audio recordings are just a few. To choose the right media for your presentation, first answer the following questions:

1. What key point or idea do you want your audience to understand or imagine more clearly?

_____

_____

2. What type of media will best convey that point?

_____

_____

Remember that different types of media are best suited to go with different types of ideas or points.

For instance, if the key point or idea you want to make clear to the audience is about how a plant or animal looks, you may choose to show a picture or video during your presentation. If the key point or idea is about the parts of a plant or animal, a diagram might be more appropriate media. If the point or idea has to do with a sound, you might decide to play an audio recording.

Once you have chosen media that fits with the point or idea you want to make clear to your audience, it's time to find or create that media.

© 2015 K12 Inc. All rights reserved.
Copying or distributing without K12's written consent is prohibited.

In many cases, you may be able to find the media you need in one of your sources. If you choose to show media from a source, be sure to give credit to that source.

Whether you find media or create it yourself, be sure that the media you use in your presentation is large enough or loud enough to be seen or heard by audience members.

After you have found or created the media for your presentation, decide when and how you will refer to it during your presentation. Consider leaving a note on one of your note cards to remind you to refer to your media at that point.

Now that you have found or created the media for your presentation, you are ready to practice delivering it.

© 2015 K12 Inc. All rights reserved.
Copying or distributing without K12's written consent is prohibited.

Name _____   Date _____

Practice a Presentation

Examine how one student practiced delivering a presentation before using a checklist to help you practice delivering your own presentation.

Review Presentation Techniques

Examine how one student practiced delivering a presentation with the help of a checklist.

Practice Your Presentation

Use the checklist to help you as you practice delivering your own presentation several times. If possible, deliver your presentation in front of a peer and/or your Learning Coach in order to get feedback. You may even wish to videotape yourself and watch.

Presentation Checklist

Use this checklist as you practice your presentation.

- Present your points in the proper order.

- Use your note cards to help you remember what points to make, but do not read directly from the note cards.

- Pronounce each word clearly as you speak.

- Speak with enthusiasm and expression.

- Speak at an appropriate pace: not too fast or too slow.

- Speak with a pleasing volume: not too loud or too soft.

- Show confidence in your knowledge of your topic.

- Stand up straight. Don't fidget.

© 2015 K12 Inc. All rights reserved.
Copying or distributing without K12's written consent is prohibited.

- Look at your audience as much as possible.

- Direct your audience's attention to the media you have chosen at the right time.

- Practice the presentation so you know what to say.

- Use standard, formal English when you speak. Do not make grammatical or usage errors.

Also consider videotaping one of your practice presentations. Watching yourself is a great way to notice your own strengths and spot weaknesses in the presentation that you need to work on.

© 2015 K12 Inc. All rights reserved.
Copying or distributing without K12's written consent is prohibited.

Peer Feedback: Tell Me About My Presentation

Have another person watch and listen to your presentation and answer the questions.

1. What is the presentation about?

   _____

2. What is the most important point, or main idea, that the speaker makes about the topic?

   _____

3. Does the speaker include interesting facts or details (a hook) as well as the main idea at the beginning of the presentation? If not, when is the main idea included?

   _____

   _____

4. Does the speaker support the main idea with facts and details? If not, how might the speaker do so?

   _____

   _____

5. Does the speaker conclude the presentation with a suitable wrap-up and by restating the main idea? If not, how might the speaker do so?

   _____

   _____

© 2015 K12 Inc. All rights reserved.
Copying or distributing without K12's written consent is prohibited.

6. What media does the speaker include in the presentation? How does the media relate to the points being made? Is the connection between the media and the content of the presentation clear? If not, how might the speaker make it clearer?

_____

_____

_____

_____

7. At what points in the presentation does the speaker speak too quickly or too slowly? Too loudly or too softly? At what points does the speaker mumble?

_____

_____

_____

8. Does the speaker often make eye contact with the audience? Does the speaker maintain good posture while speaking? If not, at what points should the speaker have looked at the audience and stood up straighter?

_____

_____

© 2015 K12 Inc. All rights reserved.
Copying or distributing without K12's written consent is prohibited.

9. Describe the tone of the speaker's voice. Does the speaker sound confident in his or her knowledge of the topic and enthusiastic about speaking to the audience? Does the speaker emphasize the right main points? If not, how might the speaker improve his or her tone and emphasis?

_____

_____

10. Does the speaker use standard, formal English, making no errors in grammar or usage? If not, note places where the language of the presentation could be improved.

_____

_____

11. After watching the presentation, do you feel as if you learned important and interesting information about the speaker's topic? If not, what could the speaker do to make the presentation better?

_____

_____

_____

© 2015 K12 Inc. All rights reserved.
Copying or distributing without K12's written consent is prohibited.

Name _____   Date _____

Deliver Your Presentation

Make a presentation on the topic you chose. Include media and deliver the presentation as you practiced it. Good luck!

Presentation Assessment

Deliver your presentation in front of an audience. Show confidence and do your best job.

© 2015 K12 Inc. All rights reserved.
Copying or distributing without K12's written consent is prohibited.

Name _____   Date _____

Your Not-So-Silent World

How many noises does nature make? More than you'd expect! In this lesson, read three poems about sounds in nature.

First Reading: "Sound of Water"

Think Ahead

See how many words can you think of to describe the sounds that water makes. Then see how many of the words you thought of are in today's first poem.

Read

Read "Sound of Water" (page 168) once silently and a second time aloud.

Discuss

1. What is the first thing you notice about the way the poem looks on the page?

2. The title of the poem is "Sound of Water." But does water have only one sound? What does the poem tell us about the sound of water?

3. Did you notice the rhyming words in the poem? Write them here in rhyming pairs:

   _____   _____

   _____   _____

   _____   _____

   _____   _____

4. Read the poem aloud again. This time, try to make each word sound like what it describes. For example, you might say the word *murmur* softly and the word *slap* sharply.

© 2015 K12 Inc. All rights reserved.
Copying or distributing without K12's written consent is prohibited.

Second Reading: "Wind"

Vocabulary

You will find this word in today's second reading.

juniper: (n.) a kind of evergreen tree or shrub
The flat, pointed leaves of the *juniper* tree almost look like hands holding the bright blue berries.

Think Ahead

You've read about the sound of water. Now you'll read about the sound of wind. Can you think of three words for the sounds that wind makes?

Read

Read "Wind" (page 169) once silently and a second time aloud.

Discuss

1. To *personify* something means to give it human qualities. Identify the words and lines that describe the wind doing human things.

2. Imagine the wind in this poem is a person. Would *shy* be a good word to describe him or her? Why or why not? What words would you choose instead?

3. Read the poem aloud again. Make the words sound like what they describe. For example, make your voice low and deep when you say, "It rumbles." Think about how will you read the line with the capitalized words ("it tells you VERY PLAINLY"). If you want to, move around the room as if you are the wind as it is described in this poem.

© 2015 K12 Inc. All rights reserved.
Copying or distributing without K12's written consent is prohibited.

Third Reading: "Galoshes"

Vocabulary

You will find this word in today's third reading.

galoshes: (n.) waterproof shoes that slip on over regular shoes

"Willy," my mom called, "it's raining cats and dogs, so please help your little sister put her *galoshes* on over her shoes."

Think Ahead

Sometimes our clothes make noises when we wear them, like the *climp-clump* of winter boots, the *rustle-hustle* of a new party dress, and the *shrr-shoosh* of comfortable pajamas. Describe a noise your most—or least—favorite clothes make when you wear them.

Read

Read "Galoshes" (page 170) once silently and a second time aloud.

Discuss

1. In the third stanza, the poet uses a made-up word, *slosh*. Find two other words the poet made up to describe the sounds of Susie's galoshes. What do those words sound like?

2. *Alliteration* is the use of words with the same or similar beginning sounds, as in "**P**eter **P**iper **p**icked a **p**eck of **p**ickled **p**eppers." Read aloud the first stanza of "Galoshes" and listen for the repeated sound.

   Susie's galoshes
   Make splishes and sploshes
   And sloshes and sloshes,
   As Susie steps slowly
   Along in the slush.

   What sound is repeated? Underline the first letter in each word that begins with this repeated sound. (For fun, see how quickly you read the stanza and still say the words clearly. Be careful—it's almost a tongue twister!)

© 2015 K12 Inc. All rights reserved.
Copying or distributing without K12's written consent is prohibited.

Activity

Making Noise
Buzz! Whir. CRASH! Clang-clang! Hiss. Purr.

Those words are examples of *onomatopoeia (ah-nuh-mah-tuh-PEE-uh),* words that imitate, or sound like, the sounds they describe. For example, the noise a cat makes sounds like the word *meow.* And in the poem "Galoshes," the made-up word *splish* sounds like galoshes in the slush.

Onomatopoeia includes:
- words for common noises, like *ding, crash,* or *boom*
- words that describe animal noises, like *bark, meow, hiss,* and *moo*
- made-up words like *splish* and *sploosh*

Write an example of onomatopoeia to describe these sounds:

Dishes dropping: _____

A rocket being launched: _____

The noise your favorite animal makes: _____

Now complete the Onomatopoeia Chart.

© 2015 K12 Inc. All rights reserved.
Copying or distributing without K12's written consent is prohibited.

Name _____   Date _____

Onomatopoeia Chart

In the boxes below, write three examples of onomatopoeia from each poem. In the last box, add your own example that *also* describes the subject of the poem. It may be a word you know or a word you make up. On the lines below the chart, tell what sound your word describes, for example:

My "Water" example is *burble*. It describes the sound of water boiling in a big pot.

"Sound of Water"	"Wind"	"Galoshes"
1.	1.	1.
2.	2.	2.
3.	3.	3.
Your Example:	Your Example:	Your Example:

My "Water" example is_____. It describes _____

_____.

My "Wind" example is_____. It describes _____

_____.

My "Galoshes" example is_____. It describes _____

_____.

© 2015 K12 Inc. All rights reserved.
Copying or distributing without K12's written consent is prohibited.

Optional: The Sound of...

Write a poem in the style of "Sound of Water." Choose a subject, such as a place, an animal, or even a person, and write a list of words that describe the sounds that go with that subject. For example:

Sound of My Baby Sister

The sound of my baby sister is:
Laugh,
Cry,
Shout,
Whine,
Burp,
Coo,
Giggle,
Wiggle,
Hug,
Love.

© 2015 K12 Inc. All rights reserved.
Copying or distributing without K12's written consent is prohibited.

Guidelines for Peer Discussion

Share your thoughts, ideas, questions, and feelings about a text with a peer or others. Listen carefully to what everyone has to say about the text. During your discussion, follow these guidelines.

1. Be prepared to discuss what you think about the text. You should have already read the assignment. Come prepared to discuss your ideas, and use examples from the text to support your thoughts and answers.

2. You will be asked questions about the text. Be ready to answer them, and bring some questions of your own to ask others, such as:

   "Who was your favorite character? Why?"

   "What was your favorite part of the text? Why?"

   "What fact did you enjoy learning? Why do you find this fact interesting?"

   "What question would you ask if you had the chance to meet the author?"

3. Listen if it's not your turn to speak. Pay attention to what others say so that you can add your ideas. Speak clearly and in complete sentences.

4. If you don't understand what someone says, ask a question, such as:

   "What do you mean when you say . . . ?"

   "Can you give an example of . . . ?"

5. If you don't agree with what someone says, explain why.

   "I don't agree with that because . . . "

6. Keep discussions positive! You can disagree, but don't argue. Be respectful.

© 2015 K12 Inc. All rights reserved.
Copying or distributing without K12's written consent is prohibited.

Name _____ Date _____

Moon and Stars

Enjoy the sounds and examine the tone of poems about the moon and stars.

First Reading: "Full of the Moon" and "The White Window"

Vocabulary

You will find these words in today's first readings.

prowl: (v.) to move carefully or secretly
The cheetah *prowled* silently in the shadows, sneaking behind the herd of gazelles.

amble: (v.) to walk casually
We *ambled* through the gardens, talking, smelling the flowers, and enjoying the sunshine.

ramble: (v.) to wander from place to place
They *rambled* from one end of the county to the other, never knowing where they would go next.

lark: (v.) to have fun; to play good-hearted jokes
I know I should be weeding the garden, but on a sunny day like this I just want to *lark* and frolic about.

two-step (n.) and **polka** (n.): two kinds of dances
In the *polka*, dancers take short, lively steps, but in the *two-step*, dancers take long, sliding steps.

© 2015 K12 Inc. All rights reserved.
Copying or distributing without K12's written consent is prohibited.

Think Ahead

The tone of your voice says almost as much as the words you choose. Imagine saying "Come here!" to a friend. Try saying it aloud now. First say it in an excited tone, then an angry tone, and then a gentle tone.

Just as you let someone know how you feel by the tone of your voice, a poem has a tone as well. The tone of a poem comes through the words and images the poet uses to express his or her attitude and emotions. The tone might be happy or sad, confident or anxious, serious or playful.

As you read these poems, think about the tone of each.

Read

Read "Full of the Moon" (page 171) and "The White Window" (page 172) once silently and a second time aloud.

Discuss

1. What words would you use to describe the dogs' behavior in "Full of the Moon"?

2. In "Full of the Moon," the poet uses onomatopoeia to describe the dogs' actions. On the lines below, write two examples of onomatopoeia from the poem.

_____   _____

3. The second line of "Full of the Moon" uses alliteration—it uses words with the same or similar beginning sounds: "The **d**ogs **d**ance out." Find another line in the poem that uses alliteration. Write it below and underline the first letter in each word that begins with the repeated sound.

_____

4. "Full of the Moon" is fun to read aloud because of the rhymes. These rhymes occur not only at the end of lines but also within lines, such as "They <u>howl</u> and <u>yowl</u>." Find two other lines with rhyming words within the line. Write the lines below and underline the rhyming words:

_____

_____

5. Is the *tone* of "Full of the Moon" serious or playful? Identify specific words and phrases in the poem that support your answer.

6. In "The White Window," the poet *personifies* the moon. He describes it as though it were a person. Identify the words and lines that describe the moon in human ways. What is the moon really doing?

7. How would you describe the *tone* of "The White Window"? Is it lighthearted, like "Full of the Moon," or is it different? Explain your answer.

Second Reading: "Escape at Bedtime"

Vocabulary
You will find these words in the third poem you will read today.

parlor: (n.) a room in a person's home for receiving visitors
We never played in the *parlor* because most of the furniture and decorations were old and fragile.

glory: (n.) majestic beauty, splendor, or great honor
The hero rode off into the sunset in a blaze of *glory*.

Think Ahead
For thousands of years, people around the world have looked up at the night sky and seen pictures of people, animals, and objects

© 2015 K12 Inc. All rights reserved.
Copying or distributing without K12's written consent is prohibited.

in the stars. We call these imaginary designs in the stars *constellations.* For example, in the constellations known as Orion and Canis Major, the ancient Greeks saw a great hunter with his faithful dog at his side.

Can you recognize any constellations, such as the Big Dipper? In Scotland (where the writer of the next poem is from), the Big Dipper is called the Plough. (*Plough* is a British spelling of *plow*.)

Read

Read "Escape at Bedtime" (page 173) once silently and a second time aloud.

Discuss

1. Who do you think the speaker might be in this poem? How old do you think he is? Where is the speaker?

2. In the first and second stanzas, what words and phrases does the speaker use to express that there are *so many* stars?

3. On the lines below, write two words or phrases the poet uses to personify the stars. What human things do the stars do?

_____   _____

4. The title of the poem is "Escape at Bedtime." What do you think the speaker is escaping from?

5. At the end of the poem, the speaker has to go to bed. Is the speaker upset? How does he feel? Why do you think he feels this way?

6. What is the rhyme scheme of the poem? (Remember, the rhyme scheme is the pattern of rhymes in a poem. Look at the word at the end of each line. Identify the rhyming words, and use a letter of the alphabet to stand for each new rhyme in a stanza.)

© 2015 K12 Inc. All rights reserved.
Copying or distributing without K12's written consent is prohibited.

Name _____   Date _____

Hoofs, Howls, and Feathers

What sounds do the rain and wind make? What does snow feel like? Today's poems answer these questions with imagination and figurative language.

First Reading: "Rain Riders"

Think Ahead

When poets use similes, metaphors, personification, and other imaginative ways of writing, they are using *figurative* language.

In your everyday conversation, sometimes you use figurative language, and sometimes you use *literal* language. When you speak literally, you use words for their plain, everyday, factual meanings. But when you speak figuratively, as poets often do, you use words in unusual and imaginative ways. For example:

Literal: My pillow is soft.
Figurative: My pillow feels like a big, puffy cloud.

Literal: Coach Anderson yells a lot but he's really a nice man.
Figurative: Coach Anderson yells a lot but he's really just a big teddy bear.

Literal: You broke Mom's favorite lamp. Now you're really in trouble!
Figurative: You broke Mom's favorite lamp. Now you're really in hot water!

Be on the lookout for figurative language in today's first poem.

Read

Read "Rain Riders" (page 174) once silently and a second time aloud.

© 2015 K12 Inc. All rights reserved.
Copying or distributing without K12's written consent is prohibited.

Discuss

1. The first line of the poem includes a word that imitates a sound, *"rat-tat-too."* What is this word an example of?

2. In the first stanza, the speaker uses figurative language. He says he "heard the Riders of the Rain." Literally, what did he hear?

3. In the second stanza, the speaker continues to use figurative language when he says, "The Riders of the Rain had gone / To tramp on other children's roofs." Literally, what has happened?

Second Reading: "Wind-Wolves"

Vocabulary

You will find these words in today's second reading.

flank: (n.) the side of a four-legged animal
After I finished brushing the *flanks* of my horse, he almost seemed to glow with health.

mere: (n.) a pond, or a small lake or marsh
The bullfrog sat on the edge of the *mere* and croaked his evening song.

phantom: (n.) a ghost
The white cat looked like a *phantom* in the dark corner of the room.

hold sway: an expression meaning "to rule, to control"
"I *hold sway* over all that I see, and even beyond," boasted the conqueror.

© 2015 K12 Inc. All rights reserved.
Copying or distributing without K12's written consent is prohibited.

Think Ahead

In one of her poems, Christina Rossetti wrote

Who has seen the wind?
Neither I nor you.

If you cannot see the wind, how do you know the wind is blowing?

Read

Read "Wind-Wolves" (page 175) once silently and a second time aloud.

Discuss

1. In the last poem, the poet figuratively described the sound of the rain as the tramping of horses' hoofs. In this poem, the poet figuratively uses two animals to describe the wind and the clouds. Which animals are they?

2. In the figurative language of the poem, the wolves are chasing the deer. What is literally happening?

3. Identify at least two words in the poem that describe the sounds the wind-wolves make.

4. The poet uses the words "ghostly" and "phantom" to describe the "trail" and the "wail" of the "wind-wolves." Why do you think the poet chose these words? How is the wind like a ghost or a phantom?

© 2015 K12 Inc. All rights reserved.
Copying or distributing without K12's written consent is prohibited.

Third Reading: "Snow in Spring"

Vocabulary

You will find this word in today's third reading.

swansdown: (n.) soft feathers of a swan
Sleeping on a pillow stuffed with *swansdown* is like sleeping on a cloud.

Think Ahead

A *metaphor* compares one thing to another, without using the words *like* or *as.* In the two poems you have read so far, you have encountered two metaphors:

- the sound of falling rain =
  the sound of horses' hoofs tramping on the roof

- the clouds blown across the sky by the wind =
  frightened deer running away from a pack of wolves

In the next poem, look for a metaphor to describe falling snow.

Read

Read "Snow in Spring" (page 176) once silently and a second time aloud.

Discuss

1. What metaphor does the poet use to describe the snow in spring?

2. *Imagery* is language that creates a mental picture by appealing to the senses. Imagery makes us see, hear, smell, taste, or feel things in our imagination. In "Snow in Spring," find examples of words that describe the snow and appeal to your senses of sight and touch.

© 2015 K12 Inc. All rights reserved.
Copying or distributing without K12's written consent is prohibited.

3. Here are two passages from the poem. Tell whether each is mainly using literal or figurative language:

    a. Feather on feather
       on feather it falls….

    b. I held seven snowflakes
       with my hands….

Optional Activity

Picturing a Metaphor

Choose one of the poems you have read today and draw a picture of the metaphors and the actions described in the poem: rain riders tramping on the rooftops, wind-wolves chasing cloud-deer, or snow-feathers falling from the sky.

© 2015 K12 Inc. All rights reserved.
Copying or distributing without K12's written consent is prohibited.

Name   Date

Wonderful Words

Today's poems are about places and creatures of fantasy. In another way, however, these poems are about words and the sounds of words, including some wonderful words you might have never heard before.

First Reading: "Grim and Gloomy"

Vocabulary

You will find these words in today's first reading.

ravenous: (adj.) very hungry
"Never get in a cage with a *ravenous* lion at feeding time," said the wise old zookeeper.

tintinnabulation: (n) the jingling, ringing sound of bells (Note: The poem turns this word into a made-up adjective, *tintinnabulous.*)
More than a hundred years ago, as sleds rushed along the roads of wintry New England villages, the *tintinnabulation* of sleigh bells filled the frosty air.

querulous: (adj.) irritable, always complaining, whiny
My little brother pleaded in a *querulous* voice, "Ah, Mom, it's early, and I'm not sleepy, so pleeeease let me stay up a little longer."

perilous: (adj.) full of danger
As we hiked along the mountain trail, our guide said, "Watch your step because there's a *perilous* drop off the edge of that cliff."

tresses: (n.) long locks of hair
The princess combed her *tresses* before going to the ball.

© 2015 K12 Inc. All rights reserved.
Copying or distributing without K12's written consent is prohibited.

bower: (n.) a sheltered place, as in a garden, covered with vines and trees
When I need some peace and quiet, I sit in the cool shade of the *bower* in the garden.

grandiose: (adj.) full of importance, or marked by an exaggerated sense of importance or greatness
The king spoke in a *grandiose* manner when he announced the building of a new museum to contain paintings of the royal family.

denizens: (n.) inhabitants, people who live in a certain place
You'll be greeted warmly by the *denizens* of that friendly neighborhood.

Think Ahead
Onomatopoeia, alliteration, and rhyme almost jump out at you in the next poem. When you read it the first time, don't worry about understanding each and every word—just enjoy the sounds and sensations.

Read
Read "Grim and Gloomy" once silently and a second time aloud.

Discuss
1. Describe the setting of the poem. Where is this "grim and gloomy" place? Identify descriptive phrases and words in the poem that describe it.

2. Describe the creatures that live in the sea. Identify adjectives that describe them.

3. The words "**g**rim and **g**loomy" are one example of *alliteration* in the poem. Identify two other examples. Write them here, and underline the letter of the repeated sound:

_____

_____

© 2015 K12 Inc. All rights reserved.
Copying or distributing without K12's written consent is prohibited.

4. The poet made up the word *sandiose*. What do you think the word might mean?

5. Can you make up another word that would fit in the poem? For example: *shell* + *delicious* = *shellicious,* an adjective that describes some of the dishes served at the feasts of the sea beasts. Write your word, its part of speech, and definition on the lines below.

_____(_____.) _____

_____

Second Reading: "Jabberwocky"

Vocabulary

You will find *many* new words in the next poem. Most of them are made up, and you can figure out what they mean by the way they sound and how they are used in the poem. Here are definitions for two *real* words that might be new to you.

shun: (v.) to stay away from
The bully was *shunned* by the rest of the children on the playground.

foe: (n.) enemy
"Halt!" cried the guard, "and identify yourself—are you friend or *foe*?"

Think Ahead
Do you know what it means to *jabber?* If you speak in a rapid way without making sense, you are jabbering. So, what do you expect from a poem titled "Jabberwocky"?

© 2015 K12 Inc. All rights reserved.
Copying or distributing without K12's written consent is prohibited.

"Jabberwocky" is a nonsense poem, but it's a nonsense poem that makes sense—in its own strange way! It was written by Lewis Carroll, the author of *Alice in Wonderland.* The poem comes from a second book about Alice and her adventures, called *Through the Looking Glass,* published in 1872.

Don't worry about the many strange, new words in "Jabberwocky." They are part of the fun of the poem. First, just listen and enjoy the fantastic sounds of the words.

Listen and Read

Listen to the audio recording of "Jabberwocky" online. The second time you listen to the poem, follow along in your book (page 179). Then try reading aloud the poem yourself.

Discuss

1. Even though some of the words may seem to make no sense, you can still follow the action. In your own words, briefly summarize what happens in the poem.

2. Identify two words used as onomatopoeia that describe the sounds of the Jabberwock and the sword.

3. In the book called *Through the Looking Glass,* Humpty Dumpty explains to Alice the meaning of some of the words in "Jabberwocky":

> "That's enough to begin with," Humpty Dumpty interrupted: "there are plenty of hard words there. 'Brillig' means four o'clock in the afternoon—the time when you begin broiling things for dinner." . . .
> "I see it now," Alice remarked thoughtfully. "And what are 'toves'?"
> "Well, 'toves' are something like badgers—they're something like lizards—and they're something like corkscrews."
> "They must be very curious-looking creatures."
> "They are that," said Humpty Dumpty, "also they make their nests under sundials—also they live on cheese."

© 2015 K12 Inc. All rights reserved.
Copying or distributing without K12's written consent is prohibited.

Choose two made-up words from the poem. On the lines below, write each word, its part of speech, and your own made-up definition for the word. Look closely at how the word is used in the poem to give you ideas for your definition. (One example has been done for you.)

___slithy___ (_adj_ .) _slippery, slimy, and snakelike_

_____(___.) _____

_____

_____(___.) _____

_____

Optional Activities

Look It Up
"Jabberwocky" became such a popular poem that some of the words Lewis Carroll invented have now become part of the English language. You can even look them up in a dictionary. Check your dictionary for definitions of the following words, or go online to www.m-w.com.

- beamish
- chortle
- galumph

Pictures of Fantasy
In "Jabberwocky," what do you think the Jabberwock, Jubjub bird, Tumtum tree, and Bandersnatch look like? Or the sea animals, beasts, and queen from "Grim and Gloomy"? If you want to, draw or paint draw one or more of these creatures of fantasy.

© 2015 K12 Inc. All rights reserved.
Copying or distributing without K12's written consent is prohibited.

Name_____ Date_____

Welcome to the Middle Ages

Enter the world of kings and castles. Become a page at a great lord's castle, and begin your quest for knighthood.

Pronunciation
feudal (FYOO-duhl)

Vocabulary
You will find these words in today's reading. Look up the definitions in the glossary.

feudal system: (n.)
In the *feudal system,* kings gave nobles pieces of land, and in return, the nobles promised to send soldiers to the king during wartime.

quintain: (n.)
When training for battle, knights would practice by charging a *quintain.*

Think Ahead
1. Look through the book. Is it fiction or nonfiction? Why?

2. Over a thousand years ago, in 476 A.D., a period of history called the Middle Ages began. Look at the timeline on page 5. Where would the year 476 fall on the timeline? The Middle Ages lasted until about the year 1500. Where would the year 1500 fall on the timeline? About how many years ago did the Middle Ages end?

3. In this book, you'll learn about the Middle Ages in England. Look at the map on page 6. What continent does it show? Which countries do you recognize? Which are unfamiliar?

© 2015 K12 Inc. All rights reserved.
Copying or distributing without K12's written consent is prohibited.

Compare the map on page 6 with a modern map. Tell three similarities and three differences.

Read
If You Lived in the Days of the Knights, pages 5-16

Questions
Answer the following questions in complete sentences in your Reading Notebook.

1. What time and place does the book describe?
2. Name the four main groups of people that were part of the feudal system.
3. What were the Crusades?
4. How could a peasant become a knight?
5. Describe a *dubbing ceremony.*

Discuss
1. Describe where a king, noble, knight, merchant, and peasant would live.
2. Were people in the Middle Ages able to easily change the group they belonged to?
3. Which life would you most like to have lived? Which would you have liked least? Think of one advantage and one disadvantage of having each life.

The Feudal System
The feudal system began during the Middle Ages. Kings, nobles, knights, and peasants traded land, loyalty, and hard work for protection.

A kingdom is a very large piece of land. The king knew he needed help defending it from enemies. So the king said to his most loyal nobles, "I will give you land if you promise to serve me and help fight the kingdom's enemies."

© 2015 K12 Inc. All rights reserved.
Copying or distributing without K12's written consent is prohibited.

The nobles agreed. But even they could not protect their land without help. So the nobles said to their finest warriors, "I will make you a knight and let you live in my great house if you will serve me and protect my land from enemies. I might even give you land of your own."

Peasants farmed the land that other people owned. They were able to stay on the land and were protected by the nobles if they farmed it. They were not allowed to leave to go somewhere else.

The feudal system connected kings, nobles, knights, and peasants. They depended on each other. You can use a *tree diagram* to show their relationships. A tree diagram is a figure that starts with one root and branches out—like a tree.

Look at the tree diagram for this example: Mary baked a cake. She gave one piece to Paul and one piece to Sue. Sue gave part of her piece to her brother Zack and some of the crumbs to the birds.

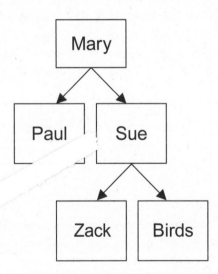

Mary and the whole cake are at the root of the tree diagram. The first two branches of the diagram show to whom Mary gave pieces of cake. The next branches of the tree diagram show to whom Sue gave parts of her piece. This tree diagram shows how the cake was shared.

© 2015 K12 Inc. All rights reserved.
Copying or distributing without K12's written consent is prohibited.

Draw a tree diagram of the king, nobles, knights, and peasants in your Reading Notebook to show how people under the feudal system shared the land. Use the tree diagram on page 10 to help you. You may illustrate your tree diagram if you wish.

A Day in the Life of Peter the Page

Pretend you live in the Middle Ages. Your name is Peter and you live at a lord's castle where you are being trained to become a knight. Each day, write a journal entry about what you see, do, and learn.

Reread pages 13-14. Then write a journal entry on the Peter the Page's Journal page. In your entry, include:

- How you feel about being away from home and why
- Three or more things you have learned as a page
- Why it is an honor to become a knight
- If you are excited about becoming a knight, and why

Remember to write the date as if you were living in the Middle Ages, and use *I, me,* and *mine* as you write. When you finish, you may illustrate your journal entry.

© 2015 K12 Inc. All rights reserved.
Copying or distributing without K12's written consent is prohibited.

Name _____   Date _____

Peter the Page's Journal

Date:_____

_____

_____

_____

_____

_____

_____

_____

_____

_____

_____

_____

_____

© 2015 K12 Inc. All rights reserved.
Copying or distributing without K12's written consent is prohibited.

Guidelines for Peer Discussion

Share your thoughts, ideas, questions, and feelings about a text with a peer or others. Listen carefully to what everyone has to say about the text. During your discussion, follow these guidelines.

1. Be prepared to discuss what you think about the text. You should have already read the assignment. Come prepared to discuss your ideas, and use examples from the text to support your thoughts and answers.

2. You will be asked questions about the text. Be ready to answer them, and bring some questions of your own to ask others, such as:

   "Who was your favorite character? Why?"

   "What was your favorite part of the text? Why?"

   "What fact did you enjoy learning? Why do you find this fact interesting?"

   "What question would you ask if you had the chance to meet the author?"

3. Listen if it's not your turn to speak. Pay attention to what others say so that you can add your ideas. Speak clearly and in complete sentences.

4. If you don't understand what someone says, ask a question, such as:

   "What do you mean when you say . . . ?"

   "Can you give an example of . . . ?"

5. If you don't agree with what someone says, explain why.

   "I don't agree with that because . . . "

6. Keep discussions positive! You can disagree, but don't argue. Be respectful.

© 2015 K12 Inc. All rights reserved.
Copying or distributing without K12's written consent is prohibited.

Name _____ Date _____

Knights and Castles

What was it like to fight as a knight and live in a castle?

Pronunciations
trebuchet (treh-byah-SHET)
hauberk (HAW-buhrk)
coif (kwahf)

Vocabulary
You will find these words in today's reading. Look up the definitions in the glossary.

dovecote: (n.)
She gathered eggs from the pigeons in the *dovecote.*

coif: (n.)
The knight wore a *coif* of chain mail underneath his helmet.

Think Ahead
During the Middle Ages, kings and nobles built castles to protect themselves, their land, and their people from invaders. A castle was designed to be a fortress. Look at the diagram on pages 17-18. What features do you think were specially included to keep enemies out?

Read
If You Lived in the Days of the Knights, pages 17-35

© 2015 K12 Inc. All rights reserved.
Copying or distributing without K12's written consent is prohibited.

Questions

Answer the following questions in complete sentences in your Reading Notebook.

1. Describe how a knight got dressed for battle.
2. How did a squire keep a knight's armor clean?
3. Why did knights wear their *coat of arms* on their shields and trappings?
4. Why did some people carry bunches of herbs and flowers to sniff outdoors?

Discuss

1. Name three weapons used during the Middle Ages. Tell who used them and how they were used.
2. Describe winter in a castle. Was it pleasant or unpleasant? Why?

A Day in the Life of Peter the Page

In today's journal entry, describe the castle you live in. Describe where you sleep, what the great hall is like, and two or more other rooms. Explain one thing you like about living in the castle and one thing you dislike.

On a separate sheet of paper, draw and label a picture of the castle where you live.

Your Coat of Arms

A *coat of arms* is a design that stands for a particular noble family. During the Middle Ages, knights wore their coat of arms on their shields, banners, and helmets, so others could identify them on the battlefield. Remember, their faces and bodies were hidden by their armor. Use the Your Coat of Arms page to design a coat of arms for Peter's family.

First, choose a color for the *field,* or background. The following colors were used during the Middle Ages: bright red, royal blue,

© 2015 K12 Inc. All rights reserved.
Copying or distributing without K12's written consent is prohibited.

sky blue, emerald green, royal purple, black, gold (yellow), and silver (white).

Next, choose the *charges* for your shield. A charge is an object that appears on the field. Animals were often used as charges. During the Middle Ages, the following animals were popular: lions, bears, boars, eagles, horses, dragons, and griffins.

You may wish to draw your animal in one of the traditional postures: standing on its hind legs facing sideways, standing on its hind legs facing you, walking, sitting, or lying down.

Most families had a saying or *motto*, like this French nobleman's: "To valiant hearts, nothing is impossible."

Write a motto for Peter's family on the line below the shield.

© 2015 K12 Inc. All rights reserved.
Copying or distributing without K12's written consent is prohibited.

Name _____   Date _____

Your Coat of Arms

Draw Peter's family shield. Write a motto on the line below the shield.

_____

© 2015 K12 Inc. All rights reserved.
Copying or distributing without K12's written consent is prohibited.

3. How were knights' clothes similar to and different from peasants' clothes? How did each person's clothing suit the work he or she did?

Read
If You Lived in the Days of the Knights, pages 36-54

Questions
Answer the following questions in complete sentences in your Reading Notebook.

1. How were *serfs* different from peasants?
2. Describe what work the sons of nobles, knights, merchants, and serfs did.
3. What did girls learn how to do?
4. Describe two kinds of medieval schools and tell who attended them.
5. How did students learn their lessons?

Discuss
1. Choose two of the crimes discussed on page 50. Describe each crime and what its punishment was.
2. Why do you think the punishments were so public? How might that relate to the fact that most people in medieval times could not read or write?
3. Describe how books were made in medieval times. Who owned books? Why do you think they were considered so valuable?
4. Reread the information about toys and games on page 44. What games do you play today that are like those that children played during the Middle Ages? Did they do any activities that you wish you could do today?

A Year in Medieval Times
Fold a piece of paper in quarters. Label the quarters *Winter, Spring, Summer,* and *Autumn.* In each box, draw a picture of an event that would take place during that season. Use details from the book for

© 2015 K12 Inc. All rights reserved.
Copying or distributing without K12's written consent is prohibited.

ideas and to make sure your drawings are *accurate. Accurate* means correct and based on facts. Being accurate means paying attention to little details and correctly describing what people wore, what tools they used, or what games they played.

After you finish drawing, write a 1-2 sentence caption for each picture.

A Day in the Life of Peter the Page

In today's journal entry, tell about an afternoon you and your friends spent having fun. Describe three or more things you did, the places you went, and the people you saw.

© 2015 K12 Inc. All rights reserved.
Copying or distributing without K12's written consent is prohibited.

Name _____   Date _____

Peter the Page's Journal

Date:_____

_____

_____

_____

_____

_____

_____

_____

_____

_____

_____

_____

© 2015 K12 Inc. All rights reserved.
Copying or distributing without K12's written consent is prohibited.

Name _____ Date _____

Travel, Medicine, and Celebrations

Visit a few medieval doctors' offices and travel in style to a grand wedding celebration.

Vocabulary

You will find these words in today's reading.

wares: (n.) goods for sale
The potter arranged his *wares* on shelves instead of on the ground so it would be easy for customers to see and reach them, but difficult for careless feet to trip over and break them.

remedy: (n.) a cure
The best *remedy* for being overtired is a good night's sleep.

leech: (n.) a kind of blood-sucking worm
Sometimes when a surgeon reattaches one of a patient's body parts, he or she will use *leeches* to control the patient's blood flow.

Think Ahead

1. Look at the picture on page 61. Do most of the people seem to be there for a haircut? Why or why not? What do you think the barber does?
2. Do you predict that there were many or few doctors in medieval times? Why?

Read

If You Lived in the Days of the Knights, pages 55–70

© 2015 K12 Inc. All rights reserved.
Copying or distributing without K12's written consent is prohibited.

Questions

Answer the following questions in complete sentences in your Reading Notebook.

1. Describe how a rich baron might move from one castle to another.
2. What dangers did travelers face on land and on the sea?
3. Did each person get his or her own bed in an inn?
4. Were all doctors in medieval times men?
5. How were sick people treated in hospitals?
6. What did barbers do?

Discuss

1. Besides knights and their families, servants, churchmen, and many guests lived in the castle, too. Some guests stayed for years at a time. Think about what you know about traveling and wars during medieval times. Why do you think some guests stayed at a castle for years?

2. Why did girls and boys marry so young?

3. How was the birthday of a noble's child celebrated ? How is that similar to and different from how children's birthdays are celebrated today?

A Day in the Life of Peter the Page

In your journal entry, describe how you (and most everyone who lives in your castle) traveled to the princess's wedding celebration at the king's castle and what happened there. Some questions to think about:

- How many people, horses, and carriages did you travel with?
- How long did the journey take? Where did you stay? Were you set upon by robbers?

© 2015 K12 Inc. All rights reserved.
Copying or distributing without K12's written consent is prohibited.

- Describe the feast. Carefully reread pages 62-64 and imagine what astonishing creations the king's cooks might have come up with to celebrate the princess's wedding.
- Did anyone have excellent manners? Did anyone behave in an unmannerly way?
- What entertainment was there?
- What happened at the ceremony?

You might also want to reread pages 40-41 to review the people who worked in castles and their jobs and page 46 to review music and musicians.

When you finish writing, you may illustrate your journal entry.

What I Know: What I Wonder

Look at the table of contents in *If You Lived in the Days of the Knights*. Did you notice that all of the chapter titles are written as questions? Did you notice, too, how each question seems to lead to even more questions?

This author had many burning questions about medieval times. Have you ever had a burning question? A burning question is something that you wonder about when you read or learn new information.

Imagine you are visiting a museum and you see an exhibit on motte-and-bailey castles. During your visit, you learn the following facts about motte-and-bailey castles:

- Long ago, people built wooden towers on top of a hill. The hill was called a *motte*.
- The land at the bottom of the hill was called a *bailey*. A moat surrounded the motte and the bailey.
- Motte-and-bailey castles were replaced by stone castles.

© 2015 K12 Inc. All rights reserved.
Copying or distributing without K12's written consent is prohibited.

What questions do you have? Even though you have learned new information, there is more that you may wonder about. These are your burning questions. In order to answer them, you would need to do research.

Now look at your Peter the Page journal entries and the projects you have completed so far. Which topics that you have read about are the most interesting to you?

Choose a topic and write at least five facts that you have learned about it in the "What I Know" column of the Burning Questions page. Then complete the "What I Wonder" column. Think of at least five questions that you still have about this topic and write them down. Research and write the answer to one or more of your questions.

© 2015 K12 Inc. All rights reserved.
Copying or distributing without K12's written consent is prohibited.

Name _____ Date _____

Peter the Page's Journal

Date: _____

_____

_____

_____

_____

_____

_____

_____

_____

_____

_____

_____

_____

© 2015 K12 Inc. All rights reserved.
Copying or distributing without K12's written consent is prohibited.

Name _____   Date _____

Burning Questions

Use the chart below to create a list of questions about something that you would like to learn more about.

I would like to know more about_____.

What I Know	What I Wonder
_____	_____
_____	_____
_____	_____
_____	_____
_____	_____
_____	_____
_____	_____
_____	_____
_____	_____

© 2015 K12 Inc. All rights reserved.
Copying or distributing without K12's written consent is prohibited.

Name _____   Date _____

The Middle Ages Today

How much of the Middle Ages is with us today?

Vocabulary
You will find these words in today's reading. If the definition is missing, look it up in the glossary.

contribution: (n.) something given for the common good
The Wright Brothers made an important *contribution* to science: they invented the first successful airplane.

tapestry: (n.)
Thread by thread, the woman wove a picture of a knight on horseback into the growing *tapestry*.

manuscript: (n.)
The first draft of my story was a *manuscript*, but I decided to type the second draft because my handwriting looked so messy.

Think Ahead
. Do you think there are still knights today? Give reasons for your prediction.
. How do you think historians have learned so much about the Middle Ages? How do they get their information?
  Imagine that an ancient farming tool has just been found at an archaeological site. What information could you get from the tool about the people who used it? What other questions might you have, and how would you find the answers?

Read
If You Lived in the Days of the Knights, pages 71-73

© 2015 K12 Inc. All rights reserved.
Copying or distributing without K12's written consent is prohibited.

Questions

Answer the following questions in complete sentences in your
Reading Notebook.

1. To whom does the Queen of England award knighthoods today?
2. Are today's knights only men?
3. Name three things historians look at to learn about the past.
4. Describe what historians can learn from one of the three things.

Discuss

1. Very few books were made during the Middle Ages. Why was it
   important for the writers during the Middle Ages to be as
   accurate as they could during their time?

2. Today, historians use those books to help them learn about the
   past. What might the consequences be for us today if a writer
   had been inaccurate a thousand years ago?

3. Think back over what you've read. How were the people who
   lived during the Middle Ages like people today? How were they
   different?

4. What do you think is the most important thing you learned? Why?

A Day in the Life of Peter the Page

Congratulations! The son of the lord of your castle has been made
a knight. The new knight wants you to be his squire. In your journal
entry, describe the knighting ceremony and answer these
questions:

- What happened before, during, and after the ceremony?
- If you become the knight's squire, what will you have to learn
  next? What will your responsibilities be?
- How do you feel about becoming a squire? Are you excited or
  nervous? What are you most looking forward to? Why?

© 2015 K12 Inc. All rights reserved.
Copying or distributing without K12's written consent is prohibited.

When you finish, you may illustrate your journal entry. Then assemble all five entries into one book.

An Illuminated Manuscript

An illuminated manuscript is something written by hand that has pictures. In an illuminated manuscript, the pictures are very detailed, and are often decorated with brilliant colors or even real gold.

Choose your favorite question from the book to write about, or research the answer to one of your own burning questions from the previous session. Draft a paragraph or more to answer the question. Revise and proofread your paragraph. When you're ready, write your final copy in your best handwriting on the Illuminated Manuscript page.

When you finish, draw and color an illumination in the box.

© 2015 K12 Inc. All rights reserved.
Copying or distributing without K12's written consent is prohibited.

Name _____

Date _____

Squire's Certificate

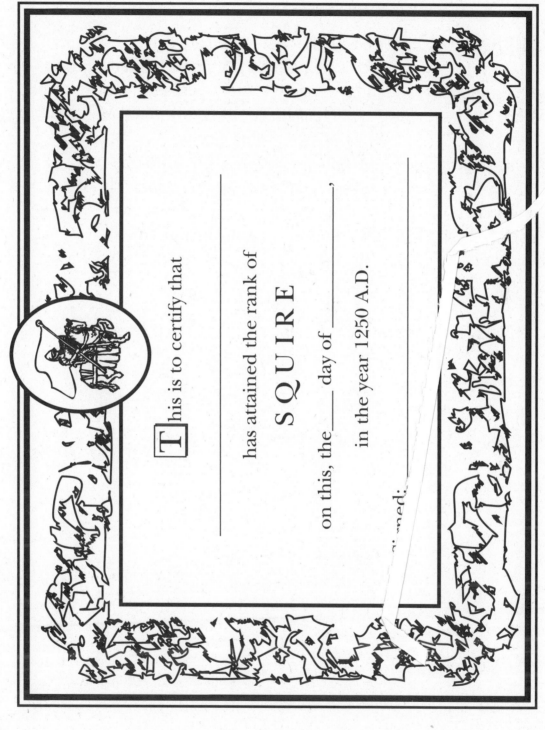

This is to certify that

_____

has attained the rank of

SQUIRE

on this, the _____ day of _____,

in the year 1250 A.D.

_____

© 2015 K12 Inc. All rights reserved.
Copying or distributing without K12's written consent is prohibited.

Name _____   Date _____

Peter the Page's Journal

Date: _____

_____

_____

_____

_____

_____

_____

_____

_____

_____

_____

_____

_____

© 2015 K12 Inc. All rights reserved.
Copying or distributing without K12's written consent is prohibited.

Name _____   Date _____

An Illuminated Manuscript

example

_____
Title

_____

_____

_____

_____

_____

_____

_____

© 2015 K12 Inc. All rights reserved.
Copying or distributing without K12's written consent is prohibited.

Name _____   Date _____

"The Rightful King of the Britons"

Who will pull the sword from the stone and be declared the rightful
King of the Britons?

Vocabulary

You will find these words in today's reading.

cheer: (n.) entertainment or welcome
We have good *cheer* around the holidays, when everyone
comes to our house to eat, sing, laugh, and talk together.

pray: (v.) to make a polite request
"*Pray* tell," she asked the librarian, "what time is it?"

feats of arms: (n.) astonishing skill or use of weapons
At the games, there will be *feats of arms* in archery—one
archer will shoot at the bull's-eye while running!

tumult: (n.) commotion; a confusion caused by a crowd of
people milling about with loud voices
Margaret doesn't like to go to the airport by herself because she
doesn't like crowds and all of the *tumult* makes her nervous.

tarry: (v.) to be slow in leaving; to linger
When we walk the dog, my brother always *tarries* behind to
look at rocks and search for bugs in the grass.

glimpse: (v.) to see quickly
I *glimpsed* the mouse for just a second before it scurried back
into its hole.

© 2015 K12 Inc. All rights reserved.
Copying or distributing without K12's written consent is prohibited.

hoarsely: (adv.) with a rough sound
After cheering too much at the soccer game, we all spoke *hoarsely* for a week.

inscription: (n.) words written or engraved on a surface
When I opened the book I received for my birthday, I saw that my mother had written a thoughtful *inscription* inside the front cover.

liege: (n.) a person who was given allegiance and service during feudal times
The knight knelt before the king and said, "I swear to serve you and fight for your kingdom, my *liege*."

anvil: (n.) a heavy iron block on which metal is shaped
The blacksmith laid the horseshoe on the *anvil* and then began pounding it into the correct shape.

Think Ahead

1. In *If You Lived in the Days of the Knights,* you learned about life in England during the Middle Ages. These stories, about King Arthur and the Knights of the Round Table, also take place during the Middle Ages in England. What kinds of people, places, and objects do you expect to find in "King Arthur"? What events might take place?

2. "King Arthur and the Knights of the Round Table" is a collection of *legends* from the Middle Ages. A legend is a story that is handed down from the past. Legends often contain historical facts, but sometimes the facts change over time and the legend becomes fiction. Legends may even contain historical characters; however, the facts about these real people may not be true. For example, the story of George Washington chopping down the cherry tree is a legend. What other legends have you read?

3. What do you remember about chivalry?

© 2015 K12 Inc. All rights reserved.
Copying or distributing without K12's written consent is prohibited.

Read

"The Rightful King of the Britons" in *Classics for Young Readers,*
Vol. 4B, pages 60-71

Questions

Answer the following questions in complete sentences in your
Reading Notebook.

1. Why do Arthur, Kay, and Sir Ector go to London?
2. According to the guard, how, when, and why does the sword in
   the stone appear?
3. Why does Arthur first pull the sword from the stone?
4. Does Arthur know what pulling the sword from the stone means?
   How do you know?
5. What happens when Sir Kay tries to return the sword to the stone?
6. What happens when Arthur tries to return the blade to the stone?
   How do Sir Ector and Sir Kay react?
7. Sir Ector is not of royal blood. Why can Arthur, his son, be king?

Discuss

1. When Arthur steps up to try to pull the sword from the stone,
   the knights in the crowd are angry. Why are they angry? Who
   calms them? How?

2. Choose three words that describe Arthur. Give an example of
   something Arthur thinks, says, or does to support each choice.

3. At the end of the story, Arthur says, "I promise you I will be a
   true king. I will do my best to be fair and just, as long as I may
   live." Do you think Arthur will be a good king? Why?

4. Will Arthur have help as the King of Briton? Predict who or what
   might help him. What challenges might he face?

© 2015 K12 Inc. All rights reserved.
Copying or distributing without K12's written consent is prohibited.

Marvelous Merlin

Merlin is one of the most famous characters in British literature. In the first paragraph of this story, he is described as "old and wrinkled—a wanderer, famous for his wisdom and skill, and welcome everywhere."

Is that a complete description of this unusual character? Is Merlin what he seems to be? Discuss these questions as you think more about Merlin:

- At the beginning of the story, Merlin tells Sir Ector that he will "certainly be present" at Arthur's knighting, even though that isn't supposed to happen for five years. What is strange about this promise? (Hint: What do you know about travel during the Middle Ages?)

- Reread the paragraph on page 70 that begins, "Silence!" What does Merlin look like? Do his looks match his voice? Why or why not? Compare and contrast this description of Merlin with how Merlin appears at the beginning of the story.

- Reread the two paragraphs on page 70 that begin, "People of Britain…." What did Merlin do when Arthur was a baby? Why do you think he chose not to tell Arthur or Sir Ector?

- An event in the Arthurian Legends that is not included in this story is that Merlin knights Arthur in the churchyard on the day Arthur pulls the sword from the stone. Merlin *is* present at Arthur's knighting, as he said he would be. Do you think Merlin knew or planned what would happen? Why?

Consider the events in the story. How would you describe Merlin? In your Reading Notebook, write your own description of Merlin and illustrate it.

© 2015 K12 Inc. All rights reserved.
Copying or distributing without K12's written consent is prohibited.

The Age of Chivalry: Courage

At the end of the last unit, you, as Peter the Page, were promoted to squire. In order to become a knight, you must learn about *chivalry:* the way a medieval knight was expected to behave. In fact, knights and their code of chivalry were so important that the Middle Ages are often called "The Age of Chivalry."

A *chivalrous* knight was expected to be courageous. Discuss the following events from the story. Decide whether the characters were being courageous. Explain how their actions show courage.

1. After Kay hears about the tournament, the story says, "he wished that he could go there and take part in it. Why should he live idle here in his father's castle when there was so much to be done elsewhere? Was it not the duty of every young knight to seek adventures wherever they could be found? How else could he prove himself worthy of his knighthood?"

2. Sir Kay does not tell the truth when Sir Ector asks how he has gotten the sword. He tells the truth after he tries to return the sword and fails.

3. The first thing King Arthur says to the people of Britain is, "I promise you I will be a true king. I will do my best to be fair and just, as long as I may live."

Now write your own definition and an example of *courage* on your My Code of Chivalry page.

© 2015 K12 Inc. All rights reserved.
Copying or distributing without K12's written consent is prohibited.

Name _____   Date _____

My Code of Chivalry

Write a definition for and an example of the quality you discuss in each lesson.

MY CODE OF CHIVALRY

Courage means: _____

_____

A courageous knight: _____

Justice means: _____

_____

A just knight: _____

Defense means: _____

_____

A knight defends: _____

Humility means: _____

_____

A knight who has humility: _____

Duty means: _____

_____

A dutiful knight: _____

© 2015 K12 Inc. All rights reserved.
Copying or distributing without K12's written consent is prohibited.

Guidelines for Peer Discussion

Share your thoughts, ideas, questions, and feelings about a text with a peer or others. Listen carefully to what everyone has to say about the text. During your discussion, follow these guidelines.

1. Be prepared to discuss what you think about the text. You should have already read the assignment. Come prepared to discuss your ideas, and use examples from the text to support your thoughts and answers.

2. You will be asked questions about the text. Be ready to answer them, and bring some questions of your own to ask others, such as:

   "Who was your favorite character? Why?"

   "What was your favorite part of the text? Why?"

   "What fact did you enjoy learning? Why do you find this fact interesting?"

   "What question would you ask if you had the chance to meet the author?"

3. Listen if it's not your turn to speak. Pay attention to what others say so that you can add your ideas. Speak clearly and in complete sentences.

4. If you don't understand what someone says, ask a question, such as:

   "What do you mean when you say . . . ?"

   "Can you give an example of . . . ?"

5. If you don't agree with what someone says, explain why.

   "I don't agree with that because . . . "

6. Keep discussions positive! You can disagree, but don't argue. Be respectful.

© 2015 K12 Inc. All rights reserved.
Copying or distributing without K12's written consent is prohibited.

Name _____ Date _____

"The City of Dreams and the Sword of Legend"

Visit Arthur's castle in the City of Dreams and follow him on a quest to win a marvelous sword.

Pronunciation
Camelot (KA-muh-laht)
Excalibur (ek-SKA-luh-buhr)

Vocabulary
You will find these words in today's reading.

vapor: (n.) watery mist
As the storm ended, curls of *vapor*, like dragon's tails, rose up from the sidewalks.

adorned: (v.) decorated
I *adorned* my hair with beads and bows.

stately: (adj.) very dignified; imposing
My grandpa is a very tall man with a deep voice and a full head of white hair, who always dresses in a suit and tie and looks very *stately*.

do homage: an expression that means to pay respect or tribute
He visits the memorial once each month to *do homage* to the soldiers who died during the war.

merits: (n.) good qualities; virtues
My sister says that she knows she'll like any book written by Beverly Cleary, but I prefer to read each and judge it on its own *merits*.

© 2015 K12 Inc. All rights reserved.
Copying or distributing without K12's written consent is prohibited.

boon: (n.) a benefit that is granted because of a request
The people who seek King Arthur's assistance in their causes ask the king for a *boon*.

plume: (n.) a big, showy feather
The ostrich *plume* she tucked in her hat was so long that it curled under her shoulder.

sentry: (n.) a guard
The *sentries* stood guard at the gatehouse.

hew: (v.) to chop
Long ago, railroad builders did not have machines or dynamite to make tunnels through mountains; they had to *hew* the rock with hammers and chisels.

Think Ahead

1. Summarize "The Rightful King of the Britons." In your summary, tell:
   - In what country and time period the story takes place
   - Why Arthur first pulls the sword out of the stone
   - What the words on the sword say
   - What Arthur promises the Britons

2. Some people believe that a king or general named Arthur once lived in Britain, but the stories of King Arthur and the Knights of the Round Table are *legends.* In your own words, tell what a legend is.

Read

"The City of Dreams and the Sword of Legend" in *Classics for Young Readers,* Vol. 4B, pages 72-82

Questions

Answer the following questions in complete sentences in your Reading Notebook.

© 2015 K12 Inc. All rights reserved.
Copying or distributing without K12's written consent is prohibited.

1. What are the two names of the city where Arthur lives?
2. Where does the king go at noon each day, and what does he do there?
3. Why does King Arthur sneak out of Camelot while everyone is asleep?
4. Why does King Arthur win the first battle with Sir Pellinore?
5. How does Arthur get Excalibur?
6. What is unusual about Excalibur's blade and scabbard?

Discuss

1. Reread the third paragraph on page 72 and the first paragraph on page 73. According to Merlin, how was Camelot made?

2. When the squire tells Arthur the story of Sir Pellinore, Arthur grows angry and decides to ride out against the knight himself. Do you think he is being wise or foolish? Do you think he makes the right choice? Why?

3. On page 76, the story says, "So, every day, men came, and women, and even children, and told the King of their wrongs. To each one, he gave judgment as it seemed most right and true. The rich and the poor came, the friendly and the rude, and all received justice according to their merits." Is Arthur keeping the promise he made in Chapter 1? Why or why not? How is he different from the old king?

The Age of Chivalry: Justice

Do you remember the tree diagram you made for the feudal system? For a long time during the Middle Ages, each group of people could tell the group below it what to do. People who were nobles did not have to be fair to people who were serfs. But chivalrous knights were expected to be just and to use their power to solve problems fairly.

Tell how Arthur resolves each of the four problems brought before him and explain why his actions are just. Then write your own definition

© 2015 K12 Inc. All rights reserved.
Copying or distributing without K12's written consent is prohibited.

and example of *justice* on the My Code of Chivalry page that you began in the last lesson. You may use your book for reference.

1. The poor man says, "A long time ago, the old king took my lands and houses from me. All my gold was stolen for his treasury, then my dear wife and I were forced to become beggars, and she died for lack of food."

2. The angry woman says, "I am your enemy, and you are no king. One of your knights killed my husband in battle. Then the knight seized our castle and lands and drove me out into the world penniless. What can I do but look to you for justice, though I hate you? All the world knows you are not the old king's son. You are not a king, and yet I am forced to call you such. I cry for justice, Arthur."

3. The child says, "A bird built its nest under my window, and every morning it woke me up with its sweet singing. But our neighbor loves no living thing, and this very day killed my bird with a stone."

4. When Arthur defeats Sir Pellinore, Sir Pellinore says, "Spare my life, and I will yield myself to you."

Camelot and Excalibur

Draw a picture of the city of Camelot or of Arthur receiving the sword, Excalibur. Use as many details from the story as you can find. When you finish drawing, write a two to three sentence caption for your illustration.

© 2015 K12 Inc. All rights reserved.
Copying or distributing without K12's written consent is prohibited.

Name _____   Date _____

"Guinevere and the Gift of the Round Table"

Many people have heard of the Round Table. Can you guess where it came from and who made it?

Pronunciation
Guinevere (GWEH-nuh-veer)
Leodegrance (LEE-oh-duh-grance)
Cameliard (cuh-MEE-lee-ard)

Vocabulary
You will find these words in today's reading.

beset: (v.) to set upon or cause trouble for
As we pitched our tent for the night, I hoped that our campsite would not be *beset* by any wild animals.

subdued: (v.) conquered
"We shall march on and fight," cried the general, "until we have *subdued* all our enemies."

poised: (v.) standing ready
The cat stood *poised* on her back legs, just about to leap into the air.

host: (n.) an army
The *host* swarmed into the valley like a troop of giant ants.

scuttled: (v.) scurried
The squirrels *scuttled* into the trees when they heard the fierce dogs barking below them.

triumphed: (v.) won
We *triumphed* over the other team.

© 2015 K12 Inc. All rights reserved.
Copying or distributing without K12's written consent is prohibited.

thronged: (v.) crowded

The shoppers *thronged* into the mall to take advantage of the sales.

clad: (v.) dressed

The bride was *clad* all in white from the top of her head to the tip of her toes.

Think Ahead

1. Summarize "The City of Dreams and the Sword of Legend." In your summary, explain:
   - How Merlin says Camelot was created
   - What happens in Camelot each day at noon and why
   - How Arthur wins the first fight against Sir Pellinore
   - How Arthur receives Excalibur
   - What Arthur does when Sir Pellinore yields to him

2. What is the *setting* of the King Arthur legends? In what time period and country do they take place?

3. What are some of the reasons that knights fought during the Middle Ages? Is it a good idea for King Arthur to send his knights to help another king? Why or why not?

Read

"Guinevere and the Gift of the Round Table" in *Classics for Young Readers,* Vol. 4B, pages 83-89

Questions

Answer the following questions in complete sentences in your Reading Notebook.

1. Merlin gives Arthur two pieces of advice before the king sets out for Cameliard. What are they?
2. Describe how Arthur is adorned when he rides into battle.

© 2015 K12 Inc. All rights reserved.
Copying or distributing without K12's written consent is prohibited.

3. Why are people able to know which knight is Arthur when the king speaks or rides into the face of danger?
4. What reward does King Arthur ask from King Leodegrance?
5. What dowry does King Leodegrance send?
6. Who made the Round Table?

Discuss

1. Is Arthur keeping the promise he made at the end of Chapter 1? How?
2. Why is the Round Table a good gift for King Arthur and all his knights? (Hint: Think about how they sit.)

The Age of Chivalry: Defense

Knights of the Middle Ages were very powerful. They protected their bodies with suits of armor, and they fought with swords and lances, which were some of the best weapons of their time. Because a knight was so much stronger than most people, he could do great harm or great good. Chivalrous knights were expected to defend the weak and the helpless, their liege lord, and the kingdom.

Discuss how King Arthur defends Camelot and Cameliard. After your discussion, write a definition and example of *defense* on your My Code of Chivalry page.

1. At Cameliard, how many enemies do King Arthur and the Thirty face? Why do you think they fight even though they are outnumbered and King Leodegrance tells them they should stay inside?

2. "The City of Dreams and the Sword of Legend," each day, the heralds cry, "Behold, the King sits in his judgment hall! If there be any who are suffering wrong, if there be any who are in trouble because of evil doers, if there be any who are in urgent need of help, let such come freely and ask for justice

© 2015 K12 Inc. All rights reserved.
Copying or distributing without K12's written consent is prohibited.

without fear!" Is Arthur defending the people by helping them solve their problems and giving them justice? Why or why not?

A Better Day

At the end of "Guinevere and the Gift of the Round Table," Merlin and the knights sing, "The old order has passed away. Now is the dawning of a better day!"

Review the paragraph below from the first story, "The Rightful King of the Britons." Then, in your Reading Notebook, write a paragraph describing two or more ways that life in England changes after Arthur becomes king, and why those changes happen.

"Sad, sad is the day," said Merlin, "for the people are without a leader. They fight among themselves. They rob their neighbors. They waste the land with fire and sword. The poor and helpless must hide themselves in the woods, for there is no safety anywhere. Many long for a king who will be strong enough to unite the country."

© 2015 K12 Inc. All rights reserved.
Copying or distributing without K12's written consent is prohibited.

Name _____   Date _____

"Pretty-Hands"

Does what you wear or where you come from change who you are on the inside? Come along on a prince's journey to become a knight and earn a chair among his brothers at the Round Table.

Vocabulary

You will find these words in today's reading.

unworthy: (adj.) dishonorable
It was *unworthy* of him to tell a lie; we expected better from him.

scullion: (n.) a kitchen helper
The *scullion* scrubbed the pots and pans and carried water from the well to the kitchen.

gallant: (adj.) courteous and brave
The *gallant* knight was kind to all and had never been bested in combat.

besieged: (v.) surrounded by an enemy army
The castle was *besieged*—every window looked out over enemy soldiers, catapults, or tents.

fie: (int.) a word used during the Middle Ages to show disgust and anger
"*Fie* upon this," cried Sir Kay, "I cannot go into battle with a rusty sword!"

vile: (adj.) disgusting
It was a *vile* mixture of dirt, rotting leaves, and old garbage.

knave: (n.) an untrustworthy or deceitful person
The *knave* stole the pie right off of the windowsill while the cook's back was turned.

© 2015 K12 Inc. All rights reserved.
Copying or distributing without K12's written consent is prohibited.

quench: (v.) to put out

I *quenched* the fire with a pail of water.

whelp: (n.) a puppy

The *whelps* barked, whined, and chased their tails.

Think Ahead

1. Summarize "Guinevere and the Gift of the Round Table." In your summary, tell:
   - What city King Arthur defends
   - Who is with him
   - What Arthur wants for a reward
   - Who makes the Round Table and why it is given to Arthur

2. In the last story, you learned that knights and fighting men from all over Britain flock to join Arthur's company. Why do you think they want to be Arthur's knights? Consider this as you read the story about Pretty-Hands.

Read

"Pretty-Hands" in *Classics for Young Readers,* Vol. 4A, pages 90-101

Questions

Answer the following questions in complete sentences in your Reading Notebook.

1. What does Gareth promise his mother so that he may go to King Arthur's court?
2. Who is Sir Lancelot?
3. Why does Sir Kay call Gareth "Pretty-Hands"?
4. Why is Lynette angry with King Arthur and Pretty-Hands?
5. What are the names of the three knights whom Sir Gareth defeats?
6. How does Gareth defeat each knight?
7. What reasons does Lyonors give for calling Pretty-Hands a knight?

Discuss

1. How do the people of Camelot feel about Gareth? Give two or more examples from the story to support your answer.

© 2015 K12 Inc. All rights reserved.
Copying or distributing without K12's written consent is prohibited.

2. Why do you think Lynette makes fun of Gareth as they start their journey? Why do you think she continues to make fun of him even after he defeats the knights?

3. You know these stories are legends. Sometimes, a legend changes as it gets passed down. In some versions of "Pretty-Hands," Gareth marries Lyonors. In others, he marries Lynette. Which woman do you think he should have married? Why?

The Age of Chivalry: Humility

Though knights were skilled warriors, brave and bold, a chivalrous medieval knight was also expected to have good manners and not boast about his own accomplishments. Discuss Gareth's character and actions. After your discussion, write a definition and example of *humility* on the My Code of Chivalry page.

1. Does Gareth's mother think that he will agree to work as a scullion for a year and a day to go to Camelot? Why? What reason does he give to explain why he agrees?

2. What do you think he means when he says, "As humble as my place will be, I shall still be a prince in mind and heart"?

3. How does Gareth behave while working in the palace kitchen? Why do you think Sir Lancelot says, "This Pretty-Hands has all the marks of a gentleman and a hero, and will someday prove himself a knight of great worth"?

4. Why do you think King Arthur lets Gareth ride his warhorse?

5. Gareth never responds rudely to Lynette's taunts. Why do you think he doesn't? How does Gareth's courtesy affect Lynette?

6. What words shine from Gareth's chair at the Round Table? Are these good words to describe Gareth? Why?

The Round Table

What have you learned about the Round Table? Complete the Round Table page.

© 2015 K12 Inc. All rights reserved.
Copying or distributing without K12's written consent is prohibited.

Name _____   Date _____

The Round Table

Fill in the blanks. Then decorate the table using details from page 92.

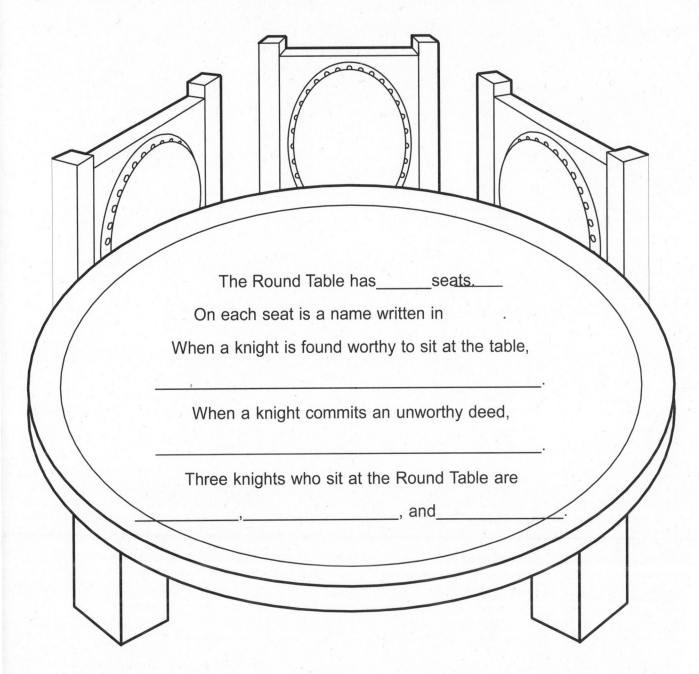

The Round Table has _____ seats. ____

On each seat is a name written in _____.

When a knight is found worthy to sit at the table,

_____.

When a knight commits an unworthy deed,

_____.

Three knights who sit at the Round Table are

_____, _____, and _____.

© 2015 K12 Inc. All rights reserved.
Copying or distributing without K12's written consent is prohibited.

Name _____ Date _____

"The Hideous Lady" and "Epilogue: The Fate of Camelot"

Find out what becomes of King Arthur, his knights, the Round Table, and the City of Dreams.

Vocabulary

You will find these words in today's reading.

loathly: (adj.) horrible, disgusting, and repulsive
The *loathly* orange had rotted into a wet, stinking mass of mold and twisting worms.

vexed: (v.) annoyed
"Don't be *vexed*," she said, laughing, "I was only teasing."

base: (adj.) low, cruel, or mean
It is *base* to hurt someone's feelings on purpose.

churl: (n.) a rude person
What *churls* they are to whisper during the candidate's speech.

straits: (n.) trouble
If you walk into the woods without a map and compass, you may find yourself lost and in terrible *straits.*

Think Ahead

1. Summarize "Pretty-Hands." In your summary, tell the following things:
   - Pretty-Hands's real name
   - The agreement he makes with his mother
   - What quest he goes on and why
   - One way he shows humility

© 2015 K12 Inc. All rights reserved.
Copying or distributing without K12's written consent is prohibited.

2. In the last story, Sir Gareth treats Lynette with courtesy even though she is quite rude to him. As you read this next story, consider how medieval knights were supposed to treat women. Think about whether the knights in this story uphold the chivalric code.

Read

"The Hideous Lady" and "Epilogue: The Fate of Camelot" in *Classics for Young Readers,* Vol. 4B, pages 102-110

Questions

Answer the following questions in complete sentences in your Reading Notebook.

1. Why does King Arthur ride out to fight the robber instead of sending one of his knights?
2. What bargain do King Arthur and the robber make?
3. What does the hideous lady say that all women desire most?
4. How does Gawain break the first half of the spell over the hideous lady?
5. How does Gawain break the second half of the spell?

Discuss

1. Do you think Arthur is wise to ride out to fight the robber himself? What is he putting at risk? Do you think he makes the right choice? Why or why not?

2. At first, Arthur rides past the robber's sister, turns his face away, and will not speak to her. When she talks to him, he will not look at her. He is behaving chivalrously? Why or why not?

© 2015 K12 Inc. All rights reserved.
Copying or distributing without K12's written consent is prohibited.

3. Gawain tells the lady that he will not look at her because she is old, ugly, and not from a noble family. The lady replies, "Ah, Sir Knight, those reasons are not so good as you suppose. For does not age bring wisdom? Are not those people beautiful who behave most beautifully? And is not nobility of mind better than nobility of birth?" Put the lady's reply in your own words. Do you think she is wise or foolish? Why?

The Age of Chivalry: Duty

The chivalrous medieval knight was expected to be brave and just, to have humility, and to protect the weak and helpless. But, above all, a knight was expected to do his duty. Doing his duty meant being the best, most chivalrous knight he could be. Doing his duty meant doing the right thing because it was the right thing to do, not because he expected to get extra rewards for it.

Discuss the questions below. After your discussion, write a definition for and example of *duty* on your My Code of Chivalry page.

1. Why does Sir Gawain offer to marry the hideous lady?

2. Why doesn't Sir Gawain mind if the other knights laugh at him?

3. If Sir Gawain had offered to marry the lady in return for money, land, or special privileges, would he be doing his duty? Why?

4. Pretend you are talking with Sir Gawain *after* he speaks with the king but *before* he marries the lady. If you ask him what his reward would be for marrying her, what do you think he would say?

5. When the lady tells Sir Gawain that he must choose which part of the day she will be beautiful, what does he choose, and why? What does she reply?

6. Why does Sir Gawain let his wife decide which part of the day she will be beautiful? How is he doing his duty? (Hint: Look at the list in the first paragraph to help you.) What is his reward?

© 2015 K12 Inc. All rights reserved.
Copying or distributing without K12's written consent is prohibited.

The Fate of Camelot

You know about how Camelot is created and you have learned how Camelot falls. Will it ever return? Complete the Fate of Camelot page and explain your ideas.

© 2015 K12 Inc. All rights reserved.
Copying or distributing without K12's written consent is prohibited.

Name _____   Date _____

The Fate of Camelot

Answer the questions in complete sentences.

1. According to the epilogue, why does the fellowship of the Round Table break and Camelot fall to ruins?

_____

_____

2. How do the knights behave similarly to or differently from the people Merlin describes on page 60, in paragraph 7?

_____

_____

3. What is most important to the people at the beginning of the legends?

_____

_____

4. What is most important to Arthur throughout the legends?

_____

_____

© 2015 K12 Inc. All rights reserved.
Copying or distributing without K12's written consent is prohibited.

The Fate of Camelot

5. What do these legends say about how people should treat each other?

_____

_____

_____

Reread the last paragraph of the epilogue, printed below. Then answer the question.

    Some people say that King Arthur is dead. Others say he is only sleeping, waiting until the people need him. Then, they say, the City of Dreams will reappear, the King will come to live in it, and right and justice will rule again.

6. Why do you think people still read and tell the legends of King Arthur and the Knights of the Round Table?

_____

_____

_____

© 2015 K12 Inc. All rights reserved.
Copying or distributing without K12's written consent is prohibited.

Name   Date

Adventures in Camelot

Choose a project and share what you've learned about the legends of King Arthur.

Think Ahead

Before you start your King Arthur project, think about what a reader expects to find when he reads a King Arthur legend. Look back through the stories and discuss the following questions. Make a list of your answers on a separate sheet of paper.

- What do all Arthurian legends have in common?
- How does an Arthurian legend begin?
- What happens in the middle of an Arthurian legend?
- How does an Arthurian legend end?

Projects

Complete one or more of the projects listed below.

Write Your Own King Arthur legend

Write an original King Arthur legend. To get started, make a word web to help you generate ideas for your writing. In the center circle, write the name of the character you'd most like to write about. It can be a character from the stories or a character you invent.

Then use the questions below to help you generate ideas and details you might want to use in your writing. You may also look back at the stories for ideas.

- Will your main character be a knight, a lady, or a person who wants to become a knight?
- What characteristics do you want your main character to have?

© 2015 K12 Inc. All rights reserved.
Copying or distributing without K12's written consent is prohibited.

- What problem do you want your main character to solve? Is there a dragon loose in the kingdom? Is there a riddle to be solved? A castle under attack?
- Will your main character solve the problem alone, or will others help?
- Will your character receive a reward at the end of the story? Will his or her name appear on a seat at the Round Table?

When you finish, circle or highlight your best ideas and use them to help you write a draft. Then revise, proofread, and publish your story. You may enjoy reading it aloud or acting it out for others.

Read More about Characters of King Arthur's Court

Research one of the Arthurian characters listed below:

- Merlin
- Guinevere
- Sir Lancelot
- Sir Percival

Read a story about the character you chose. Then do one of the following:

- Write a report that compares and contrasts the story to the other legends you have read.
- Write a letter to the main character, describing how he or she is similar to and different from the other Arthurian characters.
- Make a poster and write three or more paragraphs that compare and contrast the character to two others. Include illustrations of the characters.

Share an Arthurian Legend

Read aloud or act out your favorite Arthurian legend. Think about the following as you choose your story:

- Which story did you think was the most interesting?
- Which character did you like best?

© 2015 K12 Inc. All rights reserved.
Copying or distributing without K12's written consent is prohibited.

- Think about the characters' words and actions. Which would be the most fun to read aloud or act out? Why?

Before you perform the story, practice reading expressively. Here are some questions to think about while you practice:
- How does each character sound?
- How is the character feeling when he or she speaks? Excited? Frightened? Angry?

You may wish to make props and costumes. When you choose them, think about where the story takes place and how the people or animals in the story dress. You may look in the book for ideas and suggestions.

When you're ready, read aloud or perform your story for others.

© 2015 K12 Inc. All rights reserved.
Copying or distributing without K12's written consent is prohibited.

Name _____   Date _____

Gulliver's Travels—"A Voyage to Lilliput": Session 1

What is the strangest place you've ever visited? No matter how different that place may have seemed, it probably cannot compare to Lilliput, the kingdom in which Gulliver finds himself stranded during this section of *Gulliver's Travels*. Find out what is so special about Lilliput. See how Gulliver treats the people and handles the incredible events that fill the first three sections of "A Voyage to Lilliput."

Vocabulary

You will find these words in today's reading.

quiver: (n.) a case for carrying arrows
Robin Hood pulled an arrow from his *quiver,* aimed, and hit the middle of the target to win the competition.

mutton: (n.) lamb meat
I've never tasted *mutton,* but I would probably like it since I enjoy lamb chops.

lark: (n.) a brown-colored songbird
The bird-watcher placed a framed picture of a *lark* on the mantel in her home.

plume: (n.) the feather of a bird that is worn as an ornament
The Roman soldier's helmet was decorated with a bright red *plume.*

hilt: (n.) the handle of a sword or dagger
Theresa admired the fancy designs painted on the *hilt* of the sword in the history museum.

© 2015 K12 Inc. All rights reserved.
Copying or distributing without K12's written consent is prohibited.

Think Ahead

1. Jonathan Swift, the author of the novel, *Gulliver's Travels*, was born in Dublin, Ireland, in 1667. In 1689, Swift moved to England and began his writing career. He wrote essays and short pieces that focused on political and social issues of the time. People felt he was a talented and witty writer. In its time, *Gulliver's Travels* was so popular and seemed so realistic that many readers believed it to be a true story.

2. What does the saying "a big fish in a little pond" mean? How does being a big fish in a little pond change the way someone views the world? What if the fish were to move to a bigger pond, or the ocean? How would its views change? Think about this as you read *Gulliver's Travels.*

Read

Sections 1-3 of *Gulliver's Travels*—"A Voyage to Lilliput" in *Classics for Young Readers,* Vol. 4B, pages 112-120.

Questions

Answer the following questions in complete sentences in your Reading Notebook.

1. What country is Gulliver from and in what year does he first set sail?
2. How is Gulliver different from the Lilliputians?
3. What kingdom is the enemy of Lilliput?
4. Over what have Lilliput and its enemy been fighting a war?

Discuss

1. Gulliver is the narrator of this story. We see things from his perspective. Remember, perspective is the way a person sees or feels about events. What might readers miss as a result of only being given Gulliver's perspective?

© 2015 K12 Inc. All rights reserved.
Copying or distributing without K12's written consent is prohibited.

2. A *satire* is a literary work that uses humor to show the flaws and problems in people. It makes very serious issues seem funny and helps people think about these problems. *Gulliver's Travels* is a satire of some of the problems in society in Jonathan Swift's time. What are some of the problems that Swift might be talking about?

   (Hint: How does Gulliver treat the Lilliputians? How do they treat him? Is the war between Lilliput and Blefescu over a reasonable and important problem?)

3. Sometimes a character from literature has such a special trait that the name becomes part of our everyday language. For example, you may have read Greek myths and know that Echo is the name of a nymph who can only repeat the words that others speak. The word *echo*, which means "a repeated sound that bounces off a surface," comes from the name of this nymph.

   Example sentence: I could hear my footsteps echo off the cold, stone walls of the old castle.

   In *Gulliver's Travels*, Gulliver travels to a strange land where he meets the Lilliputians. The Lilliputians look like miniature people compared to Gulliver. The contrast between Gulliver and the Lilliputians is so descriptive that the word *lilliputian* has come to mean "very small or tiny."

   Example sentence: The baby's feet looked lilliputian when she put on her father's shoes.

   What sentences can you write using the words *echo* and *lilliputian*?

© 2015 K12 Inc. All rights reserved.
Copying or distributing without K12's written consent is prohibited.

Tell It Again

After reading the first three sections of the story, discuss the relationship between Gulliver and the Lilliputians. Talk about how Gulliver treats the Lilliputians. Think about these questions:

- What does he do to them?
- What does he not do to them?
- What does Gulliver's behavior say about his character?
- What is good and bad about being a big fish in a small pond?

Inventory

After Gulliver washes ashore in Lilliput, two Lilliputian officers search his pockets and make a report of what they find. The report contains descriptions of everyday items from the perspective of the Lilliputians. If you were a Lilliputian, how might you describe items that people commonly carry in their pockets? Complete the Inventory page from the perspective of a Lilliputian.

© 2015 K12 Inc. All rights reserved.
Copying or distributing without K12's written consent is prohibited.

Name _____ Date _____

Inventory

The Lilliputians who empty Gulliver's pockets make a report of what they find. Their descriptions of the everyday items that Gulliver carries show us their perspective. To the Lilliputians, something as simple as a handkerchief appears to be a huge rug worthy of carpeting the throne room of the emperor. Complete the chart below by describing the everyday items listed as if you were a Lilliputian looking at them for the first time.

Example:

A handkerchief a great piece of cloth, large enough to cover the emperor's throne room

Paper money _____
_____
_____
_____

A pencil _____
_____
_____
_____

© 2015 K12 Inc. All rights reserved.
Copying or distributing without K12's written consent is prohibited.

A wallet

_____

_____

_____

_____

A set of keys

_____

_____

_____

_____

© 2015 K12 Inc. All rights reserved.
Copying or distributing without K12's written consent is prohibited.

Guidelines for Peer Discussion

Share your thoughts, ideas, questions, and feelings about a text with a peer or others. Listen carefully to what everyone has to say about the text. During your discussion, follow these guidelines.

1. Be prepared to discuss what you think about the text. You should have already read the assignment. Come prepared to discuss your ideas and use examples from the text to support your thoughts and answers.

2. You will be asked questions about the text. Be ready to answer them, and bring some questions of your own to ask others, such as:

   "Who was your favorite character? Why?"

   "What was your favorite part of the text? Why?"

   "What fact did you enjoy learning? Why do you find this fact interesting?"

   "What question would you ask if you had the chance to meet the author?"

3. Listen if it's not your turn to speak. Pay attention to what others say so that you can add your ideas. Speak clearly and in complete sentences.

4. If you don't understand what someone says, ask a question.

   "What do you mean when you say . . . ?"

   "Can you give an example of . . . ?"

5. If you don't agree with what someone says, explain why.

   "I don't agree with that because . . . "

6. Keep discussions positive! You can disagree, but don't argue. Be respectful.

© 2015 K12 Inc. All rights reserved.
Copying or distributing without K12's written consent is prohibited.

Name _____ Date _____

Gulliver's Travels—"A Voyage to Lilliput": Session 2

Gulliver has sworn to defend Lilliput against the kingdom of Blefescu. Now the time has come for him to live up to his promises. Will he be able to defeat the enemy's fleet? How will the battle change his relationship with the Lilliputians? Read the final two sections of "A Voyage to Lilliput" and see how the choices that Gulliver makes affect the course of his story and teach readers about Gulliver and the other characters.

Vocabulary
You will find these words in today's reading.

prow: (n.) the pointed front part that sticks out on a ship
The wealthy yachtsman had the *prow* of his favorite boat made completely of gold.

ambassadors: (n.) official representatives of a government in a foreign country
Foreign *ambassadors* to the United States work at their nation's embassy, which is located in Washington, D.C.

treason: (n.) a crime of betrayal against one's own country
The government agent who sold secrets to his country's enemies was charged with *treason*.

perplexed: (adj.) totally uncertain or puzzled
The tourist was *perplexed* by the city's confusing subway system.

Think Ahead
1. Why does Gulliver become involved in the conflict between Lilliput and Blefescu? What does the decision to become involved tell us about Gulliver?

© 2015 K12 Inc. All rights reserved.
Copying or distributing without K12's written consent is prohibited.

2. Swift often uses humor to make serious points. As you continue to read the story, look for things that seem funny or ridiculous. Consider what serious themes or ideas may be behind Swift's humor.

Read

Sections 4-5 of *Gulliver's Travels*—"A Voyage to Lilliput" in *Classics for Young Readers,* Vol. 4B, pages 120-125.

Questions

Answer the following questions in complete sentences in your Reading Notebook.

1. What does Gulliver fear when he is fighting the fleet from Blefescu?
2. Why does the emperor of Lilliput begin to plot against Gulliver?
3. Why is Gulliver charged with treason?
4. What events allow Gulliver to return home in April 1702?

Discuss

1. The Big EndLittle End debate that causes the war between Lilliput and Blefescu seems trivial and silly to most readers. What is Swift saying about the causes of real conflicts with this fictional example?

2. What other examples of satire can you find in this story?

Choices and Consequences

Gulliver makes many choices over the course of this story. Each decision that Gulliver makes has consequences. What are the connections and what do the choices say about Gulliver? Complete the page entitled Choices and Consequences and then review and discuss your work.

© 2015 K12 Inc. All rights reserved.
Copying or distributing without K12's written consent is prohibited.

Big Idea

After completing the Choices and Consequences page, think about one of the decisions that Gulliver makes and the consequences that result from this decision. Then write two paragraphs.

- In your first paragraph, explain the choice and its consequence. Then explain what we learn about Gulliver as a result of his decision.

- In your second paragraph, explain how this choice and its consequence show one of the story's themes. Remember that a *theme* of a story is the big idea and that a story can have more than one theme. Explain the big idea that the author is talking about.

© 2015 K12 Inc. All rights reserved.
Copying or distributing without K12's written consent is prohibited.

Name   Date

Choices and Consequences

All of Gulliver's choices have direct consequences that affect both his story and the way readers see him. For example, Gulliver's choice to set sail at the start of the story eventually results in his being stranded in Lilliput. The decision also tells readers that Gulliver is an adventurous person who is not afraid of taking risks. Complete the right side of the chart to show the connection between Gulliver's choices and the resulting consequences.

Choice	Consequence
Example: Gulliver chooses to treat the Lilliputians kindly.	The Lilliputians allow Gulliver to live in their kingdom as long as he agrees to certain conditions.
Gulliver swears an oath to the Lilliputian emperor to gain his freedom.	
Gulliver refuses to help the Lilliputian emperor conquer Blefescu.	
Gulliver decides to visit Blefescu.	

© 2015 K12 Inc. All rights reserved.
Copying or distributing without K12's written consent is prohibited.

Name _____ Date _____

Gulliver's Travels—"A Voyage to Brobdingnag": Session 1

After just a few months at home, Gulliver sets sail again and eventually finds himself in Brobdingnag—a kingdom every bit as different from England as Lilliput was. Read the first three sections of "A Voyage to Brobdingnag" to see how Gulliver's perspective changes when he is no longer a big fish in a little pond, but quite the opposite!

Vocabulary
You will find these words in today's reading.

hazelnut: (n.) the nut of a small tree in the birch family
As a trained scientist, Marsha could easily tell the differences among a walnut, an acorn, and a *hazelnut*.

humanity: (n.) humankind
The elimination of smallpox, a highly contagious and deadly disease, was a victory for all of *humanity*.

burrows: (n.) holes in the ground made by animals for shelter
The rabbits quickly returned to their *burrows* whenever they sensed danger.

Think Ahead
1. Summarize the events of the story so far. Be sure to include a description of Lilliput and the Lilliputians, as well as Gulliver's relationship with them, and the lessons Gulliver (and readers) learn from Gulliver's time in Lilliput.

2. In Lilliput, Gulliver's towering size and strength gave him tremendous power. He was a big fish in a little pond. How might Gulliver change if his circumstances were to change? What does the expression "a little fish in a big pond" mean?

© 2015 K12 Inc. All rights reserved.
Copying or distributing without K12's written consent is prohibited.

Read

Sections 1-3 of *Gulliver's Travels*—"A Voyage to Brobdingnag" in *Classics for Young Readers,* Vol. 4B, pages 125-134.

Questions

Answer the following questions in complete sentences in your Reading Notebook.

1. How is Gulliver different from the Brobdingnagians?
2. How does the farmer use Gulliver to make money?
3. To whom does the farmer sell Gulliver?
4. What does the king do that insults Gulliver?

Discuss

1. How are Gulliver's concerns in Brobdingnag different from his concerns in Lilliput?
2. Why is it cruel for the farmer to make money with Gulliver as he does?

Retell the Story

After reading the first three sections of "A Voyage to Brobdingnag," discuss the relationship between Gulliver and the Brobdingnagians. Answer the following questions in your discussion:

- What does Gulliver do in Brobdingnag? What does he not do?
- How does Gulliver treat the Brobdingnagians? How do they treat him?
- What does Gulliver's behavior tell you about his character?
- What is good and bad about being a small fish in a big pond?

© 2015 K12 Inc. All rights reserved.
Copying or distributing without K12's written consent is prohibited.

Draw It!

On two separate sheets of paper, draw two pictures. In the first picture, show Gulliver in Lilliput with the Lilliputians around him. In the second picture, show Gulliver in Brobdingnag with the farmer or the royal family.

When you have finished, discuss your drawings. How are the two pictures the same? How are they different? Compare Lilliput and Brobdingnag. How does Gulliver act in each place? How does he feel in each setting?

© 2015 K12 Inc. All rights reserved.
Copying or distributing without K12's written consent is prohibited.

Name _____   Date _____

Gulliver's Travels—"A Voyage to Brobdingnag": Session 2

What else will happen to Gulliver in Brobdingnag? Will he make it home to England? Find out in the conclusion to the story.

Vocabulary
You will find these words in today's reading.

spaniel: (n.) a medium-sized, short-legged dog breed with long, droopy ears
Kathy liked to stop by the pet store on her lunch break to play with a particularly friendly *spaniel*.

trellis: (n.) a frame of crossed wood or metal that is used to support vines
Because he had no ladder, Romeo climbed up the wooden slats of the *trellis* to reach Juliet's window.

talons: (n.) the claws of a bird
The eagle swooped down and grabbed its prey with powerful *talons*.

ignorance: (n.) lack of knowledge
The college student foolishly displayed his *ignorance* when he argued about a topic that he did not truly understand.

Think Ahead
Consider Gulliver's size compared to the size of the Brobdingnagians. What unusual dangers might Gulliver face in Brobdingnag?

© 2015 K12 Inc. All rights reserved.
Copying or distributing without K12's written consent is prohibited.

Read

Sections 4-5 of *Gulliver's Travels*—"A Voyage to Brobdingnag" in *Classics for Young Readers,* Vol. 4B, pages 134-140.

Questions

Answer the following questions in complete sentences in your Reading Notebook.

1. What animals almost seriously injure Gulliver in Brobdingnag?
2. What does Gulliver tell the king about in the hopes of gaining the king's favor?
3. How long does Gulliver spend in Brobdingnag?
4. What does Gulliver show the sailors who rescued him to prove the truth of his story?

Discuss

1. Why does the king of Brobdingnag order Gulliver to never mention gunpowder again? What does the king's reaction tell you about him? What does Gulliver's attitude tell you about Gulliver? Why do you think Swift includes this exchange?

2. Why does Gulliver act strangely when he returns to England? How has his time in Brobdingnag affected him?

Speak Up!

Imagine that you are the king of Brobdingnag. Gulliver has just told you of an invention called gunpowder and some of the things that gunpowder could help you do. You are horrified by what you hear.

Plan a speech to Gulliver. You may wish to make some notes so you can remember the most important points you will make. When you are ready, explain to Gulliver why you never want to know anything else about gunpowder and why you do not want him to speak of it again. What are the possible consequences of making gunpowder in Brobdingnag? Why are those consequences bad?

© 2015 K12 Inc. All rights reserved.
Copying or distributing without K12's written consent is prohibited.

Big Idea

After completing *Gulliver's Travels*, consider the importance of perspective. Write two paragraphs on perspective.

- In your first paragraph, explain how Gulliver's perspective changes over the course of the story. How does Gulliver's behavior change? What is the connection between Gulliver's perspective and Gulliver's behavior?

- In your second paragraph, discuss the two lands. Are Lilliput and Brobdingnag really that different, or do they just seem different because of Gulliver's perspective? Do you see similarities and differences in the people? Use examples and facts from the story to support your answer.

© 2015 K12 Inc. All rights reserved.
Copying or distributing without K12's written consent is prohibited.

Name _____ Date _____

Gulliver's Travels: Review

You've finished reading *Gulliver's Travels*, and now it's time to review what you have learned. While the experiences and adventures that Gulliver had are fresh in your mind, complete the activities below.

Think Ahead

Review the main events of the story. Be sure to include Gulliver's experiences in Lilliput, the way he treats others in that kingdom, and how his perspective affects his behavior. Also, consider the differences and similarities between Lilliput and Brobdingnag, the choices that Gulliver makes, and the consequences of those choices.

Chart the Choices

Pick two of the major decisions that Gulliver makes over the course of the story. Briefly discuss your reason for choosing the decisions you did. Why are these decisions important to the story? Next, complete the Chart the Choices page.

Funny How?

Jonathan Swift, the author of *Gulliver's Travels*, was a master of satire. He used humor to make serious points about people and about society.

Read the excerpt from *Gulliver's Travels* on the next page. Discuss what is funny about the situation. Then explain the serious point that Swift is making with his humor.

© 2015 K12 Inc. All rights reserved.
Copying or distributing without K12's written consent is prohibited.

Excerpt:

"Lilliput and Blefescu," he went on to explain, "have been at war for years. Here is how the war began. Long ago, as everyone says, when people sat down to eat their eggs, they broke them on the larger end. But our present emperor's grandfather, when he was just a boy, sat down to eat an egg, and broke it at the big end, and cut one of his fingers. So the emperor, the boy's father, made a law commanding all his subjects to break the smaller end of their eggs.

"The people hated this law and rebelled. Thousands fought and many died rather than break their eggs at the smaller end. The rebels, the Big-Endians, fled to the court of the emperor of Blefescu. Since then, we have been at war."

© 2015 K12 Inc. All rights reserved.
Copying or distributing without K12's written consent is prohibited.

Name _____

Date _____

Chart the Choices

In the space provided below, draw a diagram in which you show the consequences of two of Gulliver's choices. For example, if you wanted to show the consequences of Gulliver's decision to set sail at the start of the story, it might look something like this:

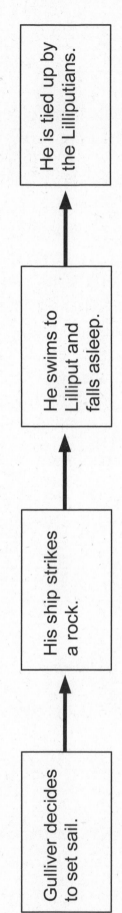

| Gulliver decides to set sail. | → | His ship strikes a rock. | → | He swims to Lilliput and falls asleep. | → | He is tied up by the Lilliputians. |

© 2015 K12 Inc. All rights reserved.
Copying or distributing without K12's written consent is prohibited.

Name _____   Date _____

Metaphors in Nature

In the toolbox of a poet's imagination, perhaps the single most important tool is *metaphor*. (Say—did you notice the metaphor in that sentence?) Metaphors make us see the world in new ways. Today, let's look at how poets use metaphor to see the natural world.

First Reading: "Fog"

Vocabulary

You will find these words in today's first reading.

harbor: (n.) a sheltered place along a coast where ships can anchor
The ships anchored in the *harbor* were safe from the storm that raged out at sea.

haunches: (n.) the hips and back part of the upper legs of an animal or person
The coyote sat on its *haunches* and howled at the moon.

Think Ahead

You know that a *metaphor* compares one thing with another, without using the words *like* or *as.* Often, the things compared don't seem alike at first—but by bringing the unlike things together, a metaphor makes us see each thing in a new way. As you read this first poem, think about what two things are being compared.

Read

Read "Fog" (page 182) once silently and a second time aloud.

© 2015 K12 Inc. All rights reserved.
Copying or distributing without K12's written consent is prohibited.

Discuss

1. What is the metaphor in this poem? Write the two things being compared in the blanks below:

   _____ = _____

2. The poet says that "the fog comes on little cat feet." What does this tell you about how the fog moves? (Think about how a cat moves when it slinks across the floor or through the grass while stalking something.)

3. This poem begins with a simple metaphor: fog = cat. But then it goes on to *extend* the metaphor. What other things does the fog do that cats do?

Second Reading: "Clouds"

Think Ahead

Do you remember the difference between *figurative* and *literal* language? Let's review:

When you speak literally, you use words for their plain, everyday, factual meanings. But when you speak figuratively, as poets often do, you use words in unusual and imaginative ways. For example:

Literal: My pillow is soft.
Figurative: My pillow feels like a big, puffy cloud.

In the next poem, we'll look at both the literal and figurative meaning of the words.

Read

Read "Clouds" (page 182) once silently and a second time aloud.

© 2015 K12 Inc. All rights reserved.
Copying or distributing without K12's written consent is prohibited.

Discuss

1. The poem describes white sheep that move or stand still on a blue hill. But the poem is not *literally* about white sheep. Instead, the white sheep are part of the *figurative language* of the poem, which includes metaphors. Explain the metaphors in the poem by filling in the blanks below:

   white sheep = _____

   blue hill   = _____

2. One metaphor in this poem compares clouds to white sheep. How are clouds like white sheep?

3. If you did not know the title of the poem, would you still know that the poet was describing clouds? What clues are in the poem?

Third Reading: "The Moon's the North Wind's Cooky"

Vocabulary
You will find these words in today's third reading.

rim: (n.) the outer edge of a curved or circular object
The *rim* of my bike's front wheel was a perfect circle, until I dented it by trying to ride over the curb.

knead: (v.) to work something by pressing and pushing with the hands
Knead the bread dough for about ten minutes, then put it in a pan to rise.

Think Ahead
Gather pencil and paper. Sketch the shapes of these phases of the moon: full, half, quarter, and crescent.

© 2015 K12 Inc. All rights reserved.
Copying or distributing without K12's written consent is prohibited.

Read

Read "The Moon's the North Wind's Cooky" (page 183) once silently and a second time aloud. (The poem uses the spelling *cooky* for the word usually spelled *cookie.*)

Discuss

1. In the first stanza, what does the North Wind do to the moon?

2. The second stanza personifies the South Wind—it describes the wind as a baker. What does the South Wind bake? What does it use for dough?

3. What happens to the "moon" that the South Wind bakes?

4. The *figurative* language of the poem describes the winds as people who bake and eat a cookie. What is *literally* going on?

5. The simple metaphor in this poem is moon = cooky. The poem goes on to *extend* that metaphor to describe the phases of the moon. Explain the metaphor by completing the following sentences:

   The poem suggests that when the moon appears to grow smaller,

   _____

   _____

   The poem suggests that when the moon appears full again,

   _____

   _____

6. Look at the last two lines of the poem. The poet separates some of the words with three periods, and he puts the words in *italics.* How do you think these words should sound when read aloud? Go ahead and read them aloud with expression.

© 2015 K12 Inc. All rights reserved.
Copying or distributing without K12's written consent is prohibited.

Guidelines for Peer Discussion

Share your thoughts, ideas, questions, and feelings about a text with a peer or others. Listen carefully to what everyone has to say about the text. During your discussion, follow these guidelines.

1. Be prepared to discuss what you think about the text. You should have already read the assignment. Come prepared to discuss your ideas, and use examples from the text to support your thoughts and answers.

2. You will be asked questions about the text. Be ready to answer them, and bring some questions of your own to ask others, such as:

   "Who was your favorite character? Why?"

   "What was your favorite part of the text? Why?"

   "What fact did you enjoy learning? Why do you find this fact interesting"

   "What question would you ask if you had the chance to meet the author?"

3. Listen if it's not your turn to speak. Pay attention to what others say so that you can add your ideas. Speak clearly and in complete sentences.

4. If you don't understand what someone says, ask a question, such as:

   "What do you mean when you say . . . ?"

   "Can you give an example of . . . ?"

5. If you don't agree with what someone says, explain why.

   "I don't agree with that because . . . "

6. Keep discussions positive! You can disagree, but don't argue. Be respectful.

© 2015 K12 Inc. All rights reserved.
Copying or distributing without K12's written consent is prohibited.

Name _____   Date _____

Metaphors in the Manmade World

Today's poets use metaphor to transform manmade objects into living creatures.

First Reading: "The Garden Hose"

Vocabulary

You will find these words in today's first reading.

serpent: (n.) a snake
The *serpent* curled up on a rock and warmed itself in the sun.

dahlia: (n.) a plant with feather-like leaves and brightly colored flowers
A bouquet of *dahlias* looks like fireworks bursting into bloom.

Read

Read "The Garden Hose" (page 184) once silently and a second time aloud.

Discuss

1. What is the metaphor in this poem? Write the two things being compared in the blanks below:

   _____ = _____

2. The poem extends the simple metaphor of hose = serpent. What does the hose do that a serpent might do?

3. If you did not know the title of the poem, would you still know that the poet was describing a garden hose? What clues are in the poem?

© 2015 K12 Inc. All rights reserved.
Copying or distributing without K12's written consent is prohibited.

Second Reading: "Steam Shovel"

Vocabulary

You will find these words in today's second reading.

crop: (v.) to cut off the top part of
The grass in the field was short where the goats had *cropped* it.

amiably: (adv.) in a friendly manner
She greets everyone so *amiably*, with a big wave and a bright smile.

Think Ahead

When you were little, did you read the book called *Mike Mulligan and the Steam Shovel?* Steam shovels were like modern bulldozers, which are used to dig and move heavy loads of dirt and rock.

Read

Read "Steam Shovel" (page 184) once silently and a second time aloud.

Discuss

1. What is the metaphor in this poem? Write the two things being compared in the blanks below:

   _____ = _____

2. The poem extends the simple metaphor of
   steam shovel = dinosaur. What does the steam shovel do that a dinosaur might do?

3. If you did not know the title of the poem, would you still know that the poet was describing a steam shovel? What clues are in the poem?

© 2015 K12 Inc. All rights reserved.
Copying or distributing without K12's written consent is prohibited.

Third Reading: "Concrete Mixers"

Vocabulary
You will find these words in today's third reading.

ponderous: (adj.) very heavy; clumsy because of great size and weight
Although *ponderous*, the whale is graceful as it swims through the ocean waters.

mahout: (n.) a word from India for an elephant's keeper and driver
The *mahout* made sure his elephant had enough to eat and drink, kept it clean and dry, and rode it proudly each day.

trough: (n.) a long box that holds food or water for animals
The pigs crowded around the *trough* as the farmer poured slops from a bucket.

bellow: (v.) to make a loud, deep cry
The giant *bellowed* so loudly that it made the mountains shake.

urban: (adj.) having to do with a city
Would you prefer to live in an *urban* area or among the farms in the country?

Think Ahead
Have you ever watched the big trucks called concrete mixers at a construction site? What do they do? If the building site is a large one, the mixers roll in one after another to pour their loads. In the next poem, the poet uses both similes and metaphors to describe concrete mixers.

Remember, both similes and metaphors compare things, but a simile uses the word *like* or *as* in the comparison. For example:

Simile: Her eyes are like shining stars.
Metaphor: Her eyes are brightly shining stars.

© 2015 K12 Inc. All rights reserved.
Copying or distributing without K12's written consent is prohibited.

Read

Read "Concrete Mixers" (page 185) once silently and a second time aloud.

Discuss

1. On the blank lines below, write any two similes from the poem:

   <u>like rows of elaphants tail to trUnk</u>

   _____

2. Most of the comparisons in the poem are similes, but the last two lines state the main metaphor. Copy that metaphor on the lines below:

   <u>Thier trunks are raising</u>

   <u>a city</u>

3. How do the "trunks" of these "urban elephants" help in the work of "raising a city"?

4. To what does the poem compare the drivers of the concrete mixers?

5. Figuratively, the "mahouts" are washing the elephants. Literally, what are the drivers of the concrete mixers doing?

6. In today's poems, you've encountered some surprising metaphors that transform manmade objects into living creatures. Which metaphor did you like best? Why?

Optional Activity

A Metaphor Riddle

If you did not know the titles to today's first two poems, they would almost be like riddles. To write your own riddle poem, follow the steps on the page called A Metaphor Riddle.

© 2015 K12 Inc. All rights reserved.
Copying or distributing without K12's written consent is prohibited.

Name _____ Date _____

A Metaphor Riddle

Use a metaphor to describe something without naming the thing itself. Then see if your friends and family can guess what you have described.

1. Choose something to describe as a riddle in metaphor. You may choose from the list below or think of your own object.

   hot dog
   seashell
   skateboard
   firefly
   airplane
   submarine
   cotton candy
   suitcase
   dandelion

2. Brainstorm a list of adjectives, verbs, and phrases that describe how your item looks, sounds, tastes, feels, or smells, and what it does.

Example: A turtle
        small
        green and brown
        has a shell—carries its house on its back
        pulls its head into its shell
        has wrinkly skin like an
        alligator moves slowly, crawls

© 2015 K12 Inc. All rights reserved.
Copying or distributing without K12's written consent is prohibited.

A Metaphor Riddle

Brainstorm your list here:

Tiger Oarenge and black, sneaky, fast

Make a list of things to which the thing can be compared.
For example, for a turtle:

    a mobile home
    a tiny dinosaur
    a slow-moving tank

Write your comparisons here:

*A sneaky snake
A fast moving race car*

Use your descriptions and comparisons to write a metaphor poem. You do not have to use rhyme in your poem, but you may if you wish.

Sample:

    I am my own mobile home.
    I move slowly on tiny dinosaur feet.
    I am a box low to the ground.
    My head disappears when I go to sleep.

© 2015 K12 Inc. All rights reserved.
Copying or distributing without K12's written consent is prohibited.

Name _____ Date _____

Seeing Metaphors

Today's poets extend an invitation: "Come look with me, and see what I see."

First Reading: "Houses"

Vocabulary
You will find this word in today's first reading.

suitable: (adj.) right for the situation, appropriate, fitting
Shorts and a tee-shirt are *suitable* clothes to wear during summer, but mittens and a snowsuit are not.

Read
Read "Houses" (page 186) once silently and a second time aloud.

Discuss
1. The first line states the basic metaphor in the poem. Identify it by filling in the blanks below:

   Houses are faces = _They are pretty_

2. The rest of the poem extends the metaphor of a house as a face. Identify two or more ways in which the poet sees specific parts of a house as parts of a face.

3. When you look at a house, can you see a face in it? Can you imagine what the poet is describing?

© 2015 K12 Inc. All rights reserved.
Copying or distributing without K12's written consent is prohibited.

Second Reading: "Pictures in the Fire"

Vocabulary

You will find these words in today's second reading.

studded: (adj.) marked or decorated, usually with small, round objects
Her jacket was *studded* with rhinestones.

crimson: (adj.) a deep red color
The sunset turned the hills from brown to *crimson*.

stalactite: (n.) a mineral formation that hangs from the roofs of caves
Stalactites hung like icicles from the cave's roof.

Think Ahead

Have you ever looked up and seen pictures in the clouds—perhaps a sailing ship, or even a dragon? In a similar way, the speaker in the next poem sees things through the eyes of the imagination.

Read

Read "Pictures in the Fire" (page 187) once silently and a second time aloud.

Discuss

1. Where is the speaker in the poem and what is she doing? Describe the scene in your own words.

2. In the fire, the speaker sees pictures of some things that you might see in everyday life, such as "a lady with a basket" and "a small boy with a dog." But she sees other things that you might only encounter in storybooks. What are some of the storybook pictures she sees?

3. Of all the pictures in the fire, which one surprised or interested you most?

4. Can you imagine one more picture you might see in a fire? Describe it.

© 2015 K12 Inc. All rights reserved.
Copying or distributing without K12's written consent is prohibited.

Third Reading: "Smoke Animals"

Vocabulary
You will find this word in today's third reading.

fierceness: (n.) dangerous wildness, ferociousness
At first, the children were so frightened by the sharks' *fierceness* that they stayed at least two steps away from the glass walls at the aquarium.

Read
Read "Smoke Animals" (page 188) once silently and a second time aloud.

Discuss
1. The title explains the basic metaphor in the poem: smoke = animals. How are the smoke animals described? Are they cuddly and sweet or frightening and mean? Identify specific words to support your answer. (Hint: look for vivid verbs.)

2. In poems like "Fog" and "Garden Hose," the poet carries the metaphor all the way through to the end of the poem. But what does the poet do to the metaphor in the last two lines of this poem?

3. Did you notice that the poem is written in pairs of rhyming lines? In a poem, what do we call two lines in a row that rhyme?

© 2015 K12 Inc. All rights reserved.
Copying or distributing without K12's written consent is prohibited.

Name _____ Date _____

Metaphors to Think About

Today's poems use metaphors to help us think about feelings and dreams.

First Reading: "Best Friends"

Think Ahead

The title of today's first poem is "Best Friends." What do you think the poem might be about?

This poem comes from a collection of poems called *Children Coming Home.* In the original collection, the title of each poem is followed by a child's name. The name of the child for this poem is "Martin D."

Read

Read "Best Friends" (page 189) once silently and a second time aloud.

Discuss

1. Did the "best friends" in the poem turn out to be what you expected?

2. Where does the speaker in the poem find his "Very Best Friends"?

3. The speaker says that these friends "know what to say to" him. What do you think these friends might really be? (Keep the clues in mind: they come from a shelf, and they "say" things to the speaker.)

4. In the third stanza, the speaker uses figurative language to describe the many things his best friends do for him:

    If I want Repairing ___
    or something to lock me up ___
    or a happy key to open me ___
    or fire when school has made me crispy-cold ___

    In your own words, what do these friends do for the speaker?

© 2015 K12 Inc. All rights reserved.
Copying or distributing without K12's written consent is prohibited.

5. The poem is not just about the "Best Friends" but also about the child who is speaking the lines. What do you think the speaker is like? What are his days like? Support your answers with specific words and phrases from the poem.

Second Reading: "Dreams"

Vocabulary
You will find these words in today's second reading.

fast: (adv.) tightly, firmly
"Hold *fast* the ropes, and pull with all your might!" cried the captain to his sailors during the storm.

barren: (adj.) not able to produce plants
There was so little water last summer that the fields became *barren,* and not a single blade of grass could be seen for miles.

Think Ahead
Do you have great dreams about things you want to do when you grow up, or places you want to visit? When you think about our world or your country, what dreams do you have for them? The next poem tells us how important dreams are by imagining what life would be like without them.

Read
Read "Dreams" (page 190) once silently and a second time aloud.

Discuss
1. The "dreams" that the poet refers to are not the kind of dreams we have when we are asleep. What kind of "dreams" are these in the poem?

2. The poet says, "Hold fast to dreams." In your own words, explain what that means.

© 2015 K12 Inc. All rights reserved.
Copying or distributing without K12's written consent is prohibited.

3. Two metaphors in the poem describe what happens if you don't "hold fast to dreams." Copy those metaphors on the lines below:

Life is a broken winged bird, life is a barren field

4. How would you describe the pictures painted by those two metaphors? What words come to mind?

5. In your own words, what do you think is the *theme* of the poem? What message, what important idea, is the poet trying to communicate to us?

Optional Activities

When Dreams Grow
Write your own poem based on "Dreams," but invent metaphors to describe what happens when dreams grow. See the page titled When Dreams Grow.

"I Have a Dream!"
Langston Hughes, the poet who wrote "Dreams," was an African-American poet who lived from 1902 to 1967. Another great African American, the Reverend Martin Luther King, Jr., also knew how important dreams are. In 1963, in Washington, D.C., he gave a great speech that has become known as the "I Have a Dream" speech. Here are some famous passages from that speech. After you read them, discuss how important it is to "hold fast" to the dreams that Dr. King describes:

> I have a dream that one day on the red hills of Georgia the sons
> of former slaves and the sons of former slaveowners will be able to
> sit down together at a table of brotherhood. I have a dream that my
> four children will one day live in a nation where they will not be

© 2015 K12 Inc. All rights reserved.
Copying or distributing without K12's written consent is prohibited.

judged by the color of their skin but by the content of their character. I have a dream today.

I have a dream that one day the state of Alabama will be transformed into a situation where little black boys and black girls will be able to join hands with little white boys and white girls and walk together as sisters and brothers. I have a dream today.

This will be the day when all of God's children will be able to sing with a new meaning, "My country, 'tis of thee, sweet land of liberty, of thee I sing. Land where my fathers died, land of the pilgrim's pride, from every mountainside, let freedom ring."

© 2015 K12 Inc. All rights reserved.
Copying or distributing without K12's written consent is prohibited.

Name _____ Date _____

When Dreams Grow

In "Dreams," Langston Hughes uses powerful metaphors to describe
what happens "if dreams die" or "when dreams go."

Write a poem like "Dreams," but invent a metaphor that describes what happens
when dreams *grow*. Use the same rhyme scheme as in "Dreams." Identify the
rhyme scheme in the stanza below:

> Hold fast to dreams   _____
>
> For if dreams die   _____
>
> Life is a broken-winged bird   _____
>
> That cannot fly.   _____

Your poem can be one or more stanzas. You may use any of the following
lines for the second line of the stanza (or make up your own):

- For when dreams grow
- For if dreams fly
- For when dreams thrive
- For if dreams soar
- For when dreams live
- For when dreams shine

To get started, you might want to make a list of words that rhyme with *grow*,
fly, *thrive*, *soar*, *live*, and *shine*.

Here is an example:

> Hold fast to dreams
> For if dreams fly
> Life is a kite
> Soaring high in the sky.

© 2015 K12 Inc. All rights reserved.
Copying or distributing without K12's written consent is prohibited.

Name _____   Date _____

"Wilbur and Orville Wright: Men with Wings"

Today, airplane travel is common. Every day, thousands of flights take off from cities and towns around the world, taking people great distances to conduct business, visit friends and family, or just enjoy a relaxing vacation. But things were quite different 100 years ago. In this story, you'll read about Wilbur and Orville Wright, two brothers who changed the world one December day in 1903 in Kitty Hawk, North Carolina.

Vocabulary

You will find these words in today's reading.

starched: (adj.) stiffened with starch, as though recently dry-cleaned
Harold buttoned his *starched* collar, put on his lucky tie, and headed off to an important business meeting.

rudder: (n.) a structure on the rear of an airplane that the pilot can move to help steer the plane in the air
The plane's *rudder* had to be fixed because the pilot noticed some problems when he tried to turn right in the air.

horsepower: (n.) a unit of measurement equal to the power that a horse can exert in pulling something
The sports car's engine was more than 250 *horsepower*.

spry: (adj.) nimble; agile; quick and precise in motion
Even at 75 years old, Grandpa was *spry* enough to dance the entire night at the wedding reception.

Think Ahead

1. Have you ever heard the phrase "If at first you don't succeed, try, try again"? What does it mean? Why is it important to not give up when problems and setbacks occur in life?

© 2015 K12 Inc. All rights reserved.
Copying or distributing without K12's written consent is prohibited.

2. Describe what an airplane looks like. When you've finished, take a look at the picture of the airplane on page 146. How is that plane different from the one you described?

Read

"Wilbur and Orville Wright: Men with Wings" in *Classics for Young Readers,* Vol. 4B, pages 142-147

Questions

Answer the following questions in complete sentences in your Reading Notebook.

1. Who were Katharine and Bishop Milton Wright and where did they live?
2. Where were the Wright brothers testing their plane in December 1903?
3. Where did the Wright brothers build their plane?
4. How long was the fourth test flight of the Wright brothers' plane?

Discuss

1. Why weren't the Wright brothers satisfied with the first three test flights of their plane?
2. How might the fact that the Wright brothers owned a bicycle shop have influenced the construction of their airplane?
3. What words would you use to describe Wilbur and Orville Wright? Support your answers with evidence from the text.

Major Places in Aviation – Part One

Where did the Wright brothers complete their historic flight? Where was their bicycle shop located? Both are important places in the history of aviation.

Before you begin this activity, you will first need to put your map together. To do so, tape the map together so that it forms a large rectangle with Section 1 on the top left, Section 2 on the top right,

© 2015 K12 Inc. All rights reserved.
Copying or distributing without K12's written consent is prohibited.

Section 3 on the bottom left, and Section 4 on the bottom right.
See the example below:

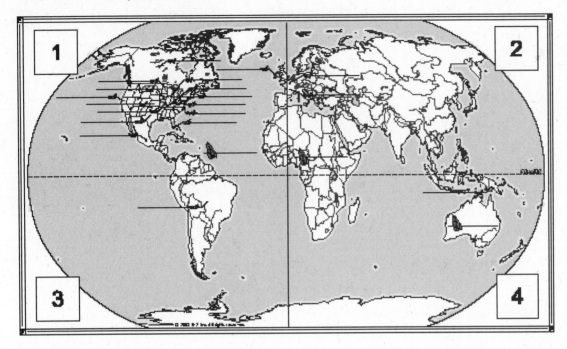

The lines on the map connect to places that were significant in the lives
of the Wright brothers. Find the following locations and use a green
colored pencil or marker to write the names of those places on the lines
on the map:

1. the place where Wilbur and Orville Wright first flew their airplane
2. the city where Wilbur and Orville Wright owned a bicycle shop

Not Giving Up

With their first flight in 1903, Wilbur and Orville Wright achieved what
seemed impossible. But they did not invent the airplane overnight. Their
success was the result of hard work and *perseverance*. To persevere is
to continue a difficult task despite setbacks or other discouragements.

On a separate sheet of paper, write one paragraph that explains why it is
important not to give up. Use the Wright brothers as an example of the
benefits of not giving up, and imagine what might have happened if Wilbur
and Orville had decided that flight was impossible after their first failure.

© 2015 K12 Inc. All rights reserved.
Copying or distributing without K12's written consent is prohibited.

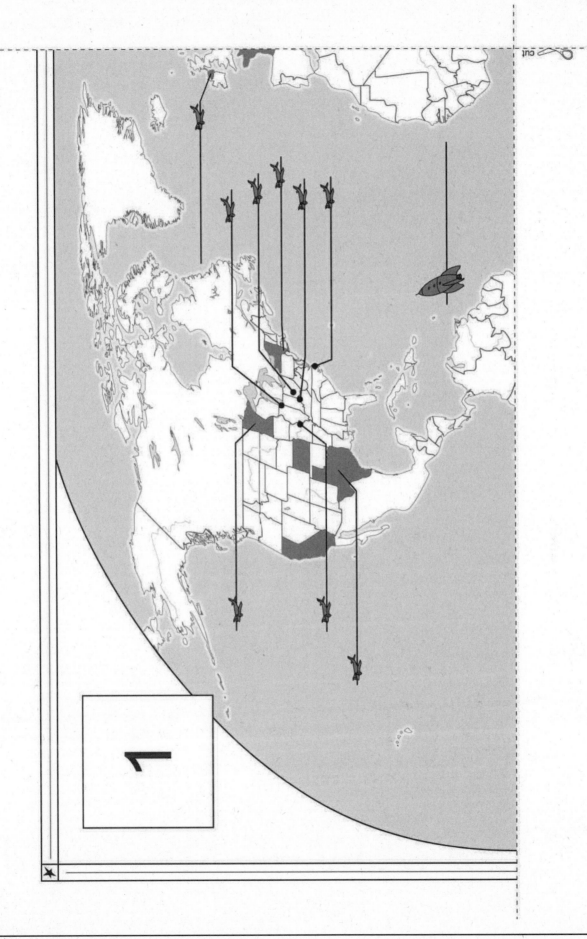

© 2015 K12 Inc. All rights reserved.
Copying or distributing without K12's written consent is prohibited.

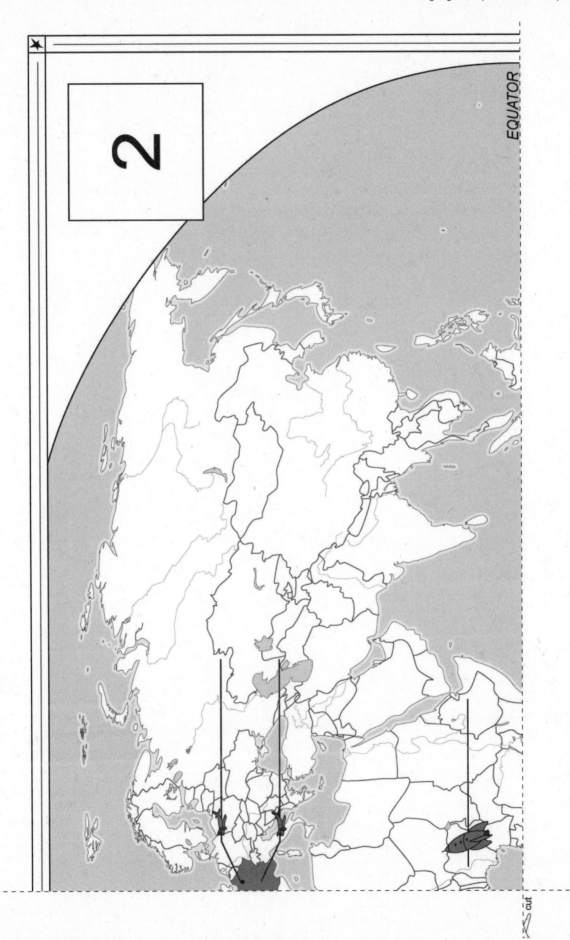

EQUATOR

2

© 2015 K12 Inc. All rights reserved.
Copying or distributing without K12's written consent is prohibited.

cut

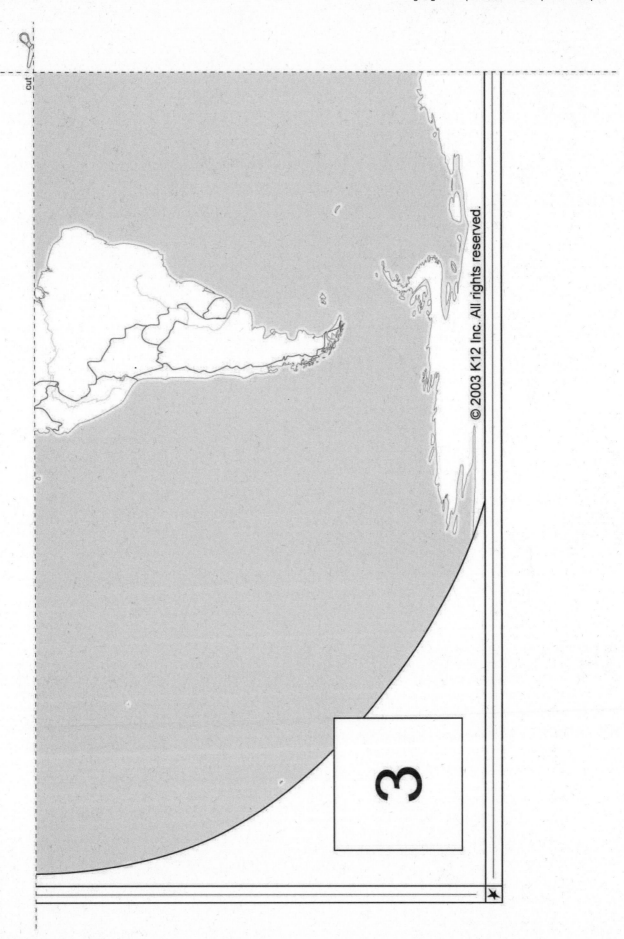

© 2003 K12 Inc. All rights reserved.

3

© 2015 K12 Inc. All rights reserved.
Copying or distributing without K12's written consent is prohibited.

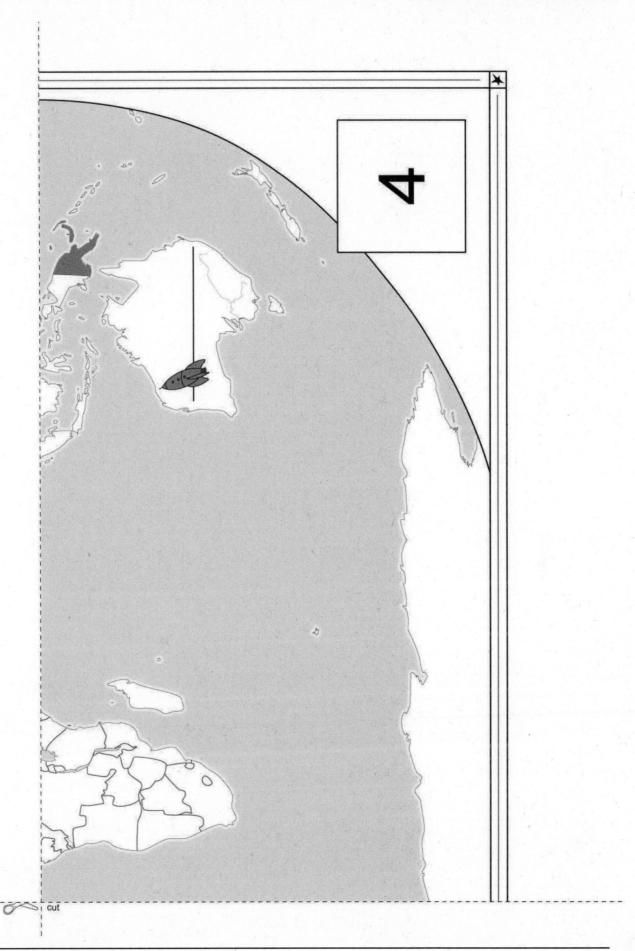

4

cut

© 2015 K12 Inc. All rights reserved.
Copying or distributing without K12's written consent is prohibited.

Name _____   Date _____

"The Challenge: Bessie Coleman's Story"

Sometimes, things get in the way of our dreams. We find that achieving our goals will be more difficult than we thought. How should we react when this happens? One of the earliest pilots faced this situation when she was young. Her name was Bessie Coleman, and she showed a lot of courage when people and problems got in the way of her dreams.

Vocabulary
You will find these words in today's reading.

aviation: (n.) the field of designing, building, and flying airplanes
Janice has always been interested in airplanes, so she studied math and science in the hopes of getting a job in the *aviation* industry when she graduated.

aviatrix: (n.) a female pilot of an airplane
Adriana has wanted to be an *aviatrix* ever since she read a biography of Amelia Earhart, the famous female pilot.

Think Ahead
1. What do you want to be when you grow up? What will you have to do to achieve that goal?
2. How would you react if someone told you that you could never achieve your dream? How would you feel? What would you do?

Read
"The Challenge: Bessie Coleman's Story" in *Classics for Young Readers,* Vol. 4B, pages 148-152.

© 2015 K12 Inc. All rights reserved.
Copying or distributing without K12's written consent is prohibited.

Questions

Answer the following questions in complete sentences in your Reading Notebook.

1. How did Bessie Coleman and her siblings earn money when they were children?
2. Where did Bessie Coleman work in Chicago?
3. Why was Bessie Coleman unable to take flying lessons in the United States?
4. Where did Bessie Coleman go to learn to fly?
5. Where can you find "Bessie Coleman Drive"?

Discuss

1. Who was Robert Abbott, and how did he help Bessie Coleman?
2. How did Bessie Coleman inspire others to become involved in aviation?

Major Places in Aviation – Part Two

Continue to label the map of the world. This time, focus on Bessie Coleman and the places that were important to her life and career. On the lines on the world map, use a red colored pencil or marker to write the names of the following places:

1. the state where Bessie Coleman grew up
2. the country where Bessie Coleman learned to fly
3. the city where you would find "Bessie Coleman Drive"

Postal Tribute

In 1995, the U.S. Postal Service honored Bessie Coleman by issuing a stamp with her picture on it. The stamp showed Bessie wearing her helmet and jacket and ready to climb into the cockpit of her plane. On a separate sheet of paper, draw your own version of the stamp. Discuss why the Postal Service might have decided to show Bessie in this way and why she deserves to be on a stamp.

© 2015 K12 Inc. All rights reserved.
Copying or distributing without K12's written consent is prohibited.

Name _____ Date _____

"Dangerous Adventure! Lindbergh's Famous Flight"

In 1927, brave young pilot Charles Lindbergh made the most famous trip across the Atlantic Ocean since Christopher Columbus. Read about the life of Lindbergh and the groundbreaking journey that made him a hero around the world.

Vocabulary

You will find these words in today's reading.

monoplane: (n.) a plane with one pair of wings
At the air show, Tommy saw a *monoplane* like the one his grandfather flew during World War II.

bureau: (n.) an agency or a department of a larger organization
After working for nearly 20 years in the *bureau,* Angela finally was promoted to the job of vice president, and now she runs three departments and supervises 300 people.

ton: (n.) a 2,000-pound unit of weight
The old bridge was not built to support more than a *ton*, so the large truck had to find another route across the river.

periscope: (n.) an instrument for viewing objects that would otherwise be blocked from view
The submarine captain ordered his men to raise the *periscope* so he could see what was happening on the surface of the water.

compass: (n.) a navigation device with a circular face and a magnetic needle
Though he was alone in the woods, the hiker was not lost because his *compass* helped him find the campground to the north.

© 2015 K12 Inc. All rights reserved.
Copying or distributing without K12's written consent is prohibited.

Think Ahead

1. Every day, hundreds of flights cross the Atlantic Ocean. The flying time from the east coast of the United States to Western Europe is between 6 and 10 hours. Today, you will be reading about the first person to make that flight, Charles Lindbergh. How long do you think it took him to make the first transatlantic flight?

2. Look at the picture on page 162 of Lindbergh flying above Paris. Predict how Lindbergh's flight was different from flights covering a similar route today.

Read

"Dangerous Adventure! Lindbergh's Famous Flight" in *Classics for Young Readers,* Vol. 4B, pages 153-162.

Questions

Answer the following questions in complete sentences in your Reading Notebook.

1. Why is Charles Lindbergh famous?
2. What is barnstorming?
3. What year-round job did Charles Lindbergh take when he was 24?
4. Why did Lindbergh name his plane the *Spirit of St. Louis?*
5. Why didn't Charles Lindbergh take a parachute with him on his journey?

Discuss

1. Describe Charles Lindbergh's flight from New York to Paris. How long did the flight take? How did Lindbergh know where he was going? What did he take with him for food? How did Lindbergh feel during the flight? Include as many details as you can remember.

© 2015 K12 Inc. All rights reserved.
Copying or distributing without K12's written consent is prohibited.

2. Why did Lindbergh want to cross the Atlantic Ocean? How were Lindbergh's reasons for crossing the Atlantic Ocean different from Wilbur and Orville Wright's or Bessie Coleman's reasons for wanting to fly?

Major Places in Aviation – Part Three

Continue to label the map of the world. This time, focus on Charles Lindbergh and the places that were important to his life and career. On the lines on the world map, use a blue colored pencil or marker to write the names of the following places:

1. the state where Charles Lindbergh grew up
2. the city that Charles Lindbergh named his plane after
3. the state where Charles Lindbergh departed on May 20, 1927
4. the first country that Charles Lindbergh passed over in Europe
5. the city where Charles Lindbergh landed on May 21, 1927

Similarities

So far, you have read about four famous figures in aviation: Wilbur and Orville Wright, Bessie Coleman, and Charles Lindbergh. How were these people similar? What character traits did they share? Did they achieve success on their own, or did others help them? What were the consequences of the decisions they made in their lives? Follow the directions on the Similarities page to complete this activity.

© 2015 K12 Inc. All rights reserved.
Copying or distributing without K12's written consent is prohibited.

Name _____   Date _____

Similarities

Based on what you've learned from reading about the Wright brothers, Bessie Coleman, and Charles Lindbergh, fill in the chart below. When you have finished, discuss your answers. How were these people similar to one another? How did the choices they made help them achieve their goals?

	The Wright Brothers	Bessie Coleman	Charles Lindbergh
Character Traits			
People Who Helped			
Important Choices Made			
Major Achievements			

© 2015 K12 Inc. All rights reserved.
Copying or distributing without K12's written consent is prohibited.

Name _____ Date _____

"Go, John Glenn!"

Three, two, one—blast off! Bessie Coleman and Charles Lindbergh certainly improved on the Wright brothers' original flight of 800 feet. By the 1960s, however, aviation was ready to make another huge step. Take a ride into outer space with John Glenn as he orbits Earth in his one-person capsule!

Vocabulary

You will find these words in today's reading.

Godspeed: (n.) from an old phrase meaning "good luck and be careful"

"*Godspeed*," said the general as he sent his soldiers off on a dangerous mission.

satellite: (n.) an object that circles another, larger object in space

The moon is a *satellite* of Earth.

orbit: (n.) the path taken by one object as it circles around another

It takes a year for Earth to complete its full *orbit* around the sun.

atlas: (n.) a book of maps

Tony always kept an *atlas* in his car in case he got lost while driving.

beacon: (n.) a source of light and guidance

The lighthouse was a *beacon* to sailors who could not see the coast from their ships.

friction: (n.) the force that results when objects come in contact with one another

The *friction* between two sticks being rubbed together can cause enough heat to start a fire.

© 2015 K12 Inc. All rights reserved.
Copying or distributing without K12's written consent is prohibited.

blunt: (adj.) not sharp; dull

The *blunt* end of a pencil is the one that has the eraser.

lunge: (v.) to move forward suddenly and quickly

The basketball player *lunged* and saved the ball just before it went out of bounds.

Think Ahead

1. What is an astronaut? What do astronauts do?
2. The "Space Race" was the name given to the competition between the United States and the Soviet Union during the 1950s and 1960s to become the first country to reach different milestones in space travel.

Read

"Go, John Glenn!" in *Classics for Young Readers,* Vol. 4B, pages 163-166

Questions

Answer the following questions in complete sentences in your Reading Notebook.

1. What was the name of John Glenn's space capsule?
2. What was *Sputnik?*
3. What problem did Mission Control notice with John Glenn's space capsule?
4. How long did John Glenn's trip into space last?

Discuss

Reread this excerpt from the story.

"I couldn't be absolutely certain whether it was the retro-pack or the heat shield tearing off…. It didn't do any good to panic at that point."

© 2015 K12 Inc. All rights reserved.
Copying or distributing without K12's written consent is prohibited.

- Describe the problem that occurred during John Glenn's trip into space.
- What were the possible consequences of this problem?
- How did John Glenn react?
- What does the quotation above tell readers about John Glenn's personality?

Major Places in Aviation – Part Six

Continue to label the map of the world. This time, focus on John Glenn and the places that he passed over as he orbited Earth. On the lines on the world map, use an orange colored pencil or marker to write the names of the following places:

1. the ocean that had lightning-flickered storms during John Glenn's trip
2. the continent with moonlight-silvered clouds
3. the continent where the city lights served as a beacon to John Glenn

Hero's Welcome

Imagine that you are a newspaper reporter who must write an article on the parade held for John Glenn. Follow the directions on the Hero's Welcome page to help you prepare to write the article. When you've finished your prewriting exercises, write two paragraphs on the event in your Reading Notebook.

© 2015 K12 Inc. All rights reserved.
Copying or distributing without K12's written consent is prohibited.

Name _____   Date _____

Hero's Welcome

Imagine that you are a newspaper reporter who has been
asked to do a story on the parade for John Glenn in 1962.
Before you begin writing, you need to prepare and make
sure that you include all the important details in your story.
For reporters, the important details of any story are the
Five W's plus How. These are the "who, what, when, where, why, and how" of
the story. Complete the chart below before writing a two-paragraph article on
the parade on a separate sheet of paper.

WHO is the article about?	
WHAT event is this article covering?	
WHEN did this event occur?	
WHERE did this event occur?	
WHY did this event occur?	
HOW did this event occur?	

© 2015 K12 Inc. All rights reserved.
Copying or distributing without K12's written consent is prohibited.

Name _____   Date _____

Firsthand Accounts

Learn about the difference between firsthand accounts and secondhand accounts. Then explore one student's comparison between a firsthand account and a secondhand account. Finally, review the assignment that you will complete to compare and contrast a firsthand account and a secondhand account.

Orville Wright's Account

Read an entry from Orville Wright's diary from the day that he and his brother first flew their airplane. Examine the information that a firsthand account can include, and learn how firsthand accounts differ from secondhand accounts.

One Student's Comparison

Review one student's comparison between the firsthand account in Orville Wright's diary and the piece about the Wright brothers in the *Classics for Young Readers* anthology. Explore the similarities and differences that the student notes, as well as how she organizes her piece. Finally, examine her use of media to help convey her points.

Your Assignment

Over the next several days, you will work to create a short piece of writing that compares a firsthand account that focuses on one of the aviators in this unit to the secondhand account about that aviator in your *Classics for Young Readers* anthology. Your piece of writing should

- be two paragraphs long
- include headlines for each section
- include a piece of media that helps to convey one of your points

You may choose any of the aviators in this unit **except** the Wright brothers.

© 2015 K12 Inc. All rights reserved.
Copying or distributing without K12's written consent is prohibited.

Read over the choices below before choosing the aviator who interests you most. Write the name of the person you choose on the line.

- Bessie Coleman
- Charles Lindbergh
- John Glenn

My piece will be about: _____

© 2015 K12 Inc. All rights reserved.
Copying or distributing without K12's written consent is prohibited.

Name _____ Date _____

Two Pieces on the Wright Brothers

by Taylor Williams

Similarities

Orville Wright's diary entry from December 17, 1903, and "Wilbur and Orville Wright: Men with Wings" are alike in several ways. Both focus on the same main event: the Wright brothers' first flights in Kitty Hawk, North Carolina. Many of the same details are in both pieces, too. Readers of each piece learn that four flights took place. They learn the length and duration of the longest flight, as well. Both pieces also explain the problems the brothers had when steering the plane. Both tell how the wind made it hard to fly on a straight and even course.

Differences

There are also differences between the two pieces. The diary entry is a firsthand account. It only tells about the events of December 17, 1903, in Kitty Hawk. It tells Orville Wright's reaction to the flights and it doesn't tell how he felt. "Wilbur and Orville Wright: Men with Wings," on the other hand, is a secondhand account, and it shows the excitement of the Wright brothers' success. Unlike the diary entry, the story tells what happened in Kitty Hawk and also how the Wright brothers' family felt when they learned about the success. Because their family was in Ohio when Wilbur and Orville were in North Carolina, there would have been no way for Orville Wright to record the family's reaction in his diary entry. The diary also gives estimated distances and durations for all four flights, but the story does not.

© 2015 K12 Inc. All rights reserved.
Copying or distributing without K12's written consent is prohibited.

Name _____   Date _____

Read and Research: Session 1

Learn about taking notes and using a graphic organizer to help plan a piece of writing. Then focus on choosing appropriate media to accompany your writing. Finally, read and take notes on firsthand and secondhand accounts related to the aviator you chose, use a graphic organizer to plan your writing, and choose the media you want to include with your work.

One Student's Research

Review one student's research efforts and the notes she took on the firsthand account in Orville Wright's diary and the piece about the Wright brothers in the *Classics for Young Readers* anthology. Explore how the student chose which ideas to include in her notes and how she used a graphic organizer to help her plan her piece. Finally, examine the media she chose to accompany her writing.

Do Your Research

Now it's time to begin doing your research and planning your comparison between firsthand and secondhand accounts of an aviator's accomplishments.

Go to the page about the aviator you chose:

- An Interview with Bessie Coleman
- Charles Lindbergh Speaks
- John Glenn's Transcript

Read the firsthand account on your aviator at least twice. Then take notes on the firsthand account in the space provided.

When you have taken notes on the firsthand account, return to the piece about your aviator in your *Classics for Young Readers* anthology. Reread that secondhand account and take notes on it, too.

© 2015 K12 Inc. All rights reserved.
Copying or distributing without K12's written consent is prohibited.

When you have finished your notes, turn to the Similarities and Differences page. Use your notes to complete the graphic organizer. You should examine how the two accounts are alike and how they are different.

Finally, in the space provided on the Similarities and Differences page, write down one idea you have for appropriate media to accompany your writing. Remember that the media should be related to the content of your writing and help audiences better understand a point you plan to make.

© 2015 K12 Inc. All rights reserved.
Copying or distributing without K12's written consent is prohibited.

Name _____   Date _____

An Interview with Bessie Coleman

Here is an excerpt from an interview that Bessie Coleman gave to a reporter from the *Chicago Defender*, a newspaper that focused on issues and events important to African Americans in the twentieth century. The interview was originally published on October 8, 1921.

Interviews are a special kind of firsthand account. An interview contains a person's account of his or her own experiences, but the information is directed by and dependent on the questions the interviewer asks. In this interview, Bessie Coleman does not decide what to talk about, but rather follows the lead of the interviewer.

After you read Coleman's interview, take notes on its main ideas and include the most important details in the space provided. Then reread "The Challenge: Bessie Coleman's story" in your *Classics for Young Readers* anthology. Take notes on that piece in the space provided, too.

Aviatrix Must Sign Away Life to Learn Trade

Miss Bessie Coleman Walked Nine Miles Each Day While Studying Aviation

Miss Bessie Coleman, 4533 Indiana Avenue, the only feminine aviatrix of the Race in the world, arrived in Chicago Saturday direct from France where she has just completed a ten months' course in aviating.

Miss Coleman was seen by a Defender reporter at her home. When asked why she took up the game of flying, she said: "Well, because I knew we had no aviators, neither men nor women, and I knew the Race needed to be represented along this racist important line, so I thought it my duty to risk my life to learn aviating and to encourage flying among men and women of the Race who are so far behind the white men in this special line, I made up my mind to try. I tried and was successful."

Not Satisfied Yet

"But I shall never be satisfied until we have men of the Race who can fly. Do you know you have never lived until you have flown? Of course, it takes one with

© 2015 K12 Inc. All rights reserved.
Copying or distributing without K12's written consent is prohibited.

courage, nerve and ambition to fly. And, too, age and health are to be given great consideration. But I am thankful to know we have men who are physically fit: now what is needed is men who are not afraid to dare death."

Miss Coleman paused a moment and with a charming smile, she continued: "I first went to Paris and decided on the school. But the first to which I applied would not take women because two women had lost their lives at the game, so I went to another school in the Somme Crotcy, the city where Joan of Arc was held prisoner by the English. There I finished my course, took the examination and passed: then afterwards I still kept flying to perfect myself. Later, I left the school in the Somme and attended another in Paris where I had lessons under an 'ace' who had brought down thirty-one German planes during the world war. Here I decided on my plane, which is a Neuport de Chasse, 130 horsepower, and with which I shall give exhibition flights in America and other countries."

© 2015 K12 Inc. All rights reserved.
Copying or distributing without K12's written consent is prohibited.

Notes on the Interview

_____

_____

_____

_____

_____

_____

_____

Notes on "The Challenge: Bessie Coleman's Story"

_____

_____

_____

_____

_____

_____

_____

© 2015 K12 Inc. All rights reserved.
Copying or distributing without K12's written consent is prohibited.

Name _____   Date _____

Charles Lindbergh Speaks

Here are excerpts from a speech that Charles Lindbergh gave three days after completing his flight from New York to Paris. Lindbergh's remarks were given at a luncheon held in his honor at the American Club of Paris on May 24, 1927.

After you read Lindbergh's speech, take notes on its main ideas and important details in the space provided. Then reread "Dangerous Adventure! Lindbergh's Famous Flight" in your *Classics for Young Readers* anthology. Take notes on that piece in the space provided too.

"There was a good deal of consideration of the type of plane to be used in the flight, but the single-motored was considered the best, and the reason for not carrying an observer was that we could carry more gasoline without one. It was impossible to miss the coastline of Europe, but we might have missed the coast of France by a few hundred miles if we had not carried enough fuel.

"…In New York we were again delayed by weather conditions and it was necessary to check up, but nothing beyond inspection was done to either the motor or the plane.

"The machine had already done 6,200 miles—over 61 hours. I think this demonstrates the reliability of the commercial motor of today and demonstrates also the reliability of planes of modern construction.

"We finally decided to leave New York, upon receiving fairly good weather reports, and after working on the plane and making ready for the flight, we left New York at 7:52 in the morning (Friday, May 20).

"Weather conditions were satisfactory over Newfoundland, but after leaving the coast it was necessary to fly over 10,000 feet because of sleet.

"Then at night we flew over 6,000 to 10,000 feet, but in the daytime we plowed through the fog. We finally picked up a course definitely about three miles north of the point on the west coast of Ireland which we had hoped to reach. I want to say that the fact that we came within three miles of that point was an accident. Had it been 25 miles, it might have been navigation.

© 2015 K12 Inc. All rights reserved.
Copying or distributing without K12's written consent is prohibited.

"During the entire trip, I saw no ship at any time. The first trace of a human being was a small fishing boat, probably ably 50 miles from Ireland.

Notes on the Speech

_____

_____

_____

_____

_____

_____

Notes on "Dangerous Adventure! Lindbergh's Famous Flight"

_____

_____

_____

_____

_____

_____

© 2015 K12 Inc. All rights reserved.
Copying or distributing without K12's written consent is prohibited.

Name _____   Date _____

John Glenn's Transcript

Here are excerpts from the transcript between John Glenn, riding in *Friendship 7*, and NASA's Mission Control, located in Cape Canaveral, Florida. These exchanges took place on February 20, 1962. They occurred as Glenn prepared for reentry into Earth's atmosphere and the conclusion of his mission.

The left column provides readers with the time and the middle column tells who is speaking. P (for *pilot*) is John Glenn. CC (for *Cape Canaveral*) is Mission Control. The right column tells what Glenn or Mission Control said. In the excerpt, "over" means that a person is ready for the other person to speak. "Roger" means that the entire message was received.

After you read the transcript, take notes on its main ideas and important details in the space provided. Then reread "Go, John Glenn!" in your *Classics for Young Readers* anthology. Take notes on that piece in the space provided, as well.

04 40 23	CC	Ah, Friendship 7, this is Cape. Over.
04 40 25	P	Go ahead, Cape. Friend 7.
...		
04 40 32	P	Ah, Roger, retracting scope manually.
04 40 36	CC	While you're doing that, we are not sure whether or not your landing bag has deployed. We feel it is possible to reenter with the retropackage on. Ah, we see no difficulty at this time in that type of reentry. Over.
04 40 51	P	Ah, Roger, understand.
04 41 10	CC	Seven, this is Cape. Over.
04 41 12	P	Go ahead, Cape. Friendship 7.
...		
04 41 33	P	This is Friendship 7. I'm on straight manual control at present time. This was, ah, still kicking in and out of orientation mode, mainly in yaw, ah, following retrofire, so I am on straight manual now. I'll back it up —

© 2015 K12 Inc. All rights reserved.
Copying or distributing without K12's written consent is prohibited.

04 41 50	CC	Standby.
04 41 53	P	This is Friendship 7. Ah, going to fly-by-wire. I'm down to about 15 percent on manual.
04 42 00	CC	Ah, Roger. You're going to use fly-by-wire for reentry and we recommend that you do the best you can to keep a zero angle during reentry. Over.
04 42 09	P	Ah, Roger. Friendship 7.

...

04 42 29	CC	Ah, Seven, this is Cape. The weather in the recovery area is excellent, 3- foot waves, only one-tenth cloud coverage, 10 miles visibility.
04 42 39	P	Ah, Roger. Friendship 7.
04 42 47	CC	Ah, Seven, this is Cape. Over.
04 42 49	P	Go ahead, Cape, you're ground, you are going out.
04 42 52	CC	We recommend that you —
04 43 16	P	This is Friendship 7. I think the pack just let go.
04 43 39	P	This is Friendship 7. A real fireball outside.
04 44 20	P	Hello, Cape. Friendship 7. Over.
04 45 18	P	Hello, Cape. Friendship 7. Over.
04 45 43	P	Hello, Cape. Friendship 7. Do you receive? Over.
04 46 20	P	Hello, Cape. Friendship 7. Do you receive? Over.
04 47 18	CC	— How do you read? Over.
04 47 20	P	Loud and clear; how me?
04 47 22	CC	Roger, reading you loud and clear. How are you doing?
04 47 25	P	Oh, pretty good.
04 47 30	CC	Roger. Your impact point is within one mile of the up-range destroyer.
04 47 34	P	Ah, Roger.

...

04 47 44	CC	This is Cape, estimating 4 50. Over.
04 47 48	P	Roger, 04 50.
04 47 53	P	Okay, we're through the peak g now.
04 47 55	CC	Ah, Seven, this is Cape. What's your general condition? Are you feeling pretty well?
04 47 59	P	My condition is good, but that was a real fireball, boy.
04 48 05	P	I had great chunks of that retropack breaking off all the way through.

© 2015 K12 Inc. All rights reserved.
Copying or distributing without K12's written consent is prohibited.

04 48 08	CC	Very good; it did break off, is that correct?
04 48 11	P	Roger. Altimeter off the peg indicating 80 thousand.
04 48 15	CC	Roger, reading you loud and clear.

Notes on the Transcript

_____

_____

_____

_____

_____

_____

_____

Notes on "Go, John Glenn!"

_____

_____

_____

_____

_____

_____

_____

© 2015 K12 Inc. All rights reserved.
Copying or distributing without K12's written consent is prohibited.

Name _____   Date _____

Similarities and Differences

You have read and taken notes on the firsthand and secondhand accounts related to the aviator you chose. Use your notes to help you complete the graphic organizer. On the left, describe the similarities between the two accounts. On the right, describe the differences. Remember that it is not necessary to write in complete sentences. You will use this graphic organizer when you begin to write the draft of your comparison. Finally, write down one idea you have for appropriate media to accompany your writing.

Similarities	Differences

Possible Media: _____

© 2015 K12 Inc. All rights reserved.
Copying or distributing without K12's written consent is prohibited.

Name _____   Date _____

Read and Research: Session 2

Learn about using a graphic organizer to help you write a first
draft. Focus on choosing an appropriate title, using headings
to organize information, and making sure that each paragraph
contains a main idea and supporting details. Examine how to
make a final decision about appropriate media to include and
the ways to begin seeking out or creating media. Finally,
write your first draft and begin to search for or create your
media.

One Student's First Draft

Review one student's first draft. Explore how the student used her completed
graphic organizer to help her write her draft. Examine the importance of a title and
headings. Review the need to state a main idea supported by details in each
paragraph. Finally, focus on the creation of appropriate media and the steps
needed to find or create it.

Write Your First Draft

Now it's time to the first draft of your comparison and contrast
between firsthand and secondhand accounts of an aviator's
accomplishments.

With both accounts and your completed graphic organizer handy,
write your draft on a separate sheet of paper. You may also choose
to type your draft on the computer.

Be sure that your draft has

- A title that lets readers know what to expect from your draft
- Headings that will help you to organize information effectively

© 2015 K12 Inc. All rights reserved.
Copying or distributing without K12's written consent is prohibited.

Remember that your piece must be at least two paragraphs long. Each of your paragraphs should begin with a sentence that states its main idea. The other sentences in your paragraphs should contain supporting details.

Do not worry if your first draft is not perfect. It does not need to be. Once you finish, you will have time to improve and correct to your draft.

Finally, decide on the media that you want to include with your writing. Remember that your media should relate to the content of your draft and help to convey an important idea or key detail to your audience. Once you have made your decision, begin to look for or create the media you chose.

© 2015 K12 Inc. All rights reserved.
Copying or distributing without K12's written consent is prohibited.

Name _____ Date _____

Polish Your Draft

Learn about using checklists to improve a piece of writing. Examine how to check that the media included with a piece is appropriate. Finally, use a checklist to improve your draft and include your media with it when you hand in your work.

One Student Improves Her Draft

Review one student's first draft. Explore how the student used a checklist to improve her draft. Examine her efforts to add and remove details, correct mistakes, use proper language, and employ transitions to connect ideas. Finally, focus on how the student finished working with her media and made certain that it was appropriate to her final piece of writing.

Improve Your Draft

Now it's time to use a checklist to improve the draft of your comparison between firsthand and secondhand accounts of an aviator's accomplishments.

With your draft and the Checklist handy, correct and improve your piece.

Be sure that your revised draft

- Contains only ideas and details that relate to your topic
- Is organized correctly so that related information is grouped together under the proper heading
- Has no grammar or spelling errors and uses formal language
- Uses transitions to smoothly connect ideas

Remember that your piece must be at least two paragraphs long. Once you have corrected and improved your draft, make a clean copy with all of your changes. Consider typing your final draft on your computer.

© 2015 K12 Inc. All rights reserved.
Copying or distributing without K12's written consent is prohibited.

When your final draft is complete, make sure that your media is appropriate to include with the piece. Check that it makes at least one point in the final draft clearer to your audience. Then determine the best way to include your media with your finished piece of writing.

Finish your final draft now.

© 2015 K12 Inc. All rights reserved.
Copying or distributing without K12's written consent is prohibited.

Name _____   Date _____

Revising and Proofreading Checklist

Use this checklist to help you improve the first draft of your piece.

☐ The writing has a proper title and headings that indicate how information will be grouped in the piece.

☐ Each paragraph begins with a sentence that clearly states its main idea.

☐ Each paragraph includes several sentences that tell details that support the main idea.

☐ Each sentence relates to its the topic.

☐ All sentences contribute to supporting the main idea.

☐ All sentences are in the proper place based on the headings in the piece and main idea of each paragraph.

☐ Ideas are connected logically and smoothly, often with the help of transition words and phrases.

☐ All sentences are complete and grammatically correct.

☐ There are no spelling errors.

☐ There are no slang words or phrases, abbreviations, or other examples of informal language.

© 2015 K12 Inc. All rights reserved.
Copying or distributing without K12's written consent is prohibited.

Name _____   Date _____

Semester Review

Review the skills you've learned and the stories you've read this semester.

Mix and Match

This semester, you've learned words that describe elements of stories and poems. For example, the word *onomatopoeia* means "words that sound like what they describe." One example of onomatopoeia is *splash,* because it sounds like the noise it describes. Match each word with the correct definition and example on the Mix and Match page.

Act It Out!

Choose one or more of the poems below to read aloud or act out.

Poems:
"Horses of the Sea"
"Concrete Mixers"
"Wind Wolves"
"Smoke Animals"
"Galoshes"

After you finish:
- Explain the metaphor of the poem. What two things are being compared?
- Describe the *theme.* What is the poet's big idea?

Look through the poems to find one example of each of the following: personification, onomatopoeia, alliteration, literal language, and figurative language.

Then discuss:
- Which poem's images do you like or remember best?
- Which metaphor is your favorite? Why?

© 2015 K12 Inc. All rights reserved.
Copying or distributing without K12's written consent is prohibited.

Name That Character!

This semester, you've met some famous story characters. Test your memory on the Name That Character! page.

What's the Big Idea?

Discuss this semester's readings.

1. Think about the stories, myths, and fables you've read this semester. Which characters did you like best? Which characters did you like least? Choose a character you admire and explain why you admire him or her.

2. How does the character change from the beginning to the end of the story? Tell one choice the character makes that helps him or her change. What does he or she learn?

3. What do you think is the theme of that character's story?

4. Find a story from your Wisdom from Around the World pages (or review the stories in the unit) that shares the same theme. What is the most important way the main characters in the two stories are alike? What is the most important way they are different?

Take Note!

When you *take notes*, you write down the most important pieces of information from something you read or hear. Complete the Take Note! page.

Main Idea and Details

Give an oral presentation summarizing *If You Lived in the Days of the Knights* OR *Nature's Way*. In your presentation, give the following information:

- The main idea of the book
- Three details
- One supported opinion

© 2015 K12 Inc. All rights reserved.
Copying or distributing without K12's written consent is prohibited.

Name _____   Date _____

Mix and Match

Write the number of the definition and the letter of the example for each word.

Perspective   Definition: ____   Example ____
Satire   Definition: ____   Example ____
Imagery   Definition: ____   Example ____
Metaphor   Definition: ____   Example ____

Definitions:

1. This is language that creates a mental picture by appealing to the senses, making readers see, hear, smell, taste, or feel things in their imaginations.

2. This is language that compares one thing to another, without using the words *like* or *as.*

3. This word refers to the way a person sees or feels about events.

4. This is a literary work that uses humor to show the flaws and problems in people. It makes very serious issues seem funny and helps people think about these problems.

Examples:

a. The Big End-Little End debate in *Gulliver's Travels* is an example of this.

b. The dewdrops were diamonds scattered on the lawn.

c. It rained on Saturday. Jane was delighted because she had just planted many new shrubs that needed water, but Sam was disappointed because he had wanted to go on a picnic.

d. The fresh sea air smelled of salt, ship's rigging, and adventure.

© 2015 K12 Inc. All rights reserved.
Copying or distributing without K12's written consent is prohibited.

Name _____ Date _____

Name That Character!

Identify the speaker of the quotation and the story title. Then reread the passage carefully and think about what you can tell about the character from the information in the passage. Write a paragraph in which you make inferences and draw conclusions about the character, based on the clues in the passage. Be sure to support your points with specific examples from the passage.

1. "Silence!" came a great voice, rumbling like thunder. An old man appeared out of the shadows. He was wrinkled and gray and bent with years, but his eyes glowed with the wisdom of the ages, and his voice struck awe into the hearts of his hearers.

    "People of Britain," he said, "would you know of this boy's parentage? Behold, I know, and I will tell you . . . I was with the old king when he died in his dark tower by the sea. On that very night, a babe was carried to me, and I knew that this child was to be the King of the Britons."

Who says this? _____

What is the title of the story? _____

What does the boy do that proves that he is king? _____

_____

What can you infer about this character, based on the clues in the passage? Be sure to support your choices with specific examples from the passage.

_____

_____

_____

_____

_____

_____

© 2015 K12 Inc. All rights reserved.
Copying or distributing without K12's written consent is prohibited.

Name That Character!

2. "His majesty received me with great joy and honor. Then he asked me to go back and bring him all the rest of his enemy's ships, so he could conquer Blefescu and rule the whole world.

"I protested that I would not bring a free and brave people into slavery. The wisest of his advisers agreed. But the emperor never forgave me. And from this time he secretly began to plot against me.

"Soon ambassadors arrived from Blefescu with humble offers of peace. An agreement was soon reached. They also heard how I refused to seize the rest of their ships. For this they were grateful, and they came to see me, and invited me to visit their kingdom. I accepted."

Who says this? _____

What is the title of this story? _____

Who is the author? _____

What can you infer about this character, based on the clues in the passage? Be sure to support your choices with specific examples from the passage.

_____

_____

_____

_____

_____

© 2015 K12 Inc. All rights reserved.
Copying or distributing without K12's written consent is prohibited.

Name That Character!

3. As the bell in the tower rang out the middle of the day, the doors were thrown wide open and the heralds cried, "Behold, the King sits in his judgment hall! If there be any who are suffering wrong, if there be any who are in trouble because of evil doers, if there be any who are in urgent need of help, let such come freely and ask for justice without fear."

   So, every day, men came, and women, and even children, and told the King of their wrongs. To each one, he gave judgment as seemed to him most right and true. The rich and the poor came, the friendly and the rude, and all received justice according to their merits.

Which character is this passage describing? _____

What is the title of this story? _____

What is the name of the king's castle? _____

What is the name of the king's sword? _____

What can you infer about this character, based on the clues in the passage? Be sure to support your choices with specific examples from the passage.

_____

_____

_____

_____

_____

_____

© 2015 K12 Inc. All rights reserved.
Copying or distributing without K12's written consent is prohibited.

Name That Character!

4. "Why, it's a game. Father told it to me, and it's lovely," she explained. "We've played it always, ever since I was a little, little girl. . . . Why, we began it on some crutches that came in a missionary barrel."

"Crutches!"

"Yes. You see, I'd wanted a doll. But when the barrel came, the lady wrote that no dolls had come in, but the little crutches had. So she sent 'em along as they might come in handy for some child, sometime. And that's when we began the game. . . . The game was to just find something about everything to be glad about—no matter what. And we began right then—on the crutches."

"Well, goodness me! I can't see anythin' to be glad about—gettin' a pair of crutches when you wanted a doll!"

She clapped her hands. "There is! There is!" she crowed. "But *I* couldn't see it either, at first. Father had to tell it to me."

"Well, then, suppose *you* tell *me*," almost snapped Nancy.

"Why, just be glad because you *don't need 'em!*" she cried. "You see, it's easy when you know how!"

Which character is this passage describing? _____

What is the title of this story? _____

What can you infer about this character, based on the clues in the passage? Be sure to support your choices with specific examples from the passage.

_____

_____

_____

_____

_____

_____

© 2015 K12 Inc. All rights reserved.
Copying or distributing without K12's written consent is prohibited.

Name _____   Date _____

Take Note!

Listen as the passage is read to you. Write down the important information from the selection. You do *not* have to write in complete sentences.

1. The name of the rocket: ——————————————————————————

2. The astronauts' names: ————————————————————————————

3. Where they were going: ——————————————————————————

4. Why they were going: ——————————————————————————

5. When they landed: ——————————————————————————

6. Two things the astronaut said: _____

_____

7. What they did when they got there: _____

8. Other important information: _____

Look back to the stories you read and Reading Notebook entries for the unit, "To Fly!" Choose one person from the unit and one person from the article. In a paragraph, describe the most important way the two people are different, and the most important way the two people are alike. What trait do they have in common?

_____

_____

_____

_____

_____

_____

© 2015 K12 Inc. All rights reserved.
Copying or distributing without K12's written consent is prohibited.